ARRL's
PIC
Programming
For Beginners

Author
Mark Spencer, WA8SME

Editor
Nancy G. Hallas, W1NCY

Production Staff

Michelle Bloom, WB1ENT

Jodi Morin, KA1JPA

Maty Weinberg, KB1EIB

Sue Fagan, KB1OKW,
Cover Design

David Pingree, N1NAS,
Technical Illustrations

A PIC programming kit is available from the ARRL, order number 0030.
Order online at **www.arrl.org/arrl-store** or call 1-888-277-5289.

Table of Contents

Foreword

Amateur Radio has a long tradition of what we affectionately call "homebrewing." Homebrewing simply means the act of building a piece of equipment with your bare hands, often in the comfort of your own home. In the earliest days of Amateur Radio, homebrewing was mandatory; there were no commercial products available. But even in this modern era of click-and-purchase Internet shopping, many hams still prefer to build their own equipment whenever possible.

One thing that has changed in recent years is the nature of what we build. Hams are increasingly attracted to the extraordinary potential of microcontrollers as tools in everything from station accessories to transceivers. As a result, they're eager to learn how to program these devices and put them to work.

In *ARRL's PIC® Programming for Beginners*, Mark Spencer, WA8SME, shows you how to "speak" the language of microcontrollers. You'll find that working with PICs is surprisingly easy, educational and, most of all, fun.

David Sumner, K1ZZ
ARRL Executive Vice President
Newington, Connecticut
March 2010

Acknowledgements and Dedication

I would like to acknowledge the contributions of *you,* the reader of this text. As a life-long learner, you are my real inspiration. At times it feels like technology is passing us by, but I am inspired by those who want to be more than just technology users…and I thank you for that.

I would also like to thank Ron Cade, W6ZQ, who reviewed the draft of this book as a student of microcontrollers. He kept me honest and true to my commitment to not to assume the reader understands what I mean.

Mark Spencer, WA8SME (and life long learner)

About the Author

Mark Spencer, WA8SME, has been a ham radio operator for over 45 years and has also held the calls G5EPV, DA1OY, and HL9AW. Mark is not sure if his interest in science and technology fostered his interest in ham radio, of if his interest in ham radio fostered his technical career path and interests. He has degrees in Metallurgical Engineering and Communications. Originally from the Detroit, Michigan area, Mark entered education as a second career following a 20 year career as an Air Force Officer flying T-38, B-52, U-2, and TR-1 aircraft.

Mark is a self-described and practicing life-long learner. This passion for learning, and helping others to learn, supports both his professional and leisure efforts. He is currently the ARRL's Education and Technology Program (ETP) Coordinator. His primary ETP responsibilities include developing curriculum leading toward wireless technology literacy, providing assistance to teachers implementing ham radio and related content in their school's curriculum, managing the ARRL ham radio equipment grant program for schools, and instructing teachers in wireless technology literacy during the Teachers Institutes.

Mark's definition of computer literacy came about during his combat experiences in Desert Storm, and that vision for computer literacy has served as his compass in developing instructional programs and in his writings. Though personally passionate about learning, each and every personal endeavor has the dual purpose of facilitating the learning of others…including this text.

Mark's current ham radio interests include ham satellites and adapting microcontroller technology to ham radio.

About the ARRL

The seed for Amateur Radio was planted in the 1890s, when Guglielmo Marconi began his experiments in wireless telegraphy. Soon he was joined by dozens, then hundreds, of others who were enthusiastic about sending and receiving messages through the air—some with a commercial interest, but others solely out of a love for this new communications medium. The United States government began licensing Amateur Radio operators in 1912.

By 1914, there were thousands of Amateur Radio operators—hams—in the United States. Hiram Percy Maxim, a leading Hartford, Connecticut inventor and industrialist, saw the need for an organization to band together this fledgling group of radio experimenters. In May 1914 he founded the American Radio Relay League (ARRL) to meet that need.

Today ARRL, with approximately 155,000 members, is the largest organization of radio amateurs in the United States. The ARRL is a not-for-profit organization that:

- promotes interest in Amateur Radio communications and experimentation
- represents US radio amateurs in legislative matters, and
- maintains fraternalism and a high standard of conduct among Amateur Radio operators.

At ARRL headquarters in the Hartford suburb of Newington, the staff helps serve the needs of members. ARRL is also International Secretariat for the International Amateur Radio Union, which is made up of similar societies in 150 countries around the world.

ARRL publishes the monthly journal *QST*, as well as newsletters and many publications covering all aspects of Amateur Radio. Its headquarters station, W1AW, transmits bulletins of interest to radio amateurs and Morse code practice sessions. The ARRL also coordinates an extensive field organization, which includes volunteers who provide technical information and other support services for radio amateurs as well as communications for public-service activities. In addition, ARRL represents US amateurs with the Federal Communications Commission and other government agencies in the US and abroad.

Membership in ARRL means much more than receiving *QST* each month. In addition to the services already described, ARRL offers membership services on a personal level, such as the Technical Information Service—where members can get answers by phone, email or the ARRL website, to all their technical and operating questions.

Full ARRL membership (available only to licensed radio amateurs) gives you a voice in how the affairs of the organization are governed. ARRL policy is set by a Board of Directors (one from each of 15 Divisions). Each year, one-third of the ARRL Board of Directors stands for election by the full members they represent. The day-to-day operation of ARRL HQ is managed by an Executive Vice President and his staff.

No matter what aspect of Amateur Radio attracts you, ARRL membership is relevant and important. There would be no Amateur Radio as we know it today were it not for the ARRL. We would be happy to welcome you as a member! (An Amateur Radio license is not required for Associate Membership.) For more information about ARRL and answers to any questions you may have about Amateur Radio, write or call:

ARRL — the national association for Amateur Radio
225 Main Street
Newington CT 06111-1494
Voice: 860-594-0200
   Fax: 860-594-0259
   E-mail: **hq@arrl.org**
   Internet: **www.arrl.org/**

Prospective new amateurs call (toll-free):
800-32-NEW HAM (800-326-3942)
You can also contact us via e-mail at **newham@arrl.org**
or check out *ARRLWeb* at **www.arrl.org/**

Introduction to Programming Microcontrollers

If you look around the room, you will probably see a number of items within the room that are controlled by microcontrollers. These small, inexpensive yet powerful, dedicated computers are in virtually everything that we use in our daily lives from microwave ovens, TV and other appliance remote controls, heating thermostats, entertainment systems, clocks, to even home pregnancy tests and electronic tooth brushes. Microcontrollers have a lot of utility for the casual electronic enthusiasts as well as the professional engineer. The purpose of this book, *ARRL's PIC® Programming for Beginners*, is to get you started on a journey to explore and use the potential of these devices.

If you are an old hand at basic electronics, you probably have spent hours putting together some electronic device to accomplish some task using discrete components in an analog circuit, for instance an oscillator, or timer, or some sort of driver for a visual display. There is a lot that you can do with analog circuits using the many (and sometimes expensive and hard to come by) individual components needed to create the circuit. In the end, the circuit probably worked with some fine tuning and adjustment, and if your design was quality, the circuit may have stayed in "tune" for quite a while.

The digital revolution has changed the electronics paradigm, and now you can do many of the things you used to do with analog circuits with digital technology better, faster, cheaper and more flexibly. You can't do everything with digital, but you sure can do some incredible things that analog circuits just couldn't do. The addition of microcontrollers into the equation has made your access to the capabilities of digital technology even easier. It just takes some effort and study to get started using microcontrollers, but once you do over-come that first hurdle, not only your creative juices start flowing, but you will be able to do something about it, digitally.

I have had to make some assumptions about you, the reader of this book.

1) I assume that you know the basics of electronics, i.e, how to identify different components, know how to determine component values, know the basic function of

the various components, can interpret a circuit diagram, and can build circuits on a prototyping board based on those circuit diagrams.

2) I assume that you know some basic electronic vocabulary, i.e., *current, voltage, frequency, period, cycle, comparator, analog* and *digital*.

3) I also assume that you have some basic knowledge of computer programming and some of the vocabulary associated with computer programming, i.e, understand the meaning of *variable, constant, label, instruction, command, opcode, operand, program, program code, goto* and *loop*. I do not assume that you are a proficient computer programmer.

4) Finally, I assume that you have a working knowledge of number systems, i.e., decimal, hexadecimal, and binary. You won't be doing extensive mathematics using these different numbering systems, perhaps just some simple addition and subtraction. There are two algebra level formulas presented in one of the chapters — that will be the extent of the mathematics content of the book.

Text Conventions

Here are a few text conventions that I am using in the body of the book:

•The mnemonics that refer to the registers and individual bits within registers will be in **UPPER CASE LETTERS** (with the exception of the working accumulator register which will be referred to in `lower case letters` — **W**-register).

•The *mnemonics* that make up the *instruction set* (opcodes) that are used in programs will be in all `lower case letters`.

•An *instruction* refers to a line of *program code* that includes an *opcode*, the *programming instruction*, and *operand*, the *register location* or *memory location* that is being sensed, modified or supplying a value (if the operand is required).

•*Decimal numbers* in the program listings will be immediately preceded with a decimal point (**.**), i.e., the number 123 will be noted as .123 to identify the number as the decimal form.

•*Hexadecimal numbers* will be listed with **0x** preceding the number, i.e., 0x1a.

•*Binary numbers* will be listed with the letter **b** preceding the binary digits between apostrophes, i.e, "b01001001". The binary number may be truncated to represent a portion of an 8-bit number, i.e., "b1111" for the lower nibble of a byte.

•When the words *set* or *clear*, and variations of those words, are used in the context of the state of a *register bit* or the *voltage state* on an *input/output pin*, the words will be in all capitals. The SET state of an I/O pin would be logic high or +5 V, the CLEAR state of an I/O pin would be logic low or 0 V (ground).

Book Structure

The structure of this book is based on a building block approach. The material presented in each chapter builds on the material in preceding chapters. So if you are going to skip around the book to focus on those topics that interest you most and you find something missing, go back and check in preceding chapters and you may find the background you need. It is important to understanding how to use microcontrollers that you have a firm grasp of the hardware inside these little computers, therefore the opening chapters of the book will explore the hardware architecture. Your *interface* between the hardware of the device and the programs that you will be authoring to exploit the capabilities of that hardware is a set of memory locations called special function registers. The next section of the book will focus on these registers and how to manipulate them. Chapter 6 is titled with the caveat of being the most important chapter, this was not a trivial use of that caveat. Spend some time on Chapter 6, it will be time well spent. Once you have an understanding of the hardware and the registers you will use to work with that hardware, the remainder of the book looks at developing the computer programming code to access the various resources at your disposal inside the microcontroller.

I have made a pledge to you, that I will avoid the tendency of assuming that you understand. I hated those college professors who would at some juncture in a lecture say, "and it is intuitively obvious to the most causal observer that this last point leads to the next very important point without further explanation." This is not to say that I will not make this mistake. I know that some points in the book will take some concentration and study to gain an understanding of the information being presented. I will try my best to present the material as clearly as I can without cluttering that clarity by over simplifying or beating a trivial point to extinction.

There are as many ways to write program code as there are programmers writing code. I know for a fact that the code examples presented in this book are not the most efficient use of valuable memory space, nor is the code designed to execute as efficiently (as fast) as possible. The programming approach I choose to take in this book is what I call the "brute force programming method." The code was developed to facilitate understanding, not for efficiency. One of my goals is to get you to write your own code as quickly as possible, writing efficient code will come over time, and frankly that is a never-ending quest of my own.

The writing and reading of this book is a personal connection between you and me. I wrote this book pretending that I am at your shoulder providing some instruction along the way. Therefore I avoided writing in the third person and I use pronouns like you, me, we and us. This is a journey that is shared between us so please excuse any politically incorrectness in my writing.

Procedure for Reading and Studying This Book

Related to the context of this book, it is designed to be read with the exercise programs displayed on your computer screen. There are screen shots of various steps of manipulating the *MPLAB® IDE* development software and using a simulator to study the program code in detail, but you should not depend on these screen shots nor the text alone, you should have the book open along side of your computer where you are running the appropriate application.

The book comes with a CD-ROM that contains the program exercises addressed in the various chapters, some background manuals and supplementary reading that you should print out before they are referenced in the chapters, and some short video clips that you can run on your computer to reinforce those topics that are more instruction intensive. You will be able to use the programs as they are on the CD to load the programs into the microcontroller, however, you will not be able to modify those programs and save them back to the CD. If you want to experiment with the programs, and I highly encourage you to do so, you will have to copy the programs onto your computer's hard drive, and then you will have full access to the program contents. The book is also based on a set of hardware that you may have elected to purchase with the book. If you chose not to purchase the hardware, that is okay, because there is nothing special or unique about the bits and pieces. The only thing is that your hardware probably will not match the illustrations in the book.

Challenge in Rapid Change; Keeping Current

Writing a book such as this is a challenge in the rapidly changing technological environment we live in today. By the time it takes to author a book, the technology upon which it is based has probably already changed to the next generation. The basic concepts are still valid, but the specific examples of software and hardware used may have undergone some revision. In light of this fact, I have attempted to take a snapshot of the technology, and have provided a version of the development software used in the illustrations of this text on the CD-ROM with the permission of the owning company Microchip. The development program *MPLAB IDE* has been and will continue to be improved and revised beyond the version 8.1 that is on the CD-ROM. Microchip has done an excellent job of making their software revisions backward compatible to help alleviate problems with software revisions. I encourage you to use the software version that is on the CD-ROM while you are using this text, but then, go to the Microchip Web site and download the latest revision of *MPLAB IDE* as you continue your career with microcontrollers. This strategy will make the illustrations in the text match what you will see on your computer screen.

The same caveat holds true for the programming hardware. The text is based on the ARRL PIC programming kit, which is essentially a clone of the Microchip PICKit2, but other programmers will work as well. It is just a simple matter to select the programming hardware you have in the configuration menu items of *MPLAB IDE*, and you will be all set. The basic code will remain unaffected.

So — I don't know about you, but I am anxious to get started.

Inside the
PIC16F676

Objective: To review the basic capabilities and internal architecture of the PIC16F676 device to provide the context for subsequent chapters. The basic functionality of the PIC16F676 and the memory resources that are used to set up the device and store the program will be introduced.

Reading: *PIC16F630/676 Data Sheet*, pages 1, 2, 5-8.

I encourage you to do a quick read-through of the assigned pages from the *PIC16F630/676 Data Sheet*, but do not get discouraged by the amount of detail presented in just a few pages. The purpose of this text is to focus your attention on, and simplify, the most relevant details required for the beginning PIC-MCU programmer.

The PIC16F676

The PIC16F676 is a 14-pin, 8-bit *microcontroller*. If you look at the device diagram and also look at the device itself, it will be obvious that it has 14-pins (see **Figure 2-1** and **Figure 2-2**). It is an *8-bit device* because the *internal architecture* of the device allows it to handle one-*byte* of data or information at a time. The device can handle data and information greater in length than one-byte by proper, and more advanced, programming techniques that are beyond the scope of this text.

Microcontroller Functions

The PIC16F676 is a good device for learning about basic MCU programming because it contains many of the basic electronic functions that make MCUs so powerful. These functions include *input/output (I/O) pins* for both digital and analog sources, *internal* and *independent timers* for counting and timing events, multiple *analog to digital converts* (ADC) to allow the MCU to work with analog voltage sources and an analog *comparator* for comparing two voltage sources. (The sister device to the PIC16F676, the PIC16F630, differs because it lacks the ADC converter features that are in the PIC16F676 device.) To accomplish this level of performance, many of the 14-pins of the device serve

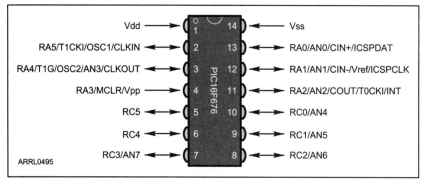

Figure 2-1 — PIC16F676 Pinout.

Figure 2-2 — PIC16F676.

multiple purposes. Two of the pins are dedicated to provide power for the device; *pin-1* is for V_{dd} (+5 V) and *pin-14* is for V_{ss} or ground.

As you explore integrated circuits you will find that device power sources are indicated in various ways and this can cause some unnecessary confusion. For instance, here you will see the *positive voltage source* listed as V_{dd}, in other cases you will see the positive voltage source listed as V_{cc}. You will also see V_{ss}, V_{ee}, or simply *GND* or *ground* for the negative voltage source. The different designations come from the internal electronic architecture of the integrated circuit and the designation depends on if there is an *n-channel FET* or an *NPN transistor* in the circuit. If there is an n-channel FET, the positive voltage source is designated as V_{dd} for the voltage supplied to the top of the n-FET *drain resistor* and V_{ss} for the voltage supplied to the bottom of the n-FET *source resistor*. If there is an NPN transistor, the positive voltage source is designated V_{cc} for the voltage supplied to the top of the NPN *collector resistor* and V_{ee} for the voltage at the bottom of the NPN *emitter resistor*. If this is not confusing enough, it really gets convoluted when there is a mix of NPN, n-FETs and p-FETs in the circuit. The bottom line and most important thing to remember is that V_{dd} or V_{cc} refers to the most positive voltage and V_{ss} to the most negative voltage. You will also see GND or ground used to refer to the negative voltage source.

Microcontroller Flexibility

The other 12 pins of the device serve different purposes as assigned by the programmer (you) when the device is set up at the beginning of the program. There will be extensive discussion on setting up the MCU in later chapters of the book because the example exercises throughout the text will demonstrate the use of each of the MCU basic functions. For instance, you can set up the PIC16F676 *pins 12* and *13* to be a comparator to compare two analog voltages relative to each other, *pin 4* to be digital input to detect when you close a switch, *pin 9* to be an ADC input to measure a voltage applied to the pin, and all the other pins as *digital output* to drive indicator *light emitting diodes* (LEDs). Each of these functions and the associated programming that will make the functions work for you will be covered in dedicated chapters in the text. For now it is important to realize that there is a tremendous amount of flexibility at your disposal inside the MCU that is limited only by your imagination and programming ability.

Internal Functional Blocks

The external 14-pins of the device are how you connect the PIC16F676 to the outside world, now let's take a look at what is going on inside the PIC16F676, at least pictorially. Take another look at Figure 1-1 on page 5 of the Data Sheet. This is a detailed block diagram of the internal workings of the device and how these internal functional blocks are interrelated. As you gain more experience with the PIC16F676, the more detailed diagram of the Data Sheet will make more sense. But for now I would like you to refer to the simplified diagram depicted in **Figure 2-3** for the following discussion.

External I/O Pins

The external I/O pins are divided into two banks of *6-pins* called *PORTA* and *PORTC*. Other, more capable MCU devices that have more I/O resources would have added ports designated *PORTB* and *PORTD*. The individual pins within the ports are designated *RA0* through *RA5* (6-pins) and *RC0* through *RC5*. You will need to be careful not to confuse the *physical pin number* with the actual *port pin designation* that will be used during programming. For instance RA0 is the physical *pin 13* of the device. If you wanted to connect an LED to RA0, you would make a physical connection between

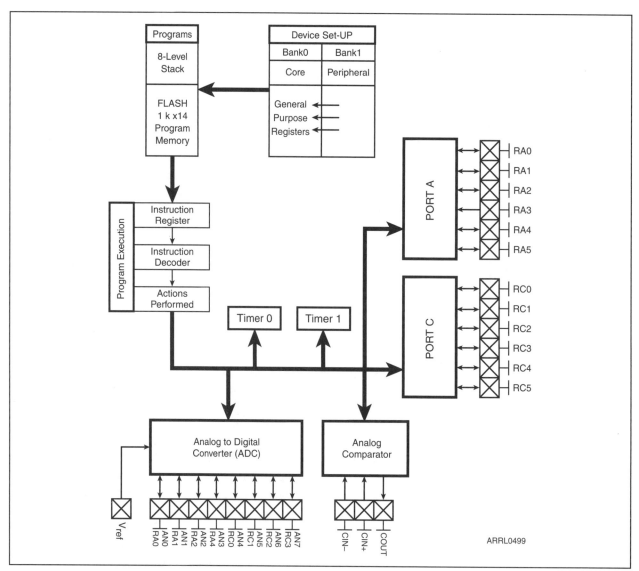

Figure 2-3 — PIC16F676 Overview.

pin-13 of the device (through a *current limiting resistor*, LED, and ground). Then in your program, to turn on the LED connected to pin-13, you would use the following programming instruction:

```
bsf    PORTA,   0
```

The opcode bsf SETS the specified bit (bit 0 (zero) of the referenced port, PORTA). SET means setting the voltage on that pin to the high value which is +5-volts. CLEARING the bit means setting the voltage on that pin to the low value or ground. There will be much more on programming throughout the text so don't get concerned at this point. Just remember that there is a difference between the physical pin number and how that pin is referred to in the program.

Uses of Pin RA3

The arrows in Figure 2-3 associated with the individual port pins indicate that data can go either into or out of the pin with the exception of RA3 which is input only. Pin

RA3 serves three special purposes: for putting the PIC16F676 into the programming mode, it serves as the device reset pin and it can also be programmed to receive digital input. Because of these special uses while the device is operating, there are restricted capabilities for this particular pin that must be kept in mind while you are developing your project.

Additional I/O Pin Purposes

As mentioned above, the I/O pins serve many purposes as dictated by the programmer. This capability is indicated pictorially in Figure 2-3 with the comparator and ADC blocks. There is one comparator module with two pins RA0 and RA1 that can be software assigned as analog inputs and one pin, RA2, that can be assigned to be the comparator output. There are eight 10-bit ADCs, four on each port that are software assigned to RA0, RA1, RA2, and RA4 (RA3 is limited and therefore does not have ADC capability) and RC0 through RC3.

These are the MCU resources available for communicating with the outside world. There are other MCU resources that are strictly used inside the device.

Internal MCU Resources

The two internal *timer modules Timer0* and *Timer1* perform powerful functions. These timers can have separate and independent clock sources and can be configured as timers or counters as defined by the programmer. This allows the timers to monitor specific I/O pins and take some programmed action at the expiration of a specified time interval or after a specified number of events while the MCU is doing other programmed tasks. For instance one of the timers can be used to "wake-up" after a specified time after the MCU is put to sleep, or placed in a low power state. Or a timer can be used to interrupt the MCU while it is performing some other task to send out serial bits to an I/O pin. This allows the MCU to perform other tasks and only dedicate resources to send out serial data when needed.

Macro View of the Memory Architecture

The MCU memory will be covered in detail in a later chapter, here we will take a macro view of the memory architecture. There are two blocks of memory depicted in the block diagram in Figure 2-3. The memory block labeled Device Setup consists of 96-bytes of random access memory (RAM) made up of byte sized registers. The bits within the individual registers are used to assign functionality to the device resources. For instance, setting the appropriate bits in the TRISA register determines if the I/O pins of PORTA are going to be input or output (either high (1) for input or low (0) for output). The area labeled General Purpose Registers is space for temporary storage of information used while the program is being executed. The memory block labeled Programs is where your program code will be stored.

Program Execution

Once your program is installed in the MCU memory, the program will begin execution (running) when power is applied. The first instruction is fetched from the first program memory location. That instruction is then decoded. And finally, actions are taken based on that decoded instruction. The process is started over again with the fetching of the next instruction. The action could be making pin assignments, doing some math on data, reacting to timer or pin inputs, or just about anything you want to happen as dictated by the program you write. That process is the reason for this book.

Summary

Inside the PIC16F676, there are two ports of six I/O pins each. The functions of these I/O pins are dictated by the programmer by setting the individual bits of a set of controlling registers that are located at specified memory locations within the device's RAM. The functions performed by the MCU include basic input/output, comparator, and ADC. There are two internal and independent timer modulates that can be used to allow the MCU to do multi-tasking. There is a bank of RAM where device resource configuration information is stored. There is a bank of working RAM where the program is stored. And finally, program instructions are fetched from the program RAM, interpreted, and actions taken based on the interpreted instruction.

By now you are probably anxious to do some actual programming of an MCU to accomplish something. The next chapter will cover the installation of the software (*MPLAB® IDE*) that you will use to develop your programs and install those programs in the PIC16F676. Once the programs are loaded into the MCU, the device is installed into the prototyping circuits you will construct to explore the power of the MCU.

Review Questions

2.1. What is the physical pin assigned to PORTA RA3?

2.2. What is the purpose of the comparator module?

2.3. What is the physical pin assigned to the ADC channel AN5?

2.4. What is the bit resolution of the ADCs within the PIC16F676?

2.5. How many internal general purpose timers are available in the PIC16F676?

2.6. How much RAM is available for your programs?

2.7. Once a PIC16F676 is programmed, how long can you expect that program to be retained in the device (if it is not over-written by another program)?

Software and
Hardware Setup

Objective: To install the *MPLAB® IDE* software on your working computer and explore the basic software functions. To construct the prototyping board hardware that will be used for the exercises in this text. Finally, load the *First Program* project into *MPLAB IDE*, build and then run the program with the PIC16F676 installed in circuit to test the *MPLAB IDE* software installation and the prototyping board setup.

Reading: *PIC16F630/676 Data Sheet*, pp 81, 82, and 84.

Microcontroller Development Tools

Microcontroller development tools are used by programmers to *author, debug, simulate* and *test*, and *load* programs into MCU devices, (Microcontrollers). The Microchip PIC® microcontrollers are supported with a number of development tools that are orchestrated under the umbrella program called *MPLAB* Integrated Development Environment (IDE). Under this programming environment, the programs that will be introduced and used in this text are the *MPASM™* Assembler and the *MPLAB SIM* Software *Simulato*r. The *MPLAB IDE* allows you to write your programs. The *MPASM* Assembler compiles the programs you write into machine language that are then loaded into the MCU device for execution. During program development, the *MPLAB Simulator* allows you to test and debug your programs in software before they are compiled and loaded into the MCU.

Development Tool Updating

The development tools are constantly being upgraded and improved at a very rapid rate. The latest program updates are usually available from Internet-based resources for download into your computer, *MPLAB IDE* is no exception. Though the updates make it easy to keep the software as up to date as technology allows, these timely updates become problematic when the software is used as the basis of instructional material as in this text. It is impractical to be able to keep pace with the rapid software updates in printed material. Consequently, this text is based on a snapshot of the software and device documentation at the time the text was written. The version of the *MPLAB IDE* used to generate the programs and graphic illustrations in this text is Version 8.10 and this version is included on the CD-ROM that accompanies this text. You are encouraged to use this software while you are going through this text, then go to the Microchip Web site and download the most recent version of the software as you continue.

Installations

With this caveat in mind, install the *MPLAB IDE* Version 8.10 on your computer from the **MPLAB Software/Software** directory on the CD-ROM. You start the installation by copying all the folders to your hard drive into a single new folder that you can easily find. Now go to this folder and find and double click on the *Install_MPLAB_ v810* icon. Follow the standard installation prompts. During the installation, accept the default directories recommended. Using the default directories will allow you to locate specific files needed later when the programming projects are set up (in particular, you will need to locate the p16f676.inc file).

Install a PIC16F676 device in the PIC programmer board making sure that you have the notch that denotes the top of the device aligned with the notch in the IC socket of the board. Also, you will be using the upper 14-pins of the socket for the PIC16F676, the bottom 4 pins are used with larger devices. Plug the connecting USB cable into your computer and let the computer install the appropriate drivers. You may have to insert the CD-ROM for the board in the drive and navigate to the appropriate directories to install the drivers. The documentation that came with the board will provide guidance on installing the drivers if there is trouble.

Launch

After you have connected the hardware, installed the proper USB driver, and completed the program installation for *MPLAB IDE* — launch *MPLAB IDE*. Have the program running during the following brief overview of the program's operation.

Overview of *MPLAB-IDE* Operation

You will notice that the *MPLAB IDE* has the classic look of a *Windows©* application with a menu bar that includes iconic representations of program features. If you move the mouse pointer and dwell over an icon, there will be a hint displayed for that icon. Clicking on the icon will launch the selected action. You can also accomplish the same thing by using the drop down menu options.

Common Operating Icons

Move the mouse pointer over the icon that is depicted in **Figure 3-1**. This is the **OPEN PROJECT** icon. A project is an umbrella file that contains the references to all the individual files that collectively are used to build a compiled program that is eventually loaded into the MCU device. The project also includes the simulator and debug windows that you set up and use during program development. You will be asked to use this icon in future chapters to load projects into *MPLAB IDE* for study.

Figure 3.1 – OPEN PROJECT Icon.

Now click on the **OPEN PROJECT** icon and navigate to the Program Files/Ch 3 Program/First Program on the CD-ROM. Click on View/Project in the menu bar. This will display the file contents of the project (**Figure 3-2**). You will see the *.asm file* which contains the program code and the *.inc file* which contains defines and constants that are particular to the device you are working with. In addition, loading this project will generate some additional icons in the menu bar.

Move the mouse pointer over the icon that is depicted in **Figure 3-3**. This is the **BUILD ALL** icon. Clicking on this icon will cause *MPLAB IDE* to use the *MPASM* Assembler to compile to program and create a machine language version of the

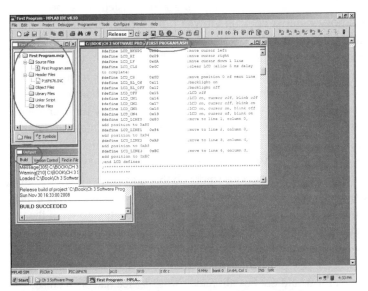

Figure 3.2 – *First Program* Project File Contents Display.

program ready for download

Figure 3.3 –
BUILD ALL
Icon.

in the PIC16F676. The program should compile without error, if there were errors; those errors will be listed in a dialog window.

Move the mouse pointer over the icon that is depicted in **Figure 3-4**. This is the **RUN** icon. Clicking on this icon will cause *MPLAB IDE* to use the *MPLAB SIM* Simulator to run the program code in software. You would use this icon along with breakpoints and Watch windows to analyze and debug your program's performance.

Move the mouse pointer over the icon that is depicted in **Figure 3-5**. This is the **ANIMATE** icon and is similar in function to the **RUN** button. The **ANIMATE** function

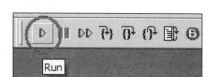

Figure 3.4 – RUN Icon.

will step through the program execution pausing on each instruction for a specified time period allowing you to follow along as the program is being executed step-by-step.

Move the mouse pointer over the icon that is depicted in **Figure 3-6**. This is the **RESET** icon. While running the program under the Simulator, the program can be reset to the beginning instruction of the program code by clicking on this icon.

Figure 3.5 – ANIMATE Icon.

Move the mouse pointer over the icon that is depicted in **Figure 3-7**. This is the **OPEN FILE** icon and allows you to open a file. This icon is used primarily for accessing other program files that contain code that you want to cut and paste into the current program file, similar to what you do in standard word processing.

Move the mouse pointer over the icon that is depicted in **Figure 3-8**. This is the **SAVE WORKSPACE** icon and allows you to save the current configuration of the project that you are working with, including Watch windows. You will be prompted if you would like to save the workspace when you attempt to close the project even if you had used this icon.

Figure 3.6 – RESET Icon.

Move the mouse pointer over the icon that is depicted in **Figure 3-9**. This is the **NEW PROJECT WIZARD** icon and the wizard will lead you through the steps needed to initiate the development of a new programming project.

The following icons allow you to access the memory of the device that is plugged into the PIC programmer's IC socket. Move the mouse pointer over the icon that is depicted in **Figure 3-10**. This is the **READ TARGET DEVICE MEMORIES** icon. Click this icon and the program contents in hexadecimal notation will be listed in a window. To view the Program Memory window, click on View/Program Memory in the menu bar and scroll down to the end of the program. Right now this program listing will be meaningless, but there is one important memory location that I want you to view. Each

Figure 3.7 – OPEN FILE Icon.

MCU device is tested in the factory before it is released for purchase. One of the tests is to calibrate the internal oscillator circuit. The calibration value is then stored in the last memory location of the device memory for later use in your program to calibrate the internal oscillator. In this case, the calibration value is 0x2c (**Figure 3-11**). The PIC MCU programming purist will record this value on the case of the MCU in the event the value is lost through reprogramming or erasing the device (more on that later). I am pointing out this feature of the *MPLAB IDE* so that in the future, if you have a device that suddenly stops working, you can check this memory location to see if the oscillator calibration value has inadvertently been corrupted. In this case the memory location would probably contain the value of 0x00h. If this were to happen, the device is still partially usable, the internal oscillator will operate, however it would not be calibrated. If the device had been erased, the calibration value would also have been erased and you would see the

Figure 3.8 – SAVE WORKSPACE Icon.

Figure 3.9 – NEW PROJECT WIZARD Icon.

Figure 3.10 – READ TARGET DEVICE MEMORIES Icon.

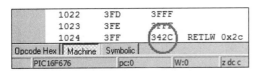

Figure 3.11 – Stored Calibration Value.

Figure 3.12 – Calibration Value Erased.

Figure 3.13 – ERASE THE TARGET DEVICE MEMORIES Icon.

Figure 3.14 – PROGRAM THE TARGET DEVICE Icon.

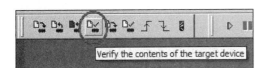

Figure 3.15 – VERIFY THE CONTENTS OF THE TARGET DEVICE Icon.

value of 0x00 as shown in **Figure 3-12**.

DO NOT CLICK THE MOUSE BUTTON IN THIS NEXT DEMONSTATION. In fact, just to be sure that nothing happens inadvertently, remove the PIC16F676 device from the PIC programmer IC socket. Move the mouse pointer over the icon that is depicted in **Figure 3-13**. This is the **ERASE THE TARGET DEVICE MEMORIES** icon. There is no real reason for you to ever use this icon. The device program memory is over-written when a new program is loaded into the device. As mentioned above, the internal oscillator calibration value is erased when the device is erased which would limit the utility of the device. There are other means to protect your code other than erasing the program memory.

Reinstall the PIC16F676 device in the PIC programmer IC socket. Move the mouse pointer over the icon that is depicted in **Figure 3-14**. This is the **PROGRAM THE TARGET DEVICE** icon. You will use this icon to send the compiled program code to the MCU device memory. First click on the **BUILD** icon to assemble the *First Program* code and then click on the **PROGRAM** icon to load the program into the MCU. The device is now ready for installation into the circuit. But before you do that, let's take a look at one more icon.

Move the mouse pointer over the icon that is depicted in **Figure 3-15**. This is the **VERIFY THE CONTENTS OF THE TARGET DEVICE** icon. When you program a device, *MPLAB IDE* automatically will compare the contents of the device memory with the assembled programmed code to verify that the programming operation was successful. You can manually compare and verify the device memory to the loaded programmed code by the use of the **VERIFY** icon.

Build and Load Program

Go ahead now and build the program and load it into the MCU. This completes the overview of the *MPLAB IDE* software and the common operating icons. You also have loaded the first example program code, the *First Program* project, compiled the program, and loaded the program into the PIC16F676. Before you can use the device in circuit, you will have to build the circuit. The following presentation will instruct you how to populate the prototyping board with the common circuits used throughout the text exercises to power the board and installed devices, as well as building the circuit required for the *First Program*.

Board Setup Outline

Hardware setup. The following board setup online assumes that you will be using the kit of parts available from ARRL. You can also opt to source the parts and programmer yourself. See the list in Appendix E. There is nothing special about the components nor is there anything critical about the board layout. This should be considered only a guide and is offered to provide some continuity between the illustrations that you will see in the book and the board layout that you will build as you

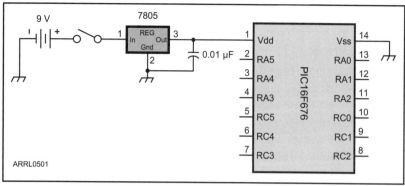

Figure 3.16 – Basic Board Setup.

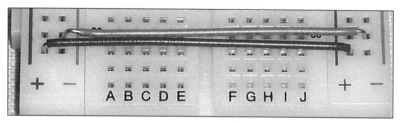

Figure 3.17 – Two Power Bus Jumpers Installed on the Bottom of the Board.

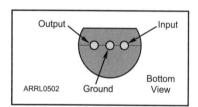

Figure 3.18 – Pin-out Diagram for the 7805 Voltage Regulator.

Figure 3.19 – Regulator Installed in the Board with the Input Pin in an Adjacent Hole as Shown.

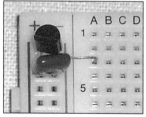

Figure 3.20 – .01µF (104) Capacitor Installed Adjacent to the Regulator.

proceed through the construction exercises in the book. As you go through the following steps to set up your prototyping board, you should refer to the schematic as well as the pictorial illustrations.

The basic board setup includes installing power bus jumpers, a voltage regulator and filter capacitor, a power switch, 9-volt battery holder, and power connections for the MCU.

The schematic for the basic setup is illustrated in **Figure 3.16**. Components will be added to this basic circuit throughout the exercises in the book.

Install two power bus jumpers on the bottom of the board as illustrated in **Figure 3-17**. You may elect to shorten and trim the jumpers to make a clean, tight fit. Color coding is not critical but it will be helpful when tracking the wiring later. The vertical red bus column will be +5-volts, the vertical blue bus column will be ground.

Review the pin-out diagram for the 7805 voltage regulator in **Figure 3-18**. The orientation of the drawing is from the bottom side (lead side) of the component. Bend the input lead of the regulator at a sharp angle close to the bottom of the case, then form a 90 degree bend in the input lead to match the holes where the regulator will be installed in the board (see **Figure 3-19**). Trim the output and the ground pins of the regulator to approximately ½ inch from the component body. Install the regulator with the output pin in the +5-V bus, the ground pin in the ground bus, and the input pin in an adjacent hole as shown in Figure 3-19.

Trim the leads of the .01uF (104) capacitor to approximately ⅜ inch. Insert the capacitor across the +5-V and ground bus pins adjacent to the regulator as shown in **Figure 3-20**.

Install the SPDT slide switch so that the center pin is in the same horizontal row of pins where the regulator input pin is connected. Install a jumper from the top pin of the slide switch to a hole on the other side of the board as illustrated in **Figure 3-21**. When the slide of the switch is positioned up, the power will be turned on.

Install the battery holder. Notice that the pins of the holder are labeled + (plus) and – (minus). When you install the battery holder, ensure that the – pin is inserted in the ground bus hole and the + pin is inserted into a hole that is adjacent to the connecting wire going to the power switch. If you inadvertently install the holder with the – pin in the +5-volt bus line, you will create a short circuit and could damage the voltage regulator (**Figure 3-22**).

This is a good time to check your wiring by installing a battery in the holder, connecting a volt meter to any conveniently exposed jumper wire connected to the +5-V and ground buses, turn on the power switch, and check for 5-V.

The final step is to install a jumper between the 5-V bus and pin 1 of the IC

Figure 3.21 – SPDT Slide Switch Installed so that Center Pin is in Same Row as Regulator Input Pin.

Figure 3.22 – Installed Battery Holder.

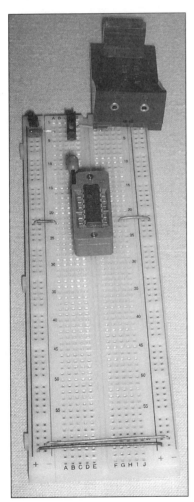

Figure 3.23 – Jumper Installed Between 5-V Bus and Pin 1 of the IC Socket.

socket and a jumper wire between the ground bus and pin 14 of the IC as illustrated in **Figure 3-23**. In this illustration you will see the use of the optional ZIF socket. Position the location of the MCU so that you can easily remove and install the IC on the board during program development but also consider giving yourself plenty of board room for developing other circuits.

First Program Components

This completes the construction of the basic board. Continue to populate the board with the components required for the *First Program*. The schematic for the *First Program* circuit is depicted in **Figure 3-24** and includes an LED with current limiting resistor connected to pin 5 of the PIC16F676 and the three conductor cable that connects the LCD unit to 5-V, ground, and pin 2 of the MCU.

The *First Program* code initializes the LCD display and then displays a welcome message. The LED will flash at 1 second intervals while the device is powered. Install the programmed PIC16F676 in the circuit and apply power. If all goes well, you will have experienced your first MCU programming success. If not, first confirm your circuit wiring and then reprogram the MCU.

After you are satisfied that your *MPLAB IDE* software is installed correctly, that the PIC programmer is integrated to your computer USB port, and your prototype board wiring is correct, you can disconnect everything and remove the LCD related cable connections and the LED related components from the prototyping board. Leave the basic board circuit in place for later exercises.

Summary

The *MPLAB IDE* is the umbrella program that allows you to develop and test your program code and to load the compiled code into the MCU memory. The PIC programmer is the hardware that you will use in conjunction with *MPLAB IDE* to load the programs into the microcontrollers. During this chapter you have installed the software, populated the prototyping

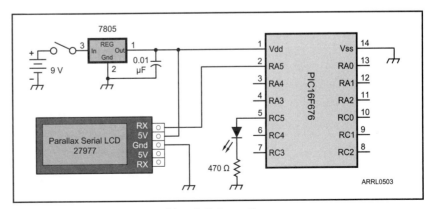

Figure 3.24 – *First Program* Circuit Schematic.

board with the basic power circuitry, and loaded your first program application to test the system.

Review Questions

3.1 What icon and *MPLAB IDE* operation must you use with caution, or not at all as recommended by the author?

3.2 If an MCU device suddenly stops working when developing your code and reloading the adjusted code in the device, what can you check in the device memory to try to troubleshoot the problem?

3.3 What is the Web URL that you can visit to find the latest version and/or check for recent updates of *MPLAB IDE*?

Program
Architechture

Objective: To model the basic program architecture that is used in the program examples and exercises of this text. The program architecture serves as an outline to organize the various components of a typical MCU program.

Reading: *PIC16F630/676 Data Sheet,* pages 56-58.

Basic Program Architecture or Outline

Keeping your programs organized will help you to keep track of what you are trying to accomplish with your program, help other users of your program to follow your logic when developing the program, and finally help you follow your own logic when you revisit the program to make adjustments and improvements at some later date. The basic program architecture or outline presented in this chapter is the architecture used for writing the programs in this text. This architecture should be considered just one example of how a program can be organized. After you become more proficient in MCU programming, you may develop an alternative architecture that makes more sense to you, or you may elect to copy the architecture of other programmers. In any case, try to use the architecture illustrated here while you are learning MCU programming.

Outline Architecture

There are a few programming lines included in this outline architecture and a few programming techniques presented. Do not get concerned if it all appears confusing because these techniques and programming instructions will be covered in detail in later chapters and are used here only to illustrate the kind of information that is included within each section of the program architecture.

For instance, in the architecture outline, you will see lines beginning with the *semi-colon* (;). The lines that begin with the ; are comment lines that are disregarded by the complier when it is translating your assembly code into machine language that is sent to the MCU's memory. The comment lines are ways to document what is going on in the code and are a way for you to communicate to yourself and other users of your program. In the programming examples of this text, I have tried to "over" comment, to state with comments even the most obvious about the code segment. I do this for instructional purposes. Commenting is an art and it will take time for you to develop your own style of commenting. But I urge you to comment your code right from the very beginning of your programming career so that you develop a habit pattern that will save you time and frustration in the future (guaranteed!). This was a hard lesson I learned.

The program outline used in this text includes:

1. **Program summary description**: information about the author, and other summary information that would be important to the application and use of the program.

2. **Directives**: tell the compiler the MCU device that is being used and any additional program files that will be used by the program. This section also includes directives that the assembler uses to configure the basic control functions of the MCU.

3. **Defines**: are simply constant and memory location labels that help make the code more readable and easier to adjust.

4. **Variable labels**: are mnemonic symbols that represent the memory locations that are reserved for the storage of variables in the General Purpose Registers section of RAM used during the program execution. Variable labels are assigned and associated to specific memory locations in this section.

5. **Reset Vector**: is the starting point of the program. On initial power-up or when the device is reset, the program is initiated at memory location 0x00. This section includes a simple call instruction to branch or jump to the memory location where the real program begins.

6. **Interrupt Vector**: like the reset vector, this is where the program will jump to upon an interrupt from one of the device resources (more on interrupts later). This section includes a call instruction to the location where your program will service the interrupt

or can contain the interrupt the service routine itself.

7. **Initialization**: is the program segment where you will set up the device resources.

8. **Main**: is where the main part of your program is located. Generally the initialization segment will only be run one time when the device is first powered up, however, the main part of the program may be looped through many, many times during the program execution.

9. **Sub-routines**: including the interrupt service routine and other sub-routines, are located at the end of the code. These routines are small program segments that are used multiple times during the main program execution and are called when needed from the main program. The use of sub-routines reduces the memory occupied by the program and simplifies the overall program.

This is what the program architecture will look like in the assembler window (the .asm) of *MPLAB IDE*. More detailed descriptions of the content of each segment are included here, using the semi-colon (;) to indicate comment lines just as would be used in an actual program. To help indicate the breaks between sections of the program, lines of asterisks (*) help to visually draw the distinction between sections. Once you have studied this outline, you will be familiar with the architecture and contents of each segment of the program when it comes time to study the programming examples in later chapters.

```
;****************************************************************************
;This section of the program file is where you will provide the program summary. Information located here
;might include the purpose of the program, any special considerations about compiling and using the
;program, the author's name and contact information, the program revision number and date, and other
;relevant information.
;****************************************************************************
```

```
;****************************************************************************
;This is where you would provide assembler directives to indicate the type of processor that this program is
;designed for and other files that contain information relevant to the processor and the program. In this
;example (and what you will be using in each exercise program for this text) the first line defines the
;MCU device as the PIC16F676 and identifies the file p16f676.inc as being associated with the program.
;The .inc file is an Include file that contains labels associated with register memory locations, constants
;associated with specific bits within the registers, and other pertinent information about a specific MCU.
;There is an .inc file for each MCU, unique to the MCU. The Include files allow you to author your code
;using labels that mirror the documentation for the MCU, making your code more readable and adaptable
;for other users.
;****************************************************************************
```

```
        list p=16F676          ;list directive to define processor
        #include <p16f676.inc>  ;processor specific variable definitions
```

```
;****************************************************************************
;This section of the code is where you would provide directives to configure the basic control functions of
;the device. The association of the labels to the specific bit configuration is included in the MCU .inc file
;and they are designed to be descriptive of the specific function. For instance in the example below, the
;WDT_OFF bit would disable the watch dog timer. To do this, the WDTE, watch dog timer enable bit
;(BIT 3) within the CONFIG register, would be CLEARED. If you were to look through the p16f676.inc
;file using WINDOWS NOTEPAD, you would find that WDT_OFF equates to 0x00. Each bit label is
;separated by the '&' symbol. The accumulation of bits is then stored in the CONFIG register which is
;located beyond the user program memory space within the device.
;****************************************************************************
```

```
        __CONFIG _CP_OFF & _WDT_OFF & _BODEN & _PWRTE_ON & _INTRC_OSC_NOCLKOUT & _MCLRE_OFF & _CPD_OFF
        ; '__CONFIG' directive is used to embed configuration word within .asm file.
        ; The labels following the directive are located in the respective .inc file.
        ; See data sheet for additional information on configuration word settings.
```

```
;****************************************************************************
```

;*Defines* are labels that are used throughout the program to identify specific memory locations
;or to identify constant values. These defines are useful when making program changes particularly
;if a memory location or constant value is used frequently in the program. Instead of having to
;go through all the code looking for each and every place the memory location or constant is
;used and making the change in the code, the user can simply change the value of the define located
;in this block of the code and they have changed all the values throughout the program.
;**

```
        #define     Bank0       0x00
        #define     Bank1       0x80
```

;**
;This is where you will *reserve* (declare) *memory* locations for storage of variables used in the program and
;associate them with a descriptive label. In the PIC16F676, the location of the 64 bytes of the General
;Purpose Registers (GPR) is between 0x20 and 0x5f in Bank 0. In the example below, the variable space
;is reserved beginning at the first memory location 0x20 and assigned the label test_byte. Using the cblock
;directive as illustrated here will result in the declarations being established in this block of GPR. In other
;MCUs, there are additional segments of GPRs, for instance in Bank 1, 2 or 3, if there is more memory
;on board the device. In the case of the PIC16F676, there is only GPR space in Bank 0.
;**

```
        cblock      0x20
        test_byte                   ;used has workspace for pin change interrupt
        minute_up                   ;used in minute segment routines
        transmit_on                 ;used as transmit on flag
        count_down                  ;used to track minute segment (1 through 5)
        message_counter             ;used in message loops
        endc
```

;**
;The *Reset Vector* is at the very beginning of the program and includes essentially a jump-to statement that
;tells the PC (the program counter) where the actual program begins. On initial power-up or reset of the
;MCU, the program counter is *cleared* (set to zero) and the program begins at the beginning, memory
;location 0x00. Therefore, the first line of code in your program needs to be a jump-to, or go-to instruction
;(goto) to where the actual beginning of the program is located. This is required because another vector,
;the *interrupt vector*, is located at memory location 0x04, just 4 bytes of memory away. The interrupt
;vector is where a jump-to will result in the event of a purposeful interrupt of your program in response to
;some defined input. Because there are only 4 bytes of memory between the reset vector and the interrupt
;vector (hardly any room for an actual program), the first line of the program needs to be a goto instruction
;to jump to where there is sufficient room to hold the main program. Likewise, for readability and
;efficiency, you will see a goto-like jump-to instruction (call) in the next section of code. In this code
;example, the program *calls*, or goes to a segment of code called Init. The ORG 0x000 stores this goto
;statement in memory location zero (0x00).
;**

```
        ORG         0x000           ;processor reset vector
        nop                         ;required by in circuit debugger
        goto        Init            ;go to beginning of program
```

;**

;The *Interrupt Vector* is where you tell the program the location of the section of code that is used to
;service an interrupt. You can configure a number of the resources on the PIC16F676 to trigger a program
;interrupt under specified conditions. For instance, you might configure the comparator to trigger an
;interrupt of the main program when one input voltage is greater than a second input voltage. When this
;condition is reached, the program counter goes to memory location 0x04 and the program resumes from
;there. The call instruction located at memory location 0x04 will cause the program to jump-to a
;subroutine program to service the interrupt and then when that section of the code is completed, the main
;program will resume at the point where it was interrupted. The `ORG 0x004` stores this call instruction in
;memory location `0x04`. Alternatively, you can enter your interrupt service code beginning at `0x04` instead
;of using the call opcode. This however puts your main code further down the editor page and may
;make your code more difficult to interpret.
;**
;

```
        ORG         0x004
        call        interrupt_service
        return                          ;interrupt trap - returns without re-enabling interrupts
```

;**
;
;Up to this point in the program architecture, the sections illustrated are pretty much universally accepted.
;The *Initialization segment* is a technique used in this text. In this section of the code, instructions are
;used to configure the registers and/or bits within specific memory locations, that control the resources of
;the device. Generally, you will configure the resources of the device one time in total, and then depending
;on the circumstances, make changes to the configuration as needed in the main body of the code. The
;Initialization section of the code is run only once during the program execution, which differentiates this
;segment of the code from the Main body of the code to be discussed later. The word "Init", located against
;the left margin of the editor screen and at the beginning of a code segment, is a label that identifies the
;segment of the code. The label is used by other instructions within the program to identify this segment of
;code. For instance, in the *Reset Vector* section above, the instruction goto Init uses the label Init to
;identify the beginning of the code segment where you want the program counter to go to upon device
;*power-up* or *reset* to initialize the device resources. This code segment is a partial example of the code
;required to configure the MCU and initialization will be covered extensively later in the text.
;**
;

```
Init
        BANKSEL     Bank1           ;switching to Bank 1
        call        0x3FF           ;retrieve factory calibration value
        movwf       OSCCAL
        BANKSEL     Bank0           ;switching to Bank0
        clrf        PORTA           ;clear port bus
        clrf        PORTC
        movlw       b'00000111'     ;comparator disconnected, low power state
        movwf       CMCON
        movlw       b'11000000'     ;globals enabled, peripherals enabled,TMR0 disabled
        movwf       INTCON
        movlw       b'10010001'     ;right justified, Vdd ref RC0 has ADC, ADC Stop, ADC
                                    ;turned on
        movwf       ADCON0
        movlw       b'00110001'     ;TMR1 prescale 1:8, internal clock, TMR1 ON    movwf
        T1CON
        BANKSEL     Bank1           ;switching to BANK1
        movlw       b'00000001'     ;TMR0 set-up: pull-ups enabled, X, internal clk, X,
                                    ;pre-scale tmr0, pre-scale 1:2
```

;**
;

;The rubber meets the road in this section of the program, the *Main Program*. This is the segment of the
;code that is executed after the MCU resources have been initialized, and this section of the code could be
;repeated over and over again, as in an infinite loop, or could be an umbrella segment of code that calls
;other segments of code called subroutines, much like a dispatcher will call on specialists to accomplish
;tasks that make up the steps of an overall project. The label for this segment of code is generally `main`,
;but that depends on the program author. The following is an example of a portion of a main program.
;**
;

```
main
        goto        turned_on
        goto        main
turned_on
        bsf         transmit_on,0       ;set transmit on flag
        movlw       time_tweek          ;adjust this value to tweek the 1 minute timer
        movwf       tmr1_count
        clrf        minute_up           ;clear minute_up flag
        bsf         T1CON,TMR1ON        ;turn on tmr1
                                        ;the code continues beyond here
```

;**
;
;Subroutines are smaller segments of code (but in reality a subroutine could be much, much larger and
;more complex than the main part of the program) that accomplish specific tasks related to the overall
;project or goal of the program. We have previously discussed the interrupt service routine which is a
;unique subroutine that determines the source of the interrupt and reacts accordingly. Other subroutines
;might be timing delays of specified lengths, math routines to do specific number manipulations, or routines
;to manipulate and control visual effects like seven-segment LEDs to display numbers or LCD displays to
;display text. The judicious use of subroutines can make your code use memory more efficiently, run more
;efficiently (in less time) or could serve as a library resource that is used in other program applications
;without major re-writing of code (as is the case with the delay subroutines used in the examples in this
;text, you will see the same delay subroutines in many of the programs in this book). Subroutines are
;defined by a unique label that is used to call the routine, and the instruction return that causes a jump back
;to the location in the calling program where the subroutine was invoked. The following code includes
;some examples of subroutines.

```
;*********************************************************************************
;Interrupt Service Routine
interrupt_service
        bcf        INTCON,GIE      ;disable global interrupts
        btfsc      INTCON,GPIF     ;check if interrupt came from port change, skip if no
        goto       port_change_interrupt
        btfsc      PIR1,TMR1IF     ;check if interrupt came from tmr1, skip if no
        call       tmr1_interrupt
        btfsc      INTCON,T0IF     ;check if interrupt came from tmr0, skip if no
        call       tmr0_interrupt
        bsf        INTCON,GIE      ;enable global interrupts
        return                     ;return from interrupt service routine
;Delay Routines
delay200ms                         ;this will produce a delay of 200mS
        movlw      .200
        movwf      tempa
    dly200ms
        call       delay1ms
        decfsz     tempa,F
        goto       dly200ms
        movlw      .64
        movwf      count
    tweek200ms
        decfsz     count,F
        goto       tweek200ms
        retlw      0
        return                     ;return from delay200ms subroutine


;*********************************************************************************
;Finally, the following segment identifies the end of the program. You can use the memory locations after
;the END statement to store tables of data or text that is used by program segments as needed.
        END

;*****************************************************************************
```

Summary

You should get in the habit of using a program organization that is similar to the example given in this chapter. Keeping your programs organized will go a long way in making your programs easier to develop and refine as well as making them more user friendly. Go over the main sections of the program again so that you reinforce the organization in your mind and also to prepare to answer the review questions that follow.

Review Questions

4.1 In which section of the program will you identify the type of device for which the program is intended?

4.2 In which section of the code will you identify additional files that contain information that is needed to complete the program?

4.3 Why do you not write the main body of the program in the reset section of the program since that is where the program counter will be starting from upon initial power-up or reset of the device?

4.4 What is the main difference between the code segment in the initialize section and the main section of the code?

4.5 List two purposes for writing code in subroutines as opposed to writing the same code in the main program?

Program Development — Starting Wizard and Using a Program Template

Objective: To illustrate how to use the *MPLAB IDE* New Project Wizard to begin program development. In this chapter you will be taken step-by-step through the process of writing an MCU program using a template. The template is a shell of a program that you can use as a starting point for future programs by making adjustments and additions to the template. Once you have the template set up for use, you will build the program into a machine language program, send it to the MCU, and then use the programmed MCU to toggle two LEDs connected to the MCU, your first real programming experience.

Reading: *PIC16F630/676 Data Sheet*, page 55

Program: **Program Files/Ch 5 Program/TEMPLATE FOR 16F676**

The *MPLAB IDE* New Project Wizard — Introduction

The *MPLAB IDE* program has a very useful function that will take you through the steps required to begin developing a program. You will be taken through the process with step-by-step instructions illustrated by computer screen shots of each step. Your computer screens may vary slightly from the illustration because each computer directory is unique and you may have your computer's operating system set up differently from my computer preferences, so do not be distracted by these differences.

The following steps assume that you have installed the *MPLAB IDE* program using the default installation. It is highly recommended that in the beginning you set up some file directories as suggested below so that the step-by-step instructions and illustrations match your live experience as much as possible. As you gain experience with the functions of *MPLAB IDE* and where required files are created during the program development process, you may elect to use a different file organization plan.

Using the *MPLAB IDE* New Project Wizard

Step 1. Using your *WINDOWS Explorer* application, create a directory on your **C-drive** named **PIC Programming** and create a sub directory within that directory named **Ch5** (**Figure 5-1**). Make a mental note of these directories because these will be the working directories where the files associated with your program will be located.

Figure 5-1 — New Directory Setup

Step 2. Launch *MPLAB IDE* and you will see the application's window as illustrated in **Figure 5-2**. Note at the top menu bar of your computer screen a green file folder with a yellow sun-burst in the corner. If you move your mouse pointer over this icon and hesitate you will see the name of this icon popup as **NEW PROJECT**. This is the *new project wizard function* that will walk you through the process of creating a new program.

Step 3. Click on the **NEW PROJECT** icon and a file management dialog box will popup and ask for a file name for the project that is going to be developed and the location within your computer's file directory where the working files will be stored (Figure 5-3). A *project is a collection of files associated with a program* that you are going to develop. As a technique, try to use descriptive project and file names to make it easier to locate these files in the future. Enter a project name "Program Template" and browse your directory until you locate the **PIC Programming/Ch 5** file folder you created in Step 1.

Step 4. The next few steps do not have to be done in a specific order, but for now, follow the order presented here. In this step you will be telling *MPLAB IDE* the type of MCU programmer that you will be using to ultimately program the device. On the menu bar: click on **PROGRAMMER /SELECT-PROGRAMMER/PICKIT 2** (**Figure 5-4**). The ARRL kit contains a programmer that is a clone of the PICKit 2. If you are using a different programmer, select it accordingly. Do not be concerned if you get an error message dialog box. Once you make this selection, *MPLAB IDE* will try to connect to the selected programmer, and if you do not have the programmer connected to the USB port of your computer, the error message will result (**Figure 5-5**). You can develop and test programs without the programmer attached to

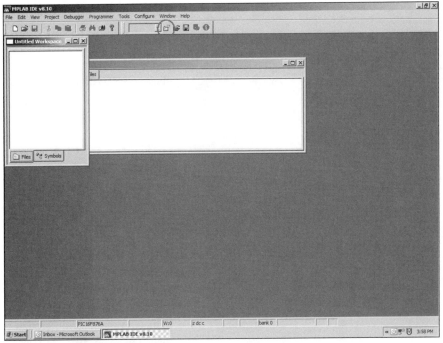

Figure 5-2 — Icon for the NEW PROJECT wizard function that walks you through the process of creating a new program.

the computer. Connecting to the programmer will be demonstrated later.

Step 5. Click on the menu bar: **CONFIGURE/SELECT DEVICE** (**Figure 5-6**) and a listing of all the MCU devices supported by *MPLAB IDE* and the *PICKit 2* programmer will be listed in the pull-down box. Scroll down the list until you find PIC16F676 and highlight that device (**Figure 5-7**). Click on OK.

Step 6. Return to the menu bar and click: **CONFIGURE/ CONFIGURATION BITS** (**Figure 5-8**). The selection screen that allows you to configure selected set-up bits for the MCU is displayed (**Figure 5-9**). Just make sure that the check box labeled

"**CONFIGURATION BITS SET IN CODE**" is checked. Remember in the last chapter one of the sections of the program architecture was the configuration section? This is the section where the _CONFIG directive and the associated specific bit selection labels were used to SET or CLEAR the individual configuration bits. By checking the box on this screen, you are telling *MPLAB IDE* to use the configuration as detailed in this section of the program code instead of using the manual bit configuration selection shown on the screen. If in the future you want to manually

select the configuration bits, simply make sure the check box is cleared and use the individual drop down options for each configuration bit to select the appropriate bit status for the device.

Step 7. In the next two steps you will be adding a couple of files that will be used by the *MPLAB IDE* to generate the program. The first file to be added is the Include file that contains the standardized labels associated with the specific device being programmed that will help make your code more readable to yourself and others. (This file was mentioned in the previous chapter.) Each MCU device has a specific Include file that is installed on your

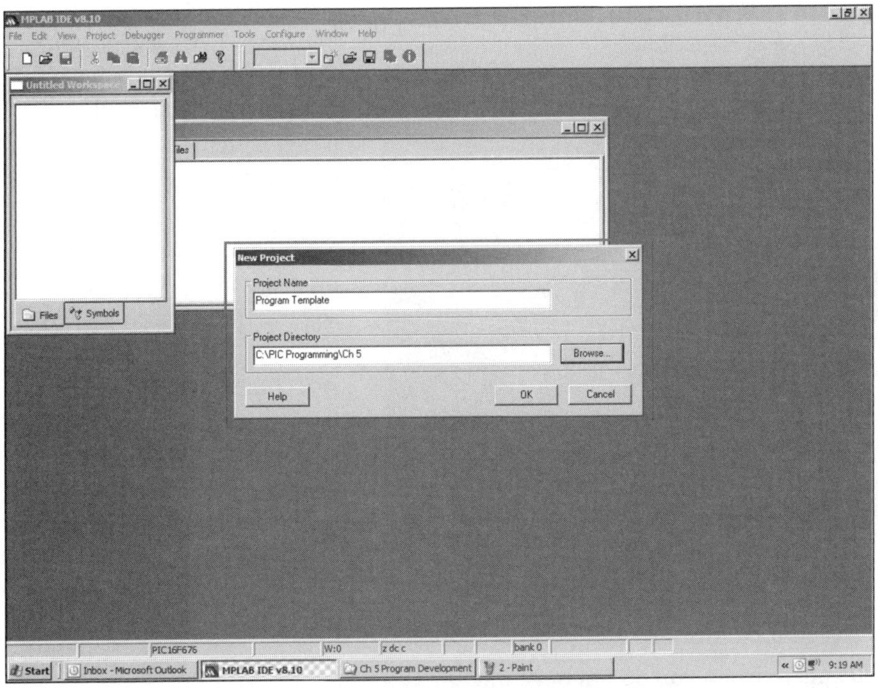

Figure 5-3 — NEW PROJECT File Management Dialog Box

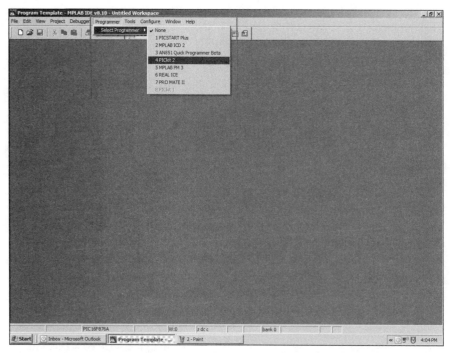

Figure 5-4 — Click on PROGRAMMER/SELECT-PROGRAMMER/PICKIT 2.

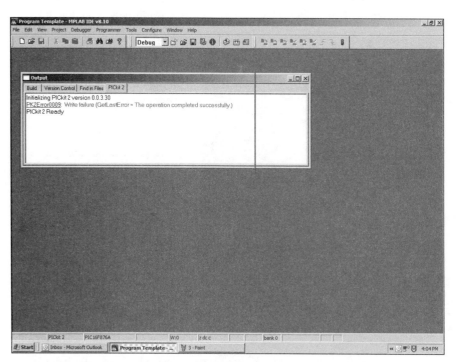

Figure 5-5 — This error message will appear when you do not have the programmer connected. Do not be concerned.

computer when you install *MPLAB IDE*; in the case of the PIC16F676, this file is named p16f676.inc. To add this file click on **PROJECT/ADD FILES TO PROJECT** on the menu bar (**Figure 5-10**). The file selection dialog box will pop up (**Figure 5-11**). Click on the "**HEADER FILES.inc**" line in the Files of Type selection box. Now navigate to where the canned .inc files are located in your file directory. If you did the default installation of *MPLAB IDE* these files will be located in: **C:\Program Files\ Microchip\MPASM Suite**. Once in this directory, scroll through the list of .inc files until you find P16F676 and select this file.

Step 8. You will next add the template file that is included on the CD ROM that accompanies this text. This template file is where the actual code of your program will be written. Insert the CD into the drive. Navigate through the directory of this CD to the file folder labeled Program Files/Ch 5 Program. Within that folder you will find a file named **TEMPLATE FOR THE P16F676.ASM** File. Copy this file and place the copy of the file into the project working directory on your C drive that you created in Step 1 (**C:\ PIC Programming\Ch 5**). If you would like, now is the time to rename this file to a more descriptive name. You may want to do this in future programs that you develop using this template. In this exercise the file name Template 16F676 is appropriate. Once the template file is installed in the project working directory, add this file to the project by clicking on **PROJECT/ ADD FILES TO PROJECT** on the menu bar (**Figure 5-12**). Navigate to the **PIC Programming/Ch 5 directory** and select the **TEMPLATE FOR THE P16F676.ASM** file.

Step 9. Click on **VIEW/ PROJECT** on the menu bar (**Figure 5-13**). This will allow you to see the files associated

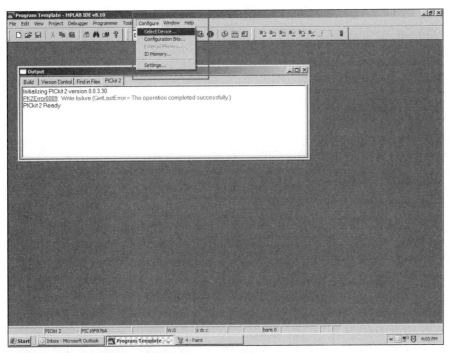

Figure 5-6 — Click on CONFIGURE/SELECT DEVICE.

with the project. You will see the directory for the project listed with the `.asm` file in the **Source Files** folder and the `.inc` file in the **Header Files** folder. If you double click on the **TEMPLATE FOR THE P16F676.ASM** file, the program working window will open and you can view and make changes to the program file (**Figure 5-14**). This is the point we want to get to so that we can start writing our programs. This would also be a good time to double click on the **P16F676. INC FILE** and view the contents of that file.

Step 10. There are just a few more steps to complete the process. The next steps will set up and configure the simulator that will allow you to run the program on your computer and debug the program before it is installed on the MCU via the programmer. The simulator is a very powerful and useful utility. Click on **DEBUGGER/SELECT TOOL/MPLAB SIM** on the menu bar (**Figure 5-15**). This selects the **MPLB IDE SIM** Simulator. Go back to **DEBUGGER/SETTINGS** (**Figure 5-16**) and a dialog box will pop up that allows you to set the device clock frequency that will be simulated (**Figure 5-17**). In the exercises in this text, you will be using the internal oscillator of the PIC16F676 which operates at 4 MHz, so select this frequency. Remember the configuration bits in Step 6 and Figure 15-9? The first configuration bit was to select the oscillator type. This is where you would make the selection for the other oscillator options available in the device (as detailed in Chapter 9 of the *PIC16F630/676 Data Sheet*.)

Step 11. In the *MPLAB IDE* menu bar find and click on the **BUILD** icon (circled in **Figure 5-18**). This application will turn your assembly code into machine language and save the program as machine language in a `.hex` file. The build process is automatic and it can happen pretty fast. If you end up with

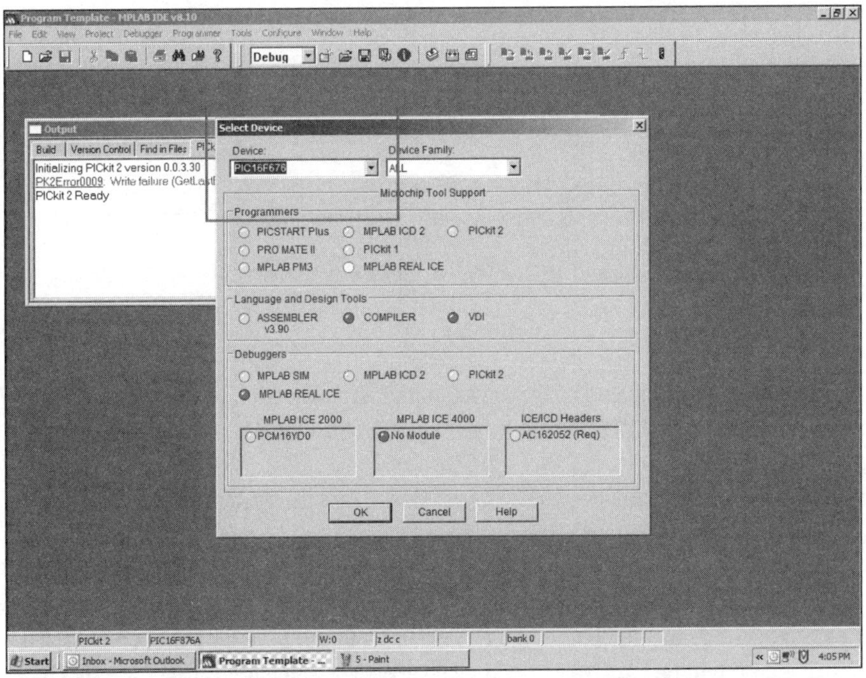

Figure 5-7 — Listing of All the MCU Devices Supported by *MPLAB IDE* and the *PICkit 2* Programmer. Highlight.

a dialog box with FAILURE and a red bar in it, there were some problems. If you followed the instructions so far, the Template program should build with no errors, and a dialog box will flash on the screen as illustrated in **Figure 5-19** momentarily and then disappear. If you select the Output window, you can verify that the build was successful (**Figure 5-20**). The Output window will also highlight areas of the code that caused a build to fail and is very helpful in de-bugging your program. The program is now ready to be sent to the MCU.

Hexadecimal File and Assembly Language File

If you look in the **PIC Programming/Ch5 directory** you will see all of the files associated with the project you just created (**Figure 5-21**). I would like to bring your attention to two of those files. The first has the extension .hex, this is a *hexadecimal file* that contains the actual program that will be loaded into the MCU in machine language, in hexadecimal form. The second file has the extension .asm, this is the *assembly language file* that contains the program in assembly language that you will be authoring very shortly. When you share files with other users, you can send them the .asm file and they can import that file into their program development software and then make changes to your program to meet their needs. Or you can send other users the .hex file so that they can directly send the program to their own devices.

Take a look at the program that is contained in the **Template for 16F676.asm** file in the editor window of *MPLAB IDE* but don't get overly concerned if you don't recognize what is going on in this program. You will learn a lot more about programming in future chapters of this text, and I will give a brief description of the program just to put the concluding activity of this chapter in context.

If you scroll down to the section of the code that looks like this:

```
        clrf    PORTA
        clrf    PORTC
        bsf     PORTA,5        ;start with pin 5 high, pin 0 low


;*********************************************************************************


;*********************************************************************************


    ;main program
    main
            movlw   b'00100001'    ;this is a mask used by the xorwf command to toggle
                                   ;pins 5 and 0
            xorwf   PORTA,f        ;XOR's the mask in the w-reg with PORTA and sets pins
                                   ;5 and 0 accordingly (toggles them-if on then off, if
                                   ;off then on
    call    delay200ms             ;this is a call to a delay subroutine that will delay
                                   ;200mS
            goto    main           ;go back and do it again
```

The first two lines that are at the end of the device initialization section of the code CLEARS all the I/O pins of both PORTA and PORTC. The third line SETS I/O pin 5 of PORTA so that 5-V is present on that pin.

The main body of the code continues by moving a "Mask" into the w-register (the working register) with 1's in bit 5 and bit 0 (which correspond to I/O pins 5 and 0 in PORTA). The next instruction does an exclusive OR comparison between the pin status of PORTA and the w-register. In an exclusive OR truth table, if both bit inputs are 0's or 1's, the outcome is 0; if the bit inputs are opposite of each other, the outcome is 1. What this means is that if PORTA I/O pin 5 is SET, then after this instruction it will be CLEARED, and vice versa. The same holds true for PORTA I/O pin 0. This will toggle those two pins on and off after each pass through this instruction.

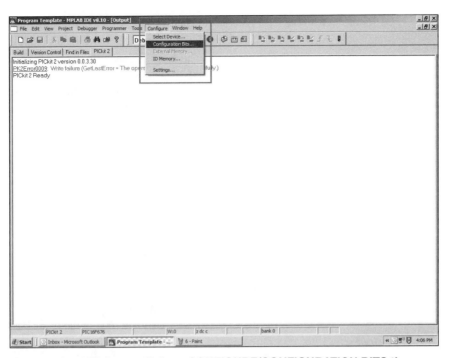

Figure 5-8 — When you click on CONFIGURE/CONFIGURATION BITS the
selection screen that allows you to configure selected set-up bits for the MCU
will be displayed.

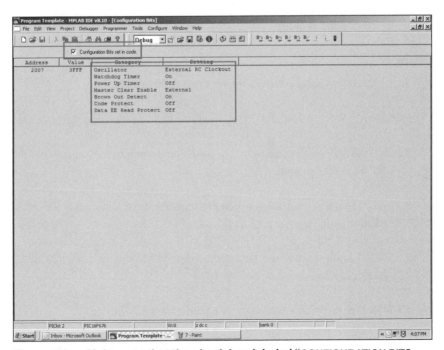

Figure 5-9 — Make sure that the check box labeled "CONFIGURATION BITS
SET IN CODE" is checked.

After the state of the PORTA pins are checked and XOR'ed, the program calls a delay subroutine that is 200 milliseconds long. Finally, after the delay, the program goes back to the beginning of main to do it all over again. The result is that LEDs that are connected to PORTA I/O pins 5 and 0 will alternately turn on and off with a period of 200 milliseconds.

Wire up the circuit illustrated in **Figure 5-22**. This circuit includes current limiting resistors and LEDs connected to pin 2 (PORTA, RA5) and pin 13 (PORTA, RA0) and ground.

A Few More Steps to Load the Program in Your Project to the MCU

Now that you have used the Project Wizard to develop your first project, let's go through a few more steps to load the program in your project to the MCU. The following steps will take you through connecting your computer to the PIC programmer, building your program (converting it from assembly language into machine language), and sending your program to the MCU RAM.

Step 12. Connect your programmer to the computer USB port and insert a PIC16F676 device into the programmer socket. In the *MPLAB IDE* menu bar, select **PROGRAMMER/ CONNECT**(**Figure 5-23**). If all goes well and the programmer and device are recognized, you should see a dialog box confirming the status (**Figure 5-24**).

Step 13. Click on the **PROGRAM TARGET DEVICE** icon in the menu bar (circled icon in **Figure 5-25**). If the programming was successful, the verification will be spelled out in the Output window (**Figure 5-26**).

You have now successfully used the Project Wizard to create a program project, inserted the required ancillary files into the project (the .inc and .asm files), selected the desired device and set up the configuration bits for the device, attached and connected your programmer, built the program, and finally installed the program on your PIC16F676 device. If you now plug the PIC into your prototyping board and turn on the power, the LEDs will flash alternately with an interval of 200 milliseconds.

Summary

During this chapter you learned how to use the *MPLAB IDE* Project Wizard to create a new project. Often you will use a program template to get you started and to shorten the program setup and development time.

Review Questions

5.1 List the steps required to list the files that make up a project.

5.2 Can you develop, test and debug programs without attaching the programmer?

5.3 Will the *MPLAB IDE* allow you to load a program into the target MCU device if the program did not assemble properly?

5.4 Which of the icons that allow you to access the target device memory should you use with great caution, or not at all?

5.5 Why is it important to use the standard default file structure when installing *MPLAB IDE* on your computer?

5.6 Which type of file is unique to each particular MCU device?

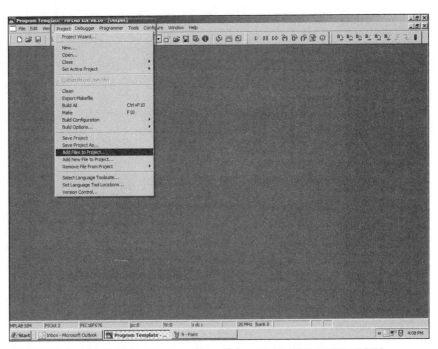

Figure 5-10 — To add the Include file, click on PROJECT/ADD FILES TO PROJECT.

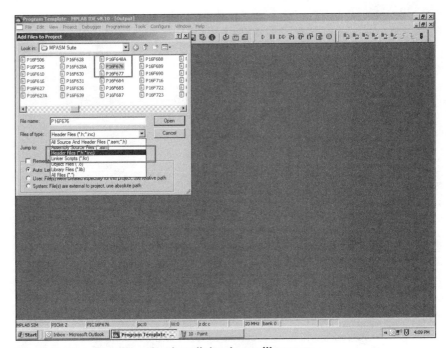

Figure 5-11 — The file selection dialog box will pop up.

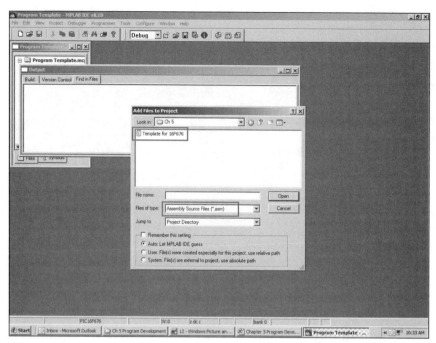

Figure 5-12 — Add this file to the project by clicking on PROJECT/ADD FILES TO PROJECT.

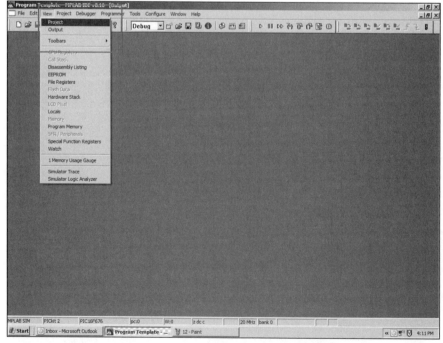

Figure 5-13 — To see the files associated with the project click on VIEW/PROJECT.

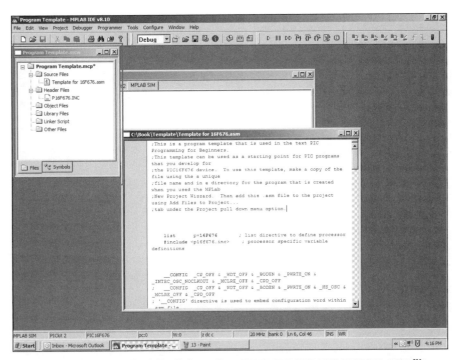

Figure 5-14 — If you double click on the TEMPLATE FOR THE P16F676.ASM file, the program working window will open and you can view and make changes to the program file.

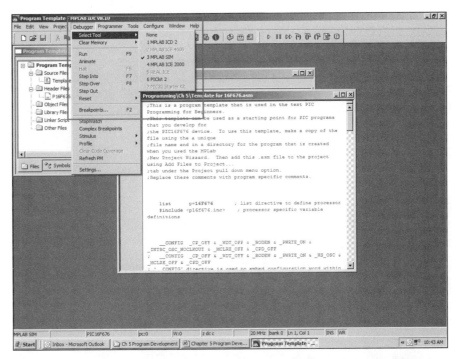

Figure 5-15 — If you double click on the TEMPLATE FOR THE P16F676.ASM file, the program working window will open and you can view and make changes to the program file.

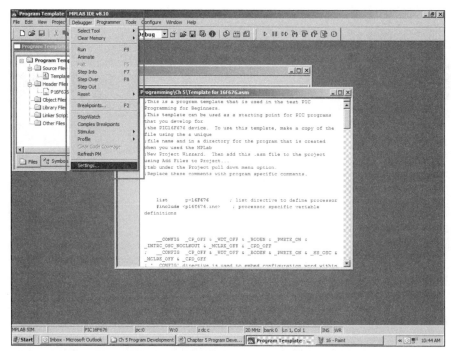

Figure 5-16 — After the MPLAB SIM Simulator is selected, go back to DEBUGGER/SETTINGS, highlighted above.

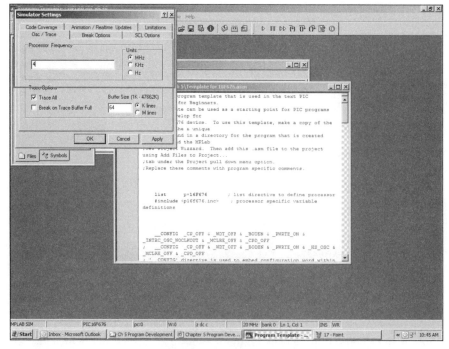

Figure 5 -17 — The dialog box pops up that allows you to set the device clock frequency that will be simulated.

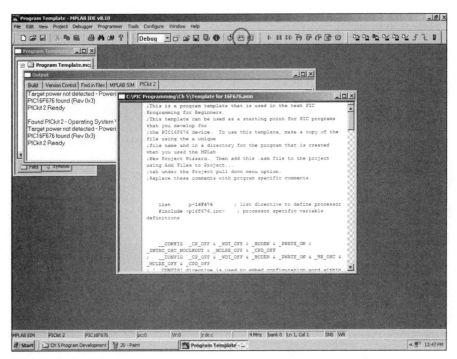

Figure 5 -18 — Click on the BUILD icon (circled above).

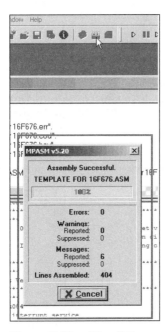

Figure 5-19 — The dialog box will flash momentarily on the screen as illustrated.

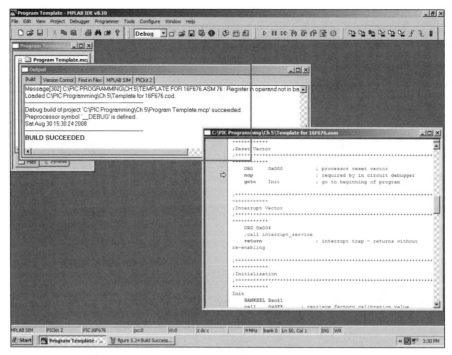

Figure 5-20 — Select the OUTPUT window to verify that the build was successful. The OUTPUT window will also highlight areas of the code that caused a build to fail and is very helpful in de-bugging your program.

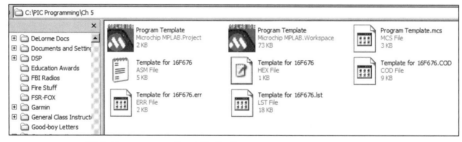

Figure 5-21 — PIC Programming/Ch5 directory showing all of the files associated with the project just created. Notice the file having the extension .hex, this is a *hexadecimal file* that contains the actual program that will be loaded into the MCU in machine language, in hexadecimal form. Notice also the file which has the extension .asm. This is the *assembly language file* that contains the program in assembly language.

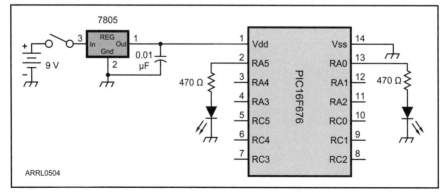

Figure 5-22 — This circuit includes current limiting resistors and LEDs connected to pin 2 (PORTA, RA5) and pin 13 (PORTA, RA0) and ground.

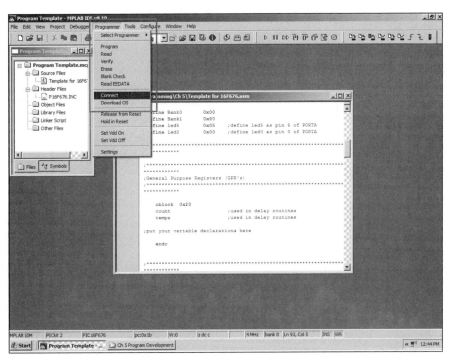

Figure 5-23 — In the *MPLAB IDE* menu bar, select PROGRAMMER/CONNECT.

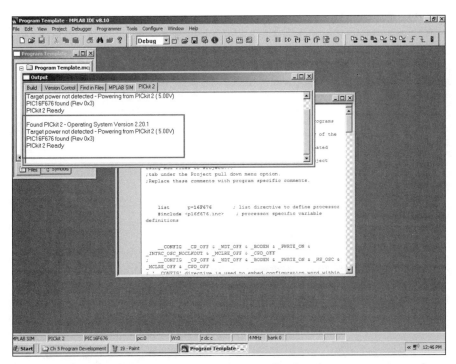

Figure 5-24 — You should see a dialog box confirming the programmer and device are recognized.

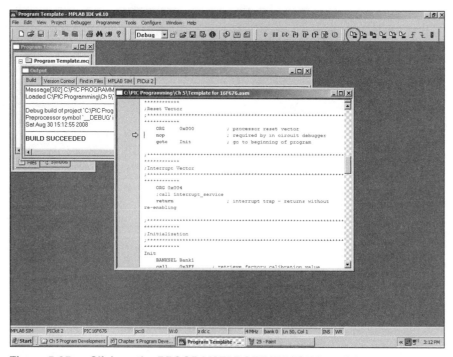

Figure 5-25 — Click on the PROGRAM TARGET DEVICE icon (circled above).

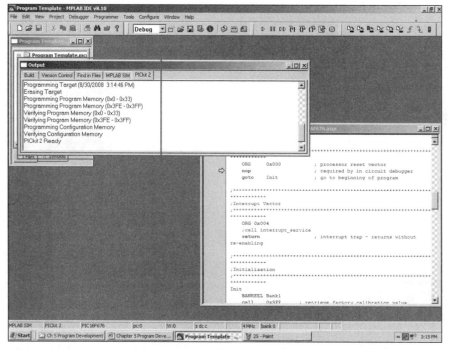

Figure 5-26 — If the programming was successful, the verification will be spelled out in the OUTPUT window as shown.

Working with Registers — the Most Important Chapter

Objective: To learn the purpose of the Special Function Registers, learn how to use memory bank switching to access Special Function Registers, and learn how to use selected Special Function Registers to configure the basic resources available in the PIC16F676.

Reading: *PIC16F630/676 Data Sheet,* pages 1, 2, 5-8, 7-13, 19-21, 27

Special Function Registers

As previously presented in the Chapter 2 "Inside the PIC16F676," there is a segment of the RAM within the device that is dedicated to device setup. This segment of RAM consists of a number of byte sized memory locations called registers that are used by the programmer to set up the resources of the device for a particular application. These registers are called Special Function Registers (SFR). Additionally there is a segment of this RAM that is used by the programmer for variables that are manipulated during the program execution. Why is understanding the use of these SFRs most important? As in any building project, as programming really is, having a firm foundation is critical to a long lasting, efficient, and useful project. If you truly understand the functions of the individual SFRs and how to access and manipulate the individual bits within those registers, you will be well on your way to understanding the PIC16F676 and how to access its full potential. I strongly urge you to spend some time with the information contained in this chapter and refer back to it often when initiating and developing your code.

Core Registers and Peripheral Registers

SFRs are divided into two sub categories, the labels of which, in reality, are just semantics and not really important to the fundamentals of understanding these registers. But touching on the semantic differences here will help in understanding the internal architecture of the PIC16F676. The two sets of registers are the core registers and the registers associated with the peripheral features of the device. The core registers deal with the basic setup, operation, and monitoring of the PIC16F676. The peripheral registers deal with the setup, operation, and monitoring of the ADC, Comparator and Timer 1 resources of the device. This chapter will focus on the core registers. The peripheral registers will be covered in later chapters that focus on each of the peripheral resources. For the time being, just be aware of the distinction between the two different sub categories of SFRs.

Device Setup Memory

You have seen previously in Figure 2-1 in Chapter 2, and in the memory diagrams of the readings that the device setup memory is divided into two banks, bank 0 and bank 1 (a portion of the memory map is duplicated in **Table 6-1**).

Bank 0 begins at memory address 0x00

Table 6-1

Device Setup Memory Map

Bank 0 memory location		Bank 1 memory location	
00h	indirect address	80h	indirect address
01h	TMR0	81h	OPTION_REG
02h	PCL	82h	PCL
03h	STATUS	83h	STATUS
04h	FSR	84h	FSR
05h	PORTA	85h	TRISA
07h	PORTC	87h	TRISC
0Ah	PCLATH	8Ah	PCLATH
0Bh	INTCON	8Bh	INTCON
0Ch	PIR1	8Ch	PIE1
0Eh	TMR1L	8Eh	PCON
0Fh	TMR1H		
10h	T1CON	90h	OSCCAL
		91h	ANSEL
		95h	WPUA
		96h	IOCA
19h	CMCON	99h	VRCON
		9Ah	EEDAT
		9Bh	EEADR
		9Ch	EECON1
		9Dh	EECON2
1Eh	ADRESH	9Eh	ADRESL
1Fh	ADCON0	9Fh	ADCON1

and ends at address 0x1f (32 bytes) and Bank 1 begins at memory address 0x80 and ends at address 0x9F (also 32 bytes). Within each bank, notice that the individual byte-sized registers are labeled with what are essentially descriptive mnemonics that help identify the function of the registers. Using these labels will help to make your code more readable. In Chapter 5, when you were developing a template for your first program, you were instructed to include an Include file (p16f676.inc) that is unique to the PIC16F676 device. Each of the different devices that you will encounter has a unique .inc file associated with it. This include file contains some valuable short cut labels or declarations that associate SFR labels that are used in the documentation for the device (and this text) to the numeric value for the specific memory location assigned to the register. For instance, the following is an extract from the file p16f676.inc.

```
STATUS       EQU     H'0003'
INTCON       EQU     H'000B'
OPTION_REG   EQU     H'0081'
PORTA        EQU     H'0005'
TRISA        EQU     H'0085'
PORTC        EQU     H'0007'
TRISC        EQU     H'0087'
```

(You can view the entire contents of this file either from *MPLAB IDE* or by using *NOTEPAD* and opening the file located at **C:\Program Files\Microchip\MPASM Suite** if you installed *MPLAB IDE* using the standard installation. It would be helpful early in your programming experience to print out the contents of the .inc file for easy reference while developing your code. The contents of the p16f676.inc file is in Appendix D.)

These labels instruct the *MPLAB IDE* complier to assign or equate the mnemonic representation of the STATUS register to the memory location 0x03, and so on. If you notice in the data memory map, the memory location for the STATUS register is in fact 0x03. Using the short hand mnemonic for the registers helps in the "readability" and understanding of your program code. For instance, if I wanted to SET the bit to switch the memory bank to Bank 1, I could use the following line of code:

```
bsf    0x03,0x05
```

This line of code bit sets the **f** register (bsf) 5th bit in the register located in memory location 0x03. The register located in memory location 0x03 is the STATUS register and the 5th bit is the Register Bank Select bit. This line of code is not particularly meaningful at first glance, however the readability can be improved by using the short hand mnemonic assignments contained in the .inc file:

```
bsf    STATUS, RP0
```

Now let's take a detailed look at the individual registers that are used to set up and manipulate the PIC16F676 resources. The format that will be used in this discussion of the individual registers will include the bank where the register is located (0, 1 or both), the descriptive mnemonic assigned to the register in the .inc file, the descriptive mnemonic assigned to the individual bits within the register (MSB [Most Significant Bit] to the left, LSB [Least Significant Bit] to the right) and a short verbal description of purpose of the individual bits.

Bank 0	STATUS						
IRP	RP1	RP0	TO	PD	Z	DC	C
Reserved	Reserved	Register Bank	Time-out bit	Power-down bit	Zero bit	Digit Carry/Borrow bit	Carry/Borrow bit

STATUS

The STATUS register is used to control the memory bank that is being addressed, to determine the reset status of the device and the status results of arithmetic operations during program execution.

Bit 0x05, or the RP0 bit is used to switch between memory bank0 and bank1. SETTING the RP0 bit switches to bank1.

There are numerous ways that the PIC16F676 can be reset, or restarted, that are beyond the scope of this text. The bit 0x04 or the TO time-out bit is SET by the internal workings of the device after initial power is applied to the device, after a CLRWDT (clear watchdog timer), or sleep instruction is executed. This bit is CLEARED after a watchdog timer time-out has occurred. The bit 0x03 or PD power-down bit is SET after initial power is applied to the device or by execution of the CLRWDT instruction. The bit is CLEARED after executing a sleep instruction. You will not be using these bits during the exercises in this text.

Bits 0x00, 0x01 and 0x02 are used to monitor the outcome of arithmetic operations performed while your programs are running.

Bit 0x02, the Z or *zero bit* is SET if the arithmetic or logic operation resulted in zero. For instance if you are incrementing an 8-bit memory location and the program increments the memory location that contains 255 (b'11111111'), the increment results in zero (b'00000000') being placed in the memory location. This operation will SET the Z bit of the STATUS register. The Z bit will be used extensively during the exercises of this text.

Bit 0x01, the DC or *digit carry/borrow bit* will be SET if there is a carry from the low nibble of a memory location into the high nibble of the memory location. For instance if a memory location contains 111 (b'01101111') and it is incremented by one the result in the memory location would be 112 (b'01110000'). Bit 4 of the memory location is SET due to a carry condition and therefore the DC bit in the STATUS register will be SET. The DC bit will not be used during the exercises of this text.

Bit 0x00, the C or *carry/borrow bit* will be SET if there is an operation that results in a '*overflow*', or *carry out of the MSB*, of an 8-bit memory location. For example, back to a memory location that contains 255 (b'11111111'). If 1 were added to this memory location the result would be 256 (b'1 00000000'.) The result would have overflowed the MSB of a word sized memory location or variable by 'carrying' the overflow to the upper byte of the word. In this case, the C bit would be SET to indicate that a carry had occurred (and also the Z bit would be set because the operation also SET the original byte to zero). The C bit will be used extensively during the exercises of this text.

Bank 1	OPTION_REG Option Register						
RAPU	INTEDG	T0CS	T0SE	PSA	PS2	PS1	PS0
PORTA Pull-up Enable	Interrupt Edge Select bit	TMR0 Clock Source Select bit	TMR0 Source Edge Select bit	Prescaler Assignment bit	Prescaler Rate Select bit	Prescaler Rate Select bit	Prescaler Rate Select bit

OPTION_REG

The *OPTION_REG register* is used to control various resource options including Timer0 (TRM0), Watch Dog Timer (WDT), RA2/INT interrupts and/or if *weak pull-up resistors* are enabled on the PORTA I/O pins.

SETTING bit 0x07, **RAPU**, will disable the weak pull-up resistors on PORTA I/O pins. The weak pull-up resistors provide a +5-volt current source on the I/O pins that ensure the appropriate pins are in a high state when not purposely placed in the low state. The RAPU pin enables or disables all pull-up resistors, the individual resistors are addressed in the WPUA Pull-up Register that will be covered later. This bit will be used in exercises in this text.

SETTING bit 0x06, **INTEDG**, will allow the rising edge of a triggering signal attached to pin RA2 to generate an interrupt. Interrupts will be covered in detail in a subsequent chapter. CLEARING INTEDG will allow the falling edge of the triggering signal to generate an interrupt.

Bit 0x05, **T0CS**, assigns the clocking source for Timer0. SETTING the bit causes the TMR0 to respond to the clocking signal attached to pin RA2 while CLEARING the bit causes TMR0 to use an internal clock source.

If T0CS is SET and the TMR0 clock source is attached to RA2, then SETTING bit 0x04, **T0SE**, will increment TMR0 on the rising edge of the clock signal; CLEARING T0SE will increment TMR0 on the falling edge.

Bit 0x03, **PSA**, assigns the prescaler to either TMR0 or the WDT. SETTING PSA assigns the prescaler to WDT. CLEARING PSA will assign the prescaler to TMR0 and this bit will be used in exercises in this text.

The three bits 0x00 though 0x02, **PS2:PS0** (which signifies PS2, PS1 and PS0) determines the prescaler rate. Refer to the table on page 12 of the *PIC16F630/676 Data Sheet* for the full table of bit values to set the prescaler. As an example, if you want to increment TMR0 every 8th clock count, in other words divide the clock counts by a factor of 8, you would SET PS2:PS0 to b'010' (PS2=0, PS1=1, PS0=0). This essentially increases the usable time delay of TMR0 eight times.

Bank 1	PCON Power Control Register						
X	X	X	X	X	X	POR	BOD
Unimplemented bit	Unimplemented	Unimplemented	Unimplemented	Unimplemented	Unimplemented	Power-on Reset Status	Brown-out Detect Status

PCON

The *Power Control Register* is rarely changed by the casual MCU programmer. This register essentially contains flags that can be used to test if the device has been reset (forced to start the program from the beginning) due to power interrupts, or power first applied to the device (Power-on Reset), or if the reset occurred because of a reduction in the power source voltage below the "brown-out" level, typically 2.1-volts. In this specific register, the flags are opposite to the other flag registers, SET being no reset, CLEAR being a reset occurred.

Bit 0x01, **POR**, *Power-on Reset* Status will be CLEARED if a power-on reset of the device occurred. You SET this bit in software to reset the flag so that a subsequent power-on reset can be indicated.

Bit 0x00, **BODIE**, *Brown-out Detect Status* will be CLEARED if a brown-out condition reset the device. You SET this bit in software to reset the flag so that a subsequent brown-out reset can be indicated.

Bank 1	OSCCAL Internal Oscillator Calibration Register						
CAL5	CAL4	CAL3	CAL2	CAL1	CAL0	X	X
6-bit Signed Oscillator Calibration bit	6-bit Signed Oscillator Calibration bit	6-bit Signed Oscillator Calibration bit	6-bit Signed Oscillator Calibration bit	6-bit Signed Oscillator Calibration bit	6-bit Signed Oscillator Calibration bit	Unimplemented	Unimplemented

OSCCAL

The *Internal Oscillator Calibration Register* is a specialized register that you use to store an *oscillator calibration value* that is determined at the time the PIC16F676 device is manufactured. The calibration value is stored in a specific memory location within the MCU's flash RAM. This calibration value can be useful if you intend to use the internal oscillator of the device as the clock source and timing issues are critical. This calibration value can improve the accuracy of the internal oscillator and therefore the accuracy of the clock. There are some specific precautions that you need to consider when using this calibration value. The calibration value is unique to the specific device, and the calibration value is perishable if you ever totally erase the flash RAM of the device. You can read the calibration value using *MPLAB IDE*, record the value for the device for future reference, and later program this value into the OSCCAL register when the device is re-programmed. Better yet, do not erase the device RAM! In normal use, the previous program stored in RAM will be over written by the new program so there should seldom be a need to erase a device (unless you want to protect some code that had been previously installed on the device). This precaution will be emphasized again in other areas of the text.

While you are studying the code examples in this book, you will see the specific program code that is needed to take the factory determined oscillator calibration value stored in the RAM and transfer this value into the OSCCAL register. This is the segment of the code that accomplishes that task:

```
BANKSEL    Bank1        ;command line to select Bank 1 where the calibration value is
                        ;stored (location 3FF)
call       0x3FF        ;retrieves factory calibration value and puts it into the W
                        ;register (working register)
movwf      OSCCAL       ;move the contents of the W register into the OSCCAL register
                        ;(also located in Bank 1)
BANKSEL    Bank0        ;command line to go back to Bank 0 where the bulk
                        ;of the program work is performed.
```

Don't get concerned about understanding this segment of the program code. That is the purpose of this book and the code will be covered in detail later. Basically what is happening with these four lines of code;

1. Switch over the RAM bank 1 so that the calibration value can be accessed;

2. Put this value into a working register where we can do something with the value;

3. Move the value from the working register into the OSCCAL register (you will soon learn that virtually every movement of values from one register [memory location] to another register must pass through the **w** [working] register;)

4. Switch back to bank 0 where most of the program operations will occur. After each instruction line, the information following the semi-colon (;) represents a comment statement. These statements are ignored by the *MPLAB IDE* and are not part of the program. These comments are for communicating with the programmer and reader of the code to help explain what is happening within the code.

Bank 1		TRISA PORTA Tri-state Register					
X	X	TRISA5	TRISA4	TRISA3	TRISA2	TRISA1	TRISA0
Unimplemented	Unimplemented	RA5	RA4	RA3	RA2	RA1	RA0

Bank 1		TRISC PORTC Tri-state Register					
X	X	TRISC5	TRISC4	TRISC3	TRISC2	TRISC1	TRISC0
Unimplemented	Unimplemented	RC5	RC4	RC3	RC2	RC1	RC0

Tri-state Registers — TRISA and TRISC

Tri-state Registers. The I/O pins of the PIC16F676 are arranged in two banks of 6-pins each and are called PORTA and PORTC. Other MCU devices may have additional or less ports. There is a Tri-state Register for each port labeled TRISA and TRISC for the PIC16F676. The TRIS# registers control the directionality of the individual pins within a port. SETTING the appropriate bit in the TRIS# register will cause the corresponding pin to be an input, CLEARING the bit will cause the corresponding pin to be an output. When a pin is assigned to be an input pin, the pin is placed in a high impedance state. This assumes that the pin resources have not been assigned to another peripheral resource such as a Comparator or ADC resource. There is one additional exception on PORTA I/O pin 3 (RA3). This pin can only be used as an input because it serves a dual purpose as the master reset pin.

Bank 1	WPUA Weak Pull-up Register						
X	X	WPUA5	WPUA4	X	WPUA2	WPUA1	WPUA0
Unimplemented	Unimplemented	RA5	RA4	Unimplemented	RA2	RA1	RA0

Weak Pull-up Register WPUA

Weak Pull-up Register. PORTA I/O pins have pull-up resistors internally connected to the I/O pins (with the exception again of I/O pin (RA3)). These pull-up resistors provide an internal current source that will hold the associated pin high when the pin is in the input state and not deliberately pulled low by an external action (such as closing a switch). By SETTING the appropriate bit, the weak pull-up resistor on the associated pin will be enabled. You must also globally enable all the weak pull-up pins by SETTING the RAPU bit in the OPTION_REG register. In other words, you would allow the appropriate pull-up to be enabled by SETTING the bit in the WPUA register, then actually enable all the allowed pull-ups by SETTING the RAPU bit in the OPTION_REG register. PORTA I/O pin 3 does not have a weak pull-up resistor again because of the dual purpose of this pin. PORTC does not have any weak pull-up resistors at all.

Bank 1	ANSEL Analog Select Register						
ANS7	ANS6	ANS5	ANS4	ANS3	ANS2	ANS1	ANS0
RC3	RC2	RC1	RC0	RA4	RA3	RA2	RA0

ANSEL

The Analog Select Register is the final register that will be covered in this chapter. This register allows you to assign either analog or digital resources to the selected I/O pin depending if there will be analog or digital voltages applied to the pin. For instance, if there will be strictly +5 or 0 V applied to a pin from a digital source, the ANSEL register would be setup as digital "channel." On the other hand, if analog voltages are going to be compared with the Comparator, or measured with the ADC resources, the ANSEL register would be set up as an analog "channel." Not all pins of PORTA or PORTC can have analog resources assigned to them and therefore some I/O pins are strictly digital and there is no capacity to control the analog or digital channel assignment to those pins. This is why only PORTA RA0, RA1, RA2 and RA4 (again PORTA I/O pin 3 (RA3) has a dual purpose therefore is an out of sequence exception), and PORTC RC0, RC1, RC2, and RC3 have associated ANSEL bits because either ADC or Comparator resources can be assigned to these pins. SETTING the appropriate bit will assign that pin as an analog input pin, CLEARING the appropriate bit will assign the pin as a digital I/O pin.

SETTING the ANSEL bit will also automatically disable the digital circuitry associated with the pin, disable the weak pull-up resistors on the pin, and disable any interrupt-on-change assigned to the pin. Care also must be taken to ensure that if a pin is to be used as an analog input pin, that the bit in the associated TRIS# register is also SET to make the pin an input pin.

These are some of the most important core registers that will be used in the next chapter when we discuss setting up resources of the PIC16F676 device in the early part of the program. There are other registers that are specific to particular MCU resources that will be covered in the detail in the chapters that cover the specific peripheral resources.

Summary

Registers are special memory locations that are made up of 8-switches (bits) that allow you to set up the resources available within the PIC16F676 to accomplish specific tasks. The registers are assigned a descriptive label that will be used when we write programs. The individual bits within each register can be either SET or CLEARED. It is up to the programmer to SET or CLEAR the register bits to set up the device resources as needed.

The STATUS register is used to control the memory bank that is being addressed, to determine the reset status of the device and the results of arithmetic operations performed during program execution.

The OPTION_REG is used to control various resource options including Timer0 (TRM0), Watch Dog Timer (WDT), RA2/INT interrupts and/or if weak pull-up resistors are enabled on the PORTA I/O pins.

The OSCCAL register is a specialized register where you load an oscillator calibration value that is determined at the time the PIC16F676 device is manufactured and stored in a specific memory location within the MCU's flash RAM to improve the oscillator and clock accuracy.

The TRISA and TRISC registers control the directionality of the individual pins within a port and makes the individual I/O pins input (Tri-state, high impedance) or output.

The WPUA register determines if pull-up resistors are internally connected to the I/O pins of PORTA (with the exception again of I/O pin 3 (RA3) which can be assigned dual purposes that conflict with output operations). PORTC has no internal pull-up resistors.

The ANSEL register allows you to assign either analog or digital resources to the selected I/O pin depending if there will be analog or digital voltages applied to the pin.

Review Questions

6.1 Define SET and CLEAR.

State the appropriate register and bit to accomplish the following actions. In your answer list the register label name, the actual memory location in hexadecimal, the bit label and the bit number. Use the question 6.2 as the example.

6.2 Which bit is manipulated to switching to Bank 1?

6.3 What register and bit would you read to determine if an arithmetic action resulted in a zero result?

6.4 Enable the weak pull-up resistors on PORTA 2?

6.5 Disable all weak pull-up resistors associated with PORTA?

6.6 To what register would you load the factory determined internal oscillator calibration value?

6.7 How would you configure the appropriate registers to make PORTA, 0;PORTA, 2, and PORTA, 4 as digital outputs, and PORTA, 1 as an analog input.

Instruction Set
Overview

Objective: To briefly review the instruction set or opcodes that are available to build programs for the PIC16F676 device. The review will include examples of how the instructions are implemented in code.

Reading: *PIC16F630/676 Data Sheet*, pages 71-82.

Computer Program Languages

A *computer program* is a collection of instructions or commands that are arranged to accomplish some task. The collection of instructions and the rules that must be followed to use those instructions (called *syntax*) make up the *computer program language.* There are a number of different computer languages that range from those that are considered *high level* languages that are more like the language we use in everyday life, to *low level* languages that are somewhat like everyday language but with a structure that is related to the language used by the computer, to *machine* language that is the collection of instructions or *commands* in binary form that are actually used by the computer. *Assembly language* which is a low level language presented in this text is a bridge between higher level languages and machine language. To use assembly language, the user needs a firm understanding of the internal architecture of the MCU being programmed. In addition, the user needs to break up the end task to be accomplished in to small manageable sections. For example, consider the act of tying your shoes. A computer program to accomplish this task in a high level language might be "tie your right shoe; then tie your left shoe." An assembly language program might be "locate right shoe; grasp left end of shoe lace in left hand and right end of shoe lace in right hand; cross your right and over your left hand"…and so on. A machine language program would go into further detail and look at the neural impulses needed to move the muscles in your arms and hands. Why would one want to work with assembly or machine language? The bottom line is execution speed and efficiency. The trade-off is that it will take more time and thought to develop an assembly language program and it in all likelihood would be limited for use to one MCU device or the related family of devices for which the program is developed.

Assembly Language Instructions Set Categories

Now with that daunting context in mind, it really isn't that difficult to use assembly language. The vocabulary of the assembly language used by the PIC16F676 and the related family of Microchip microcontrollers consists of only 35 words. And just as in any language, there is a small number of vocabulary words that are used often, others used infrequently. The assembly language instruction set is divided into **four basic categories**: operations that manipulate a *byte*, operations that manipulate *bits*, operations that use *literal numbers (constants)*, and operations that control the *program flow*. The action words in the assembly language vocabulary are called *opcodes*. The byte, bit, memory location, or program line that is being acted upon, changed, or manipulated in the operation is called the **operand.**

The *MPLAB IDE* is an umbrella software package that manages a number of other software packages that are used to develop the program. The *Editor* is a word-processor-like program where you will author the program. The *MPASM Assembler* translates the assembly language code that you develop in the *Editor* into the machine language code that is loaded into the MCU program memory. The *Simulator* allows you to run the program code within software to monitor the flow of the program, predict execution times and debug the program. The assembler looks for the vocabulary words of the assembly language that are used within the context of the accepted syntax for the language. If the vocabulary or the syntax are used in error, the assembler will terminate the assembly process and give you a hint as to the error(s) that need attention. If the vocabulary or the syntax are correct, the assembler will generate a collection of files, including the machine language file, that facilitate the loading of the program into the MCU. Using the vocabulary within the rules specified by the syntax does not necessarily mean that your program will run correctly, just that you followed the rules. Making your program also run correctly requires the use of the simulator, and some trial and error.

The Instruction Set or Opcodes of Assembly Language

The remainder of the chapter will detail the opcodes that make up the vocabulary of the assembly language. There are a few conventions to keep in mind during this discussion. The letter f refers to a register that is the target of the opcode and the register could be a *Special Function Register* (SFR) or a variable memory location. The letter w refers to the w-register. Virtually all actions on registers need to pass through the w-register. Consider the w-register as your working register. The letter k refers to a constant. A constant is some static numerical value that can be assigned an alias in the definition section of the program code or it can be an actual number. Constants can be in decimal form (identified with a period [.] before the number — .123), hexadecimal form (identified with 0x at the beginning of the hex number — 0x7b), or binary form (identified by a leading b and the binary numbers between apostrophes — b'01111011'). The letter d refers to the destination register where the result of the opcode action will be stored. If d=0 then the result will be stored in the w-register, if d=1 then the result will be stored in the target register (f) of the opcode. In the code examples in this text you will see the letters f and w used in place of the numbers 1 and 0. If you review the contents of the PIC16F676 .inc file you will find that the letters f and w are defined as aliases for the numbers 1 and 0 respectively. The letters are used in place of the numbers to make the code more readable and more consistent with the instruction set summary that is included in the device documentation.

The STATUS Register

There is one more topic that needs to be discussed before getting into the specifics of the opcodes — *the STATUS register*. The STATUS register is modified when many of the opcodes are executed and it is important to be familiar with how and when this SFR is changed. Of the 8-bits in the STATUS, the most commonly monitored bits are the *Zero bit*, Z and the *Carry/Borrow bit*, C.

Bank				STATUS			
RP	RP1	RP0	TO	PD	Z	DC	C
Reserved	Reserved	Register Bank	Time-out bit	Power-down bit	Zero bit	Digit Carry/Borrow bit	Carry/Borrow bit

STATUS

The STATUS Register contains flags that are SET or CLEARED by arithmetic operations, specific reset conditions, and a control bit for register bank selection. The reset flags will not be covered in this text. *The Digit Carry/Borrow flag bit, DC*, is SET when there is an overflow of a nibble within an operand. This flag is not used during the exercises of this text. *The Register Bank bit, RP0*, is used extensively to switch between the memory banks by using BANKSEL. If RP0 is SET, memory bank 1 is accessed, with RP0 CLEAR, memory bank 0 is accessed. The *Zero flag bit, z*, is SET when an arithmetic operation or other operation on an operand results in 0x00. If Z is CLEAR the result was not zero. The *Carry/Borrow flag bit, C*, has two uses. If the C bit is SET, then an arithmetic operation on an operand resulted in an overflow from 0xff to 0x00. If the

C bit is CLEAR, an overflow did not occur. The C bit also accepts the bit that falls out of a register. When the bits are rotated either left or right, the old contents of the C bit is rotated back into the register.

Opcode Descriptions

```
addlw          Add literal and w

Syntax:        addlw           k
STATUS bits affected:    C, DC, Z
```

The `addlw` opcode takes the literal operand and adds it to the contents of the w-register. The result is loaded into the w-register overwriting the previous contents of that register. The PIC16F676 is an 8-bit device so arithmetic operations that use numbers greater than 255 or have a result greater than 255 will require the use of binary math techniques and *multi-byte levels*. There are comprehensive libraries of multi-byte level math routines posted on the Microchip Web site that can be accessed and incorporated in your code with minor modification depending on the MCU device. In the code exercises in this text, this opcode is used primarily to convert the numbers 0 through 9 into the ASCII code needed to display those numbers as text on an LCD. This requires adding 48 to the number to convert the number into the equivalent ASCII code (well within 1-byte). This opcode is used with moderate frequency.

Example code:

```
movlw          .48
addlw          .123
addlw          b'01111011'
addlw          0x7b
```

```
addwf          Add w-register and f

Syntax:        addwf,          f or d
STATUS bits affected:    C, DC, Z
```

The `addwf` opcode is similar to `addlw` except that the contents of the f register are added to the w-register. The result is either loaded into the f or w-register as set by the operand letter identifier or the number 1 or 0. This opcode is used infrequently.

Example code:

```
movlw          .23
movwf          var1
movlw          .48
addwf          var1, f
```

In this case the operation would add 23 and 48 and the result loaded into and overwriting the contents of var1.

```
movlw          .23
movwf          var1
movlw          .48
addwf          var1, w
```

In this case the sum would be loaded into and overwriting the contents of the w-register.

---

andlw   AND the literal and w-register

Syntax: andlw, k
STATUS bits affected: Z

Table 7.1 – Boolean Truth Table for the AND Operation

Input		Output
A	B	
0	0	0
0	1	0
1	0	0
1	1	1

The andlw opcode takes the literal operand and logically ANDs it with the contents of the w-register with the result loaded into the w-register. **Table 7-1** contains the Boolean truth table for the AND operation.

This opcode is useful to mask specific bits within a byte. This opcode is used with moderate frequency primarily in masking operations.

```
movfw       var1
andlw       b'11110000'
```

This code masks the low nibble of the byte in var1 and stores the high nibble, unchanged, into the w-register (the low nibble is returned to b'0000').

andwf   AND w with f register

Syntax: andwf, d or f
STATUS bits affected: Z

The andwf opcode is similar to andlw. andwf takes the contents of the operand variable or memory location and logically ANDs it with the contents of the w-register with the result loaded into either the w or f register. This opcode is used infrequently.

Example code:

```
movfw       var1
andwf       var2, w
```

This code compares the contents of var1 and var2 with the result placed in the w-register leaving the contents of var2 unchanged.

bcf   CLEAR the specified bit in the f register

Syntax: bcf   var1, 2
STATUS bits affected: None

The bcf opcode is used to manipulate (CLEAR) a single bit within the operand register. This opcode is used frequently.

Example code:

```
bcf        OPTION_REG, RAPU
```

This code CLEARS bit 7 of the OPTION_REG to enable individually enabled weak pull-up resistors. RAPU is defined in the PIC16F676.inc file as equal to 7. An alternative form for this instruction would be:

```
bcf        OPTION_REG, 7
```

bsf   SET the specified bit in the f register

Syntax: bsf   var1, 2
STATUS bits affected: None

The bsf opcode is used to manipulate (SET) a single bit within the operand register and is the opposite opcode to bcf. This opcode is used frequently.

Example code:

```
bsf         OPTION_REG, RAPU
```

This opcode SETS bit 7 of the OPTION_REG to disable weak pull-up resistors. RAPU is defined in the PIC16F676.inc file as equal to 7. An alternative form for this instruction would be:

```
bsf         OPTION_REG, 7
```

```
btfss       Test a specified bit in f, skip next instruction if the bit is SET
```

```
Syntax:  btfss var1, 7
STATUS bits affected: None
```

The opcode is used to make branching decisions based on the state of an individual bit within the operand register. If the bit of interest is SET, the next instruction is skipped and a nop instruction is executed instead (this makes the number of instruction cycles the same regardless of whether the next instruction is skipped or executed). The program continues with the instruction following the skipped instruction. If the bit of interest is CLEAR, the next instruction is executed. This opcode is used frequently.

Example code:

```
btfss       INTCON, T0IF
goto        no_TMR0_interrupt
movwf       var1
```

This code checks the status of the TMR0 interrupt flag in the INTCON register. If the bit is SET (an interrupt occurred) the next goto opcode is skipped and the program continues with the movwf instruction. If the bit is CLEAR (an interrupt did not occur) the goto instruction is executed.

```
btfsc       Bit test f, skip next instruction if CLEAR
```

```
Syntax:  btfsc var1, 7
STATUS bits affected: None
```

The opcode is the opposite of the btfss opcode and also used to make branching decisions based on the state of an individual bit within the operand register. If the bit of interest is CLEAR, the next instruction is skipped and a nop instruction is executed instead. (This makes the number of instruction cycles the same regardless of if the next instruction is skipped or executed.) The program continues with the instruction following the skipped instruction. If the bit of interest is SET, the next instruction is executed. This opcode is used frequently.

Example code:

```
btfsc       INTCON, T0IF
goto        TMR0_interrupt
movwf       var1
```

This code checks the status of the TMR0 interrupt flag in the INTCON register. If the bit is CLEAR (an interrupt did not occur) the next goto opcode is skipped and the program continues with the movwf instruction. If the bit is SET (an interrupt occurred) the goto instruction is executed.

```
call      Call to execute a subroutine
```

```
Syntax:  call   subroutine_label
STATUS bits affected: None
```

The `call` opcode causes a jump to the subroutine that is identified by the label in the operand. Upon a subroutine `call`, the program counter for the first instruction to be executed on return from the subroutine is pushed onto the hardware Stack and a jump to the subroutine is executed. There is limited stack space so the number of nested calls to subroutines must be considered. After the return from the subroutine, program counter is pulled from the Stack, to cause a jump back to the calling program. This opcode is used frequently.

Example code:

```
call      interrupt_service
```

```
clrf      CLEAR the register or variable f
```

```
Syntax:  clrf   var1
STATUS bit affected: Z
```

The `clrf` opcode CLEARS the contents of the operand variable or register to `0x00` and also SETS the `z` bit of the STATUS register. This opcode is used with moderate frequency.

Example:

```
clrf      var1
```

```
clrw      CLEAR the W-register
```

```
Syntax:  clrw
STATUS bit affected: Z
```

The `clrw` opcode CLEARS the contents of the w-register to `0x00`. There is no operand needed for this instruction since the w-register is implied by the opcode. The `z` bit of the STATUS register is SET by the execution of this opcode. This opcode is used with moderate frequency.

Example:

```
clrw
```

```
clrwdt    CLEAR the Watchdog Timer
```

```
Syntax:  clrwdt
STATUS bits affected: TO, PD
```

The opcode `clrwdt` resets the Watchdog Timer and the prescaler when it is assigned to the Watchdog Timer. This opcode also CLEARS the TO and PD interrupt flags in the STATUS register. There is no operand argument for this opcode. This opcode is used infrequently.

Example:

```
clrwdt
```

comf   Complement the contents of the f register

```
Syntax:       comf        var1, d or f
STATUS bit affected:   Z
```

The opcode comf complements the contents of the operand variable or register and loads the result into either the operand target register or the w-register. Complementing a binary number turns 0's into 1's and 1's into 0's. For instance if the contents of var1 was b'00001111', the result of executing comf var1, f would result in the value b'11110000' being loaded into var1. Complements are frequently used in *two's complement arithmetic*. The subtrahend is turned into a two's complement which is the negative of the absolute value of the subtrahend. Once the subtrahend is negative (complemented) it can be added to accomplish the subtraction. The two's complement method of subtraction has the advantage of not requiring that the sign of the number to be analyzed to determine whether the operation is addition or subtraction. This opcode is used infrequently and primarily in binary mathematics algorithms.

Example:

```
comf         var1, w
```

---

decf   Decrement the contents of the operand.

```
Syntax:       decf        var1, d or f
STATUS bit affected: Z
```

The opcode decf decrements the contents of the operand variable or register and the result is loaded into the f or w-register as specified. If the decrement results in zero, the Z bit is SET in the STATUS register. This opcode is used infrequently.

Example:

```
decf         var1, f
btfss        STATUS, Z
goto         not_zero_routine
movfw
```

---

decfsz   Decrement the contents of the operand and the next instruction is skipped if the result is zero.

```
Syntax:       decfsz      var1, d or f
STATUS bit affected: Z
```

The opcode decfsz decrements the contents of the operand variable by 1 and places the result either in the f or w-register. This opcode is frequently used in controlled loops that require a definite number of iterations. The variable used as a counter is loaded with a starting value equal to the number of iterations. The counter variable is decremented at the end of each loop iteration. The result of that decrement is tested if the result is zero, and a loop back or loop exit is executed accordingly. In this case, the results of decfsz would have to be loaded back into the f register for the counter scheme to function. This opcode is used frequently.

Example:

```
            movlw    .8
            movwf    counter
loop

            loop code here

            decfsz   counter, f
            goto     loop
```

After loading the number of desired loop iterations into the variable counter, the counter variable is decremented at the end of the loop, the Z flag tested to see if the counter has been decremented to zero, and the loop is executed again until the counter reaches zero.

```
            goto     Unconditional jump or branch to a labeled program segment

            Syntax:  goto      routine_to_do_something
            STATUS bit affected:    None
```

The goto opcode causes a jump to some labeled segment of the program code. The program counter is loaded with the address of the code segment and the program execution continues at that new location. This opcode is used frequently.

Example:

```
wait_for_button
            btfss    PORTA, 2
            goto     button_pressed
            goto     wait_for_button
```

In this code the PORTA pin 2 is sensed. If the pin is SET, the button has not been pressed, the next instruction is skipped, and the goto wait_for_button loop continues to wait for the button press. When the button is pressed, the pin is CLEAR, and the next instruction is executed to jump to the button_pressed code.

```
            incf     The operand register is incremented by one.

            Syntax:  incf      var1, d or f
            STATUS bit affected: Z
```

This opcode is the opposite of decf. The opcode incf increments the contents of the operand and the result is loaded into the f or w-register as specified. If the increment results in an overflow from 0xff to 0x00, the Z bit is SET in the STATUS register. This opcode is used infrequently.

Example:

```
            incf     var1, w
            btfss    STATUS, Z
            goto     not_zero
```

incfsz   The operand register is incremented by one, the result is loaded into the w-register or the operand, and the next instruction is skipped if the result of the increment is zero. This opcode is similar but opposite to decfsz.

```
Syntax:   incfsz      var1, d or f
STATUS bit affected: Z
```

The opcode incfsz increments the contents of the operand variable or register by 1 and places the result either in the f or w-register. This opcode can be used in controlled loops that require a definite number of iterations. The variable used as a counter is loaded with a starting value equal to 256 minus the number of iterations. The counter variable is incremented at the end of each loop iteration, the result of that increment is tested if the result is zero, and a loop back or loop exit is executed. In this case, the results of incfsz would have to be loaded back into the **f** register. This opcode is used infrequently.

Example:

```
        movlw    248
        movwf    counter
loop

        loop code here

        incfsz    counter, f
        goto     loop
```

The code will load the counter variable with a starting value of 248. Each time through the loop, the value of counter will be incremented by 1. When counter increments through 0xff to 0x00, the Z flag will be SET and the program will exit the loop and continue with the rest of the program.

---

iorlw   Inclusive ORs the literal with the w-register with the result loaded into the w-register.

```
Syntax:   iorlw k
STATUS bit affected: Z
```

The iorlw opcode takes the literal operand and logically ORs it with the contents of the w-register with the result loaded into the w-register. **Table 7-2** contains the Boolean truth table for the OR operation. This opcode is used infrequently.

Example code:
```
        movfw    var1
        andlw    b'01010101'
```

Table 7.2 — Boolean Truth Table for the OR Operation

Input		Output
A	B	
0	0	0
0	1	1
1	0	1
1	1	1

iorwf   Inclusive ORs the contents of the w-register with the contents of the operand register. The result is loaded into either the w-register or the operand.

```
Syntax:  iorwf, d or f
STATUS bit affected: Z
```

The `iorwf` opcode is similar to `iorlw`. `iorwf` takes the contents of the operand variable or memory location and logically ORs it with the contents of the w-register with the result loaded into either the f or w-register. This opcode is used infrequently.

Example code:

```
movfw    var1
iorwf    var2, w
```

This code compares the contents of var1 and var2 with the result placed in the w-register leaving the contents of var2 unchanged.

---

movf   The contents of the operand register are moved back into the operand register or the w-register.

```
Syntax:  movf   var1, f
STATUS bit affected: Z
```

The `movf` opcode allows you to move the contents of the operand register into itself or the w-register. The opcode `movfw` also will accomplish this task. (This opcode is not listed in the device documentation.) The instruction `movf var1, f`, which moves the contents of the register `var1` back into `var1` seems a bit redundant, however, because the z flag of the STATUS register is affected by the move if the contents of the register be zero. This is a way to test the contents for zero. This opcode is used infrequently; `movfw`, however, is used very frequently.

Example code:

```
movf     var1, f
```

Move the contents of `var1` and store it back into `var1`, the Z flag is affected if the contents were zero.

```
movf     var1, w
```

Move the contents of `var1` into the w-register. The instruction `movfw var1` could also have been used.

---

movlw   The literal operand is loaded into the w-register. The literal operand can be a defined constant, a decimal number (.123), a hexadecimal number (0xfa), a binary number (b'00100001), or an ASCII code representation of a character ('A').

```
Syntax:    movlw  .45
STATUS bit affected: None
```

The 8-bit literal is loaded into the w-register, the Z bit of the STATUS register is not affected by this operation. This opcode is used frequently.

Example code:

```
movlw    b'10000010'
movlw    'C'
movlw    .75
movlw    0xff
```

```
movwf          The contents of the W-register is loaded into the operand register.
```

```
Syntax:   movwf  var1
STATUS bit affected: None
```

The contents of the W-register is loaded into the operand register, the **z** bit of the STATUS register is not affected by this operation. This opcode is used frequently.

Example code:

```
movlw     .75
movwf     var1
```

This code loads the literal 75 into the W-register and then loads the contents of the W-register (75) into the `var1` variable location.

```
nop            This opcode performs no operation except to hold time for one instruction
               clock cycle.
```

```
Syntax:   nop
STATUS bit affected: None
```

The `nop` opcode is frequently used as a place holder for debugging purposes and is also frequently used to fine tune delay subroutines to a specific number of instruction cycles.

Example code:

```
            movlw     .8
            movwf     counter
delay_loop
            nop
            nop
            goto      exit_delay
```

```
retfie         This opcode is used to return the program control to the main program
               after an interrupt has been serviced by a subroutine.
```

```
Syntax:   retfie
STATUS bit affected: None however, INTCON, GIE is SET
```

Upon executing the `retfie` opcode, the program counter is pulled from the Stack and the GIE flag of the INTCON register is SET to allow global interrupts. This opcode is used frequently.

Example code:

```
interrupt_service
            bcf       INTCON, T0IE
            bcf       INTCON, T0IF
            nop
            retfie
```

retlw   This opcode loads the W-register with the value of the literal operand just prior to returning the program control to the main program.

```
Syntax:    retlw    .123
STATUS bit affected: None
```

Upon executing the `retlw` opcode, the W-register is loaded with the literal operand and the program counter is pulled from the Stack to cause a return to the calling program at the end of the subroutine. This opcode is used with moderate frequency particularly when data tables are used.

Example Code:
get_data

```
movlw      temp
addwf      PCL, f
retlw      'a'
retlw      'b'
retlw      'c'
```

In the above subroutine, the location of the required data byte in the table is loaded into the variable `temp` prior to the subroutine call. The value in `temp` is loaded into the W-register and then added to the program counter. This causes a jump to the appropriate line of data where the literal value of the data byte is loaded into the W-register by the `retlw` opcode before program control is returned to the calling program.

---

rlf   This opcode rotates the contents of the operand register one bit left through the C bit of the STATUS register.

```
Syntax:    rlf      var1, f
STATUS bit affected: C
```

The `rlf` opcode rotates the contents of the operand register one bit left and puts the MSB into the C bit of the STATUS register after the previous contents of the C bit is rotated into the LSB of the operand register. The result is either loaded back into the operand or the W-register as assigned. This opcode is used frequently particularly in serial communications subroutines and/or ADC operations. This opcode can also be used to multiply the contents of the operand by 2.

Example code:

```
bcf        STATUS, C
rlf        low_byte, f
rlf        high_byte,
```

This code begins by clearing the C bit of the STATUS register to avoid corrupting the operand with the previous contents of the C bit. The low byte of a 16-bit number is rotated left one bit, with the MSB placed in the C bit. The high byte of the 16-bit number is then rotated left by one bit with the contents of the C bit from the previous operation placed in the LSB of the high byte of the number. This operation multiplied the 16-bit number by 2.

return   This opcode terminates a subroutine and pops the program counter off the Stack to return control back to the calling program.

```
Syntax:   return
STATUS bit affect: None
```

Care should be taken to ensure that nested subroutine calls do not corrupt the limited Stack space available. This opcode is used very frequently.

Example code:
delay1mS

```
          movlw     .198
          movwf     count
          nop
          goto      $+1
          goto      $+1
dly1mS

          goto      $+1
          decfsz    count, F
          goto      dly1mS
          return
```

rrf   This opcode rotates the contents of the operand register one bit right through the C bit of the STATUS register.

```
Syntax:   rrf    var1, f
STATUS bit affected: C
```

The rrf opcode rotates the contents of the operand register one bit right and puts the LSB into the C bit of the STATUS register after the previous contents of the C bit is rotated into the MSB of the operand register. The result is either loaded back into the operand register or the w-register as assigned. This opcode is used frequently particularly in serial communications subroutines and/or ADC operations. This opcode can also be used to divide the contents of the operand by 2.

Example code:

```
          bcf       STATUS, C
          rrf       high_byte, f
          rrf       low_byte, f
```

This code begins by clearing the C bit of the STATUS register to avoid corrupting the operand with the previous contents of the C bit. The high byte of a 16-bit number is rotated right one bit, with the LSB placed in the C bit. The low byte of the 16-bit number is then rotated right by one bit with the contents of the C bit from the previous operation placed in the MSB of the high byte of the number. This operation divides the 16-bit number by 2.

sleep   This opcode is used to terminate the execution of the program and place the MCU device in a low power consumption state.

```
Syntax:   sleep
STATUS bits affected: TO and PD
```

Specific changes on certain resources will "wake" the device from the sleep condition. This opcode is used infrequently.

Example code:

```
movf        PORTA, f
movlw       b'00001000'
movwf       INTCON
sleep
bsf         PORTC, 3
```

The use of sleep requires some careful programming consideration. In the above code, the GIE bit of the INTCON register is CLEARED to disable global interrupts prior to the device being put into the low power consumption state. When a change occurs on an I/O pin of PORTA, the device wakes up and the next instruction after the sleep opcode is executed. Had the GIE bit been SET to enable interrupts, an interrupt would have been executed after that next instruction (bsf PORTC, 3) was executed which may or may not have had the intended consequences. In other words, if interrupts are enabled prior to executing sleep, the wake stimulus will generate an interrupt. If interrupts are disabled prior to executing sleep, the wake stimulus will cause the program to continue at the point after the device was placed in the sleep mode.

---

sublw   This opcode subtracts, using 2's complement methods, the contents of the W-register from the literal operand with the result loaded back into the W-register.

```
Syntax:     sublw   .123
STATUS bits affected: C, DC, and Z
```

The sublw opcode allows for simple 8-bit subtraction. Subtraction of larger numbers would require other programming algorithms (similar to those required for addition of numbers larger than 8-bits). The STATUS register Z bit is SET if the result of the operation is zero. The status of the C and DC bit will require some thought. The subtraction actually is accomplished by the addition of two's complement numbers and therefore the polarity of these bits is reversed. This opcode is used infrequently.

You must use care to ensure that the subtrahend (the number in the W-register) is the lesser of the two numbers being subtracted or you will get unintended results. For instance, let's take a look at the code to accomplish 3 - 2. The number 2 is first loaded into the W-register and then the contents of the W-register are subtracted from the literal operand 3 with the result loaded back into the W-register:

```
movlw       .2
sublw       .3
```

At the end of this operation, the W-register would contain b'00000001' or decimal 1, and the C and DC bits of the STATUS register are SET (remember that in subtraction the polarity of these bits is reversed so SET means no carry or borrow).

Now let's take the opposite case and accomplish 2-3. The number 3 is first loaded into the W-register and then the contents of the W-register are subtracted from the literal operand 2 with the result loaded back into the W-register.

```
movlw       .3
sublw       .2
```

At the end of this operation, the w-register would contain b'11111111' or decimal 255, and the C and DC bits of the STATUS register are CLEAR (again remember that in subtraction the polarity of these bits is reversed so CLEAR means a carry or borrow did occur). Certainly not the answer expected! To make sense of this result you would need to complement the contents of the w-register using a variable location and the comf opcode and then add one to the result. The best thing to do, however, is to avoid these complications and make sure the content of the w-register is the lesser of the two numbers.

---

subwf	This opcode subtracts, using 2's complement methods, the contents of the w-register from the operand variable with the result loaded back into the w-register or the operand variable as directed.

```
Syntax:   subwf   var1, f or w
STATUS bits affected: C, DC, and Z
```

The same precautions as listed for sublw above apply to this use of this opcode. This opcode is used infrequently.

Example code:

```
movlw          .3
movwf          var1
movlw          .2
subwf          var1, f
```

The literal value 3 is first loaded into the variable var1, next, the literal value of 2 is loaded into the w-register and this value is subtracted from var1 (the number 3) with the result returned to var1. The STATUS Z bit is CLEAR (non zero result) and the DC and C flags are SET indicating no carry or borrow operation.

---

swapf	The opcode swapf swaps (or exchanges) the nibbles within the operand register. The low nibble (bits 0 - 3) replace the high nibble (bits 4 - 7) and vice versa. The results are loaded back into the operand register, or variable, or into the w-register as directed.

```
Syntax:   swapf   var1, f or w
STATUS bit affected: None
```

The real power of this opcode comes from the fact that the Z bit of the STATUS register is not affected even if the result of the nibble movement is zero. This is useful in preserving the contents of the STATUS register during interrupt subroutine calls. Movements of register contents into and out of temporary variable locations to preserve the pre-interrupt contents using movf or movfw opcodes could corrupt the STATUS Z bit state because if zero is being moved, the Z bit will the SET. However, if you swapf into the temp variable location and then again swapf out of the temporary variable location, the integrity of the original number is retained and the Z bit is unaffected by this opcode even if the value of zero is being moved. This opcode is used infrequently but is very useful in interrupt service subroutines to restore the contents of the w-register and the STATUS resister to pre-interrupt states.

Example code:

```
movwf       w_temp
swapf       STATUS, w
movwf       status_temp
swapf       status_temp, w
movwf       STATUS
swapf       w_temp, f
swapf       w_temp, w
retfie
```

The `movwf` opcode does not affect the Z bit so the contents of STATUS is preserved. After the STATUS byte is recovered, the multiple `swapf` opcodes return the W-register to the pre-interrupt state without corrupting the STATUS byte (the Z bit in particular).

`xorlw`   Exclusive XORs the literal with the W-register with the result loaded into the W-register.

```
Syntax:    xorlw      k
STATUS bit affected: Z
```

The `xorlw` opcode takes the literal operand and logically XORs it with the contents of the W-register with the result loaded into the W-register. **Table 7-3** contains the Boolean truth table for the XOR operation. This opcode is used frequently, particularly when toggling I/O pin states and for comparing two numbers for equality.

Table 7-3 — Boolean Truth Table for the XOR Operation.

Input		Output
A	B	
0	0	0
0	1	1
1	0	1
1	1	0

Example code:

```
movfw       var1
xorlw       b'01010101'
```

In this code, if the individual comparable bits are 1 then the associated bit will be CLEARED in the W-register. If the individual comparable bits are not both 1, then there is no change in the associated bit in the W-register.

`xorwf`   Exclusive XORs the contents of the W-register with the contents of the operand register. The result is loaded into either the W-register or the operand.

```
Syntax:    xorwf, d or f
STATUS bit affected: Z
```

The `xorwf` opcode is similar to `xorlw`. `xorwf` takes the contents of the operand variable or memory location and logically XORs it with the contents of the W-register with the result loaded into either the f or W-register. This opcode is used frequently to toggle I/O pin states, if SET then it will be CLEARED, if CLEAR then it will be SET.

Example code:

```
movfw       var1
xorwf       PORTA, f
```

This code compares the contents of var1 and var2 with the result placed in the PORTA register. If LEDs were tied to the PORTA resources, those LEDs would be toggled on and off in relation to the bit pattern loaded into the var1 variable location.

Assembler Directives

So far we have been reviewing the instruction set or opcodes of assembly language. These are mnemonic representations of machine language instructions that the *MPLAB IDE* Assembler translates into machine language that makes up the actual program instructions that are executed by the MCU. In the example program code that is included in the following chapters of this text, you will find additional lines of code that appear similar to opcodes, but they are in fact very useful and powerful assembler directives.

Assembler directives, as stated, appear in the source program code, but generally they are not translated into opcodes or instructions. *Directives* are commands that are used to control the *assembler* and the *assembly process*. Directives help make the code transferable, translatable, and portable to other PIC-MCUs.

The following list of directives are used in the example code of this text, however this is only a partial listing of the directives. More detailed information about individual directives and how they can be applied in your code can be found in the *MPLAB IDE* Help files.

Directives

```
list
```

```
Syntax: list p=PIC name
```

The `list` directive is used in the code examples to set the intended processor type. The processor type can also be set in the *MPLAB IDE* under the **CONFIGURE** menu options. The list directive takes precedence over the **CONFIGURE** menu options when the check box is checked in the menu options.

Example code:

```
list       p=16F676        ;list directive to define
processor
```

```
#include
```

```
Syntax: #include <pfile.inc>
```

The files specified in the `#include` directive are read and integrated into the program code as additional source code. The effect is as if the `#include` file were typed into your source code. The p16f676.inc file contains constant definitions that connect specific numerical constants, register locations, and mnemonic label representations for registers and individual bits that mirror the device documentation to facilitate program readability. It is a good idea to print out the contents of the device .inc file for reference during code development. Code source files that contain commonly used portable code such as delay and math routines can be accessed by other programs through the include directive. There is an extensive library of useful code that is available on the Microchip Web site that can be integrated into your code through proper definition of variables and use of the `#include` directive (unfortunately an advanced topic that is beyond the scope of this text).

Example Code:

```
#include   <p16f676.inc>   ;processor specific variable
                           ;definitions
```

```
        __config
```

```
Syntax:  __config _AAA&_BBB&_CCC
```

The __config directive sets the PIC-MCU's configuration bits within the configuration word register, a 14-bit register. The configuration bits include: *Bandgap Calibration*, *Data Code Protection*, *Code Protection*, *Brown-out Detect Enable*, *RA3/MCLR pin function*, *Power-up Timer Enable*, *Watchdog Timer Enable*, and *Oscillator Selection* bits. These bits can also be configured using the **CONFIGURE/CONFIGURATION BITS** menu option. The __config directive takes precedence over the **CONFIGURE/CONFIGURATION BITS** menu selection when the appropriate check box is checked in the menu options.

It is important that the list and #include directives precede the __config directive so that the assembler knows the device type before setting the configuration bits and where to find the mnemonic representations. The mnemonic representations used for the individual configuration bits, either on or off, are defined in the device .inc file. These mnemonics help in making the code more readable.

Example code:

```
    __CONFIG  _CP_OFF & _WDT_OFF & _BODEN & _PWRTE_ON & _INTRC_
OSC_NOCLKOUT & _MCLRE_OFF & _CPD_OFF
```

```
        #define
```

```
Syntax: #define variable    literal
```

The #define directive defines a mnemonic substitution label that represents a literal constant. The literal constant can be a number or a string. During assembly whenever the label is encountered in the code, the literal constant is substituted.

Example code:

```
#define   Bank0   0x00
#define   Bank1   0x80
#define   CS      0x03
#define   LED1    PORTA, 0
```

```
        org
```

```
Syntax:   org    0x00
```

The org directive sets the program origin at the address specified in the defined expression. When the device is first powered-up or a reset is forced, the program counter will begin at the location specified by the org directive. The other common origin definition is the location for interrupts.

Example code:

```
    org       0x00      ;for processor reset vector
    nop                 ;required by in circuit debugger
    goto      Init      ;go to beginning of program
    org       0x04      ;for interrupt vector
    goto      interrupt_service
    return
```

cblock and endc

Syntax: cblock
           endc

The cblock directive assigns variable name labels to specific memory addresses
within the memory locations reserved as *General Purpose Registers*. The memory
addresses begin at the memory address that is the operand of the cblock directive and
end with the endc directive. In the case of the PIC16F676, the General Purpose Register
memory space runs from 0x20 through 0x5f. In other devices with extended memory,
the General Purpose Registers may be divided among numerous pages of memory. The
cblock directive would then be used to dictate the memory location of specific variables
in specific memory pages.

Example code:

```
cblock      0x20
w_temp
status_temp
endc
```

In this code example, the variable w_temp would use the memory address of 0x20,
status_temp would use 0x21 and so on.

---

banksel

The banksel directive is a convenient way to switch between the memory banks
with code that is more readable than addressing the individual register bank (bank
select) bits within the STATUS register (in the case of the PIC16F676 device). The
label that represents the bit pattern that specifies the memory bank is defined before the
banksel directive is implemented.

Example code:

```
#define     Bank0       0x00
#define     Bank1       0x80
```

Then later in the code:

```
BANKSEL     Bank1           ;select bank1
call        0x3FF           ;retrieve factory calibration value
movwf       OSCCAL
BANKSEL     Bank0           ;select bank0
```

---

dt

Syntax: label dt   'A', 'B', variable_label, .123,
                        b'00010010'

The dt directive generates a series of retlw instructions in a data table that will load
the W-register with the 8-bit value of the offset argument and return that value in the
W-register to the calling program code as if the retlw opcode were executed. The offset
for the desired value in the data table is added to the low byte of the program counter
which causes a jump to the desired value and an retlw opcode is executed.

Example code:
table_get

```
          movfw    temp
          addwf    PCL,f
tabledt            LCD_LINE0,'P','o','t'
```

In this code segment, the offset is passed through the variable temp. The offset is loaded into the w-register which in turn is added to the program counter. This causes a jump to the desired location within the data table. The dt directive generates a retlw opcode with the desired table data value returned to the calling program in the w-register.

```
end
Syntax: end
```

The end directive indicates to the assembler that the code is complete. There should be one end directive. Care should be exercised so that unwanted end directives are not included within include files or partial assembly may result.

Summary

The instruction set or opcodes are the meat of assembly language. There are 35 opcodes, or words, that make up the vocabulary of the assembly language. The opcodes are mnemonics that help the programmer to create more readable code. The opcode vocabulary words are recognized and translated by the assembler into machine language instruction code that is uploaded to the MCU program memory. The opcodes generally have associated operand arguments that are variable memory locations, registers, or specific bits that are manipulated when the opcode is executed. Opcode operations can be byte-oriented, bit-oriented, or control the program flow. The execution of some of the opcodes also will affect specific bits within the STATUS register. Additionally, there is a set of assembly directives that look similar to opcode instructions but are used to control the assembler during the assembly process. The use of directives help to make your code transferable, translatable, and portable.

Review Questions

7.1 Does the movf instruction affect the Z flag of the STATUS resister?

7.2 What value would the instruction movf var1, f serve?

7.3 What precautions should you consider when executing nested call instructions?

7.4 Which of the opcode instructions is useful if you want to toggle an I/O pin to turn on and off an attached LED?

7.5 What kind of information is included in the device .inc file? What directive would you use to include the contents of the device .inc file in your program code?

7.6 Which INTCON bit is automatically SET when the retfie opcode is executed?

7.7 When using the rrf and/or the rlf opcodes to rotate bits through the C bit of the STATUS register, what are some precautions that you need to consider?

7.8 Is it possible to move values from one memory location or register directly into another? If so, write a sample of code that would accomplish this task.

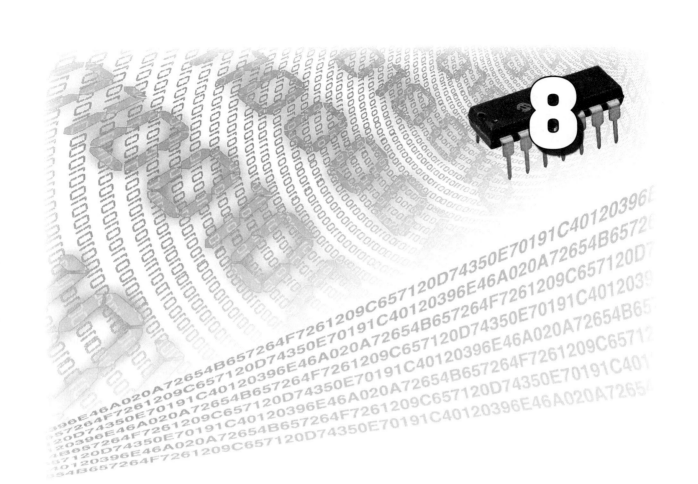

Device
Setup

Objective: To learn to configure the special features of an MCU and initialize the Special Function Registers to configure the device resources for a particular application.

Reading: *PIC16F630/676* Data Sheet, pages 55-71.

Writing Preliminary Code

Before you can start writing the code for your particular application, you will need to write some preliminary code to configure the MCU device resources. This preliminary code can be divided into two broad categories, special features that are controlled by the *configuration word* and the *special function registers*. The configuration word can be set and modified either with an *assembler directive* or by *manipulating switches* in *MPLAB IDE* **DEVICE SETUP** menu options. The special function registers are generally configured at the beginning of the program code as will be illustrated or can be also modified during the run-time section of the program code.

Configuring the Special Features

Figure 8-1
CONFIGURE
Drop Down Menu/
CONFIGURE/
CONFIGURE BITS

When you first start to construct your program code, you should give some thought to how you want to configure the special features and use the resources available on your chosen MCU. Let's take a look at the possibilities for the special features. The majority of these features are not relevant for most of the applications you are likely to write. Consequently you will use the defaults for most of the special features.

There are two ways to configure the special features of the device. First, you can set up the configuration using the *MPLAB IDE* **CONFIGURE** menu option. With the device selected by clicking on **CONFIGURE/SELECT DEVICE**, clicking on the **CONFIGURE/ CONFIGURE BITS** menu option will open the **BIT SELECT** dialog window (**Figure 8-1** then **Figure 8-2**). The **CONFIGURATION BIT** dialog window lists the individual bits that can be SET, the *down arrow* adjacent to the selected bit will bring down the available options. The *default bit settings* for all except the oscillator configuration will be used for the programming examples in this text. You are encouraged to study the assigned reading material to learn the specifics of the other special features. The various oscillator options will be discussed below.

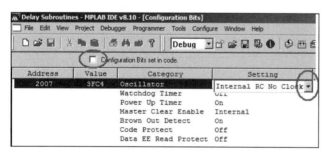

Figure 8-2 – 1. Check Box for "Configuration Bits Set in Code" 2. The oscillator configuration used in all the program examples in this text is the INTERNAL OSCILLATOR WITH NO CLOCK OUTPUT as illustrated above right.

Oscillator Options

There are eight different *oscillator options* available on the PIC16F676. The option selected depends on the application. For applications requiring a high accuracy or high frequency system clock, one of the *external crystal options* should be selected. Provisions for a *high speed crystal* or *resonator* (HS), *nominal crystal* or *resonator* (XT), or *low power crystal* (LP) are available by selecting the appropriate switch setting from the pull down menu options. Clock frequencies up to 20 MHz are possible with the use of external crystals or resonators with the tradeoff being a higher component count for loading capacitors and also losing two I/O pin resources that are used to connect the crystal or resonator to the device. For applications requiring a specific clock frequency but not necessarily high speed or accuracy, the *RC oscillator options* would be selected. The clock signal is generated by a resistor-capacitor circuit combination connected to the internal oscillator circuitry. The actual clock frequency generated with the RC circuit depends on the supply voltage, the values and tolerances of the components, the characteristics of the MCU device and the operating temperature. There are two RC oscillator modes. In both modes, the RC circuit is connected to the *RA5 pin*. In one mode, the clock frequency is output on the *RA4 pin*. This would remove two I/O pins from use. In the second mode, the clock frequency is not put on an I/O pin and therefore only pin RA5 is unavailable for use as an I/O resource.

The final oscillator options use the *internal oscillator*. For the PIC16F676, the internal oscillator runs at 4 MHz which gives an instruction cycle or clock frequency of 1 MHz. One mode outputs the 1 MHz clock frequency on the RA4 pin and consequently that pin would not be available for general purpose I/O in this mode. The second mode does not output the clock frequency and the I/O resource is available. There is a special note of caution when using the internal oscillator resource. The internal oscillator of the device is tested and calibrated at the factory before the device is released for sale. A device specific calibration value is stored in the device memory which the user can read and then load into a SFR called *OSCCAL*. The caution is that if the user elects to erase the device memory for some reason, this calibration value will also be erased and the accuracy of the internal oscillator will be in jeopardy. There is really no reason to erase a device, any code you write and store on the device will overwrite the previous code. If code security is a question, you can set the code protection bits in the configuration word and the code cannot be read by an unauthorized user. A work-around as a precaution would be to read the device memory using *MPLAB IDE* and noting the calibration values for each particular device. Later, if the device is inadvertently erased, these archived values can be loaded into the OSCCAL register. The best precaution however is not to erase the device in the first place.

The oscillator configuration used in all the program examples in this text is the INTERNAL OSCILLATOR WITH NO CLOCK OUTPUT as illustrated in the settings of Figure 8-2. Note the check box in Figure 8-2 labeled **CONFIGURATION BITS SET IN CODE**. If this box is checked, the configuration that is specified in the program code takes precedence over the configuration bits as set in this dialog window and this is the preferred method used in the programming examples of this text. So if you view this window while exploring the programs of this text, you will see this check box checked. Once checked, the configuration bits are set by the __config directive at the beginning of the program code and this will be discussed next.

In Chapter 7, assembler directives were introduced. These directives are used by the assembler to accomplish specific tasks that are related to the program, but they are not part of the actual program. The __config directive used by the assembler to set the desired configuration bits can be done manually using the **CONGIFURE** menu option described above. The advantage of using the __config directive is that the programmer controls the configuration bits and this is done independently of the end user. This ensures that the device is configured to match the code regardless of the settings that the end user might specify (or neglect to specify). The __config directive is used in conjunction with literal constants that are represented by labels that are specified within the include file (pic16F676.inc) that is attached to the program with the #include directive. Remember the include files contain definitions of memory locations and constants using mnemonics that are consistent with the device documentation and are device specific. Each device has its own unique .inc file. If you view the contents of the pic16F676.inc file you will see this listing of labels and assigned constants:

```
;================================================================
;
;       Configuration Bits
;
;
;================================================================
```

_CPD	EQU	H'3EFF'
_CPD_OFF	EQU	H'3FFF'
_CP	EQU	H'3F7F'
_CP_OFF	EQU	H'3FFF'
_BODEN	EQU	H'3FFF'
_BODEN_OFF	EQU	H'3FBF'
_MCLRE_ON	EQU	H'3FFF'
_MCLRE_OFF	EQU	H'3FDF'
_PWRTE_OFF	EQU	H'3FFF'
_PWRTE_ON	EQU	H'3FEF'
_WDT_ON	EQU	H'3FFF'
_WDT_OFF	EQU	H'3FF7'
_LP_OSC	EQU	H'3FF8'
_XT_OSC	EQU	H'3FF9'
_HS_OSC	EQU	H'3FFA'
_EC_OSC	EQU	H'3FFB'
_INTRC_OSC_NOCLKOUT	EQU	H'3FFC'
_INTRC_OSC_CLKOUT	EQU	H'3FFD'
_EXTRC_OSC_NOCLKOUT	EQU	H'3FFE'
_EXTRC_OSC_CLKOUT	EQU	H'3FFF'

The mnemonics are selected to help make the labels for the bits more representative of the bit function and more readable. For instance _CP stands for the *code protection bit on*, _CP_OFF stands for *code protection off*. _INTRC_OSC_NOCLKOUT stands for the *internal RC oscillator resource selected with no clock output*, this is the configuration used in the example programs of this text. The individual bit settings are logically AND'ed together to form the configuration word that the assembler then loads into the MCU. The assembler directive would look like this:

__CONFIG _CP_OFF & _WDT_OFF & _BODEN & _PWRTE_ON & _INTRC_OSC_
NOCLKOUT & _MCLRE_OFF & _CPD_OFF

This translates into Code Protect off, Watch Dog Timer off, Brown-out Detect Enabled, Power-up Timer Enabled on, Internal RC Oscillator with no clock output, RA3 reset pin function is off (internal tied to V_{dd}), and Data Code Protect off.

Configuring the Special Function Registers (SFRs)

Now let's turn our attention to configuring the special function registers. The SFRs are used to configure the resources that are available within the MCU device including PORT input/output, ADC, comparator, timer and interrupt resources. The details of these various resources are covered in subsequent dedicated chapters that follow. The remainder of this chapter will cover a suggested standardized way to initialize the SFRs based on the desired configuration of the device resources.

Planning How to Use the Available Resources — Developing the Circuit Diagram for the Project

Before configuring the resources, you will have to put some thought into how you want to utilize the available resources and how the external devices and components will be attached to the MCU. A good way to accomplish this is to develop the circuit diagram for the project. For instance, your application may call for user interface push buttons with pull-up resistors, indicator LEDs with current limiting resistors, and an SPI temperature sensor that requires data, clock and chip select lines. While you are developing the circuit diagram, it would be a good time to consider the physical layout of the components in the final project. Pay attention to potential crossing circuit board traces or interconnecting wires, depending on the type of circuit board being used. Crossing interconnections may dictate the physical layout of components and which MCU pin is dedicated to a specific resource. The development of the circuit diagram, parts layout on the circuit board and assignment of MCU resources to specific pins is an iterative process and just as much an art as a science. Good thought and planning at this stage of project development will make the software development more efficient.

List the Pin Assignments

As the circuit diagram for the project begins to take form, start listing the pin resources into the following categories:

Output pins
Digital input pins - no weak pull-up resistors required
Digital input pins - that require weak pull-up resistors
Analog input pins
Comparator configuration and pins required
ADC(s) required and pin assignments
Timer resources required and pin assignments for external inputs to timers

List the Software Function Requirements

After the pin resources are defined, list the software specific configurations that also will be initialized in the SFRs:

Timer 0 and/or Timer 1 interrupts required
Prescaler requirements for timer resources
ADC output left or right hand justified in the ADC output registers
ADC interrupt required
Comparator voltage reference
Comparator output
Comparator interrupt required
PORT change interrupt required

Armed with this listing of pin assignments and software function requirements, you are now ready to author the device initialization code to configure the SFR bits. An example of a generalized initialization code for the PIC16F676 that you will see in the example programs in this text is listed below. There are, of course, more elegant and more efficient ways to configure the SFRs, however, I encourage you to follow this example until you become more proficient in writing code.

```
;******************************************************************************
;Initialization
;******************************************************************************
    Init
                BANKSEL     Bank1
                call        0x3FF           ;retrieve factory calibration value
                movlw       OSCCAL
                BANKSEL     Bank0           ;select bank0
                Movlw       b'00000000'
                movwf       PORTA           ;clear port bus
                movlw       b'00000000'
                movwf       PORTC
                movlw       b'00000111'     ;turn off comparator module
                movwf       CMCON;
                movlw       b'00000000'     ;interrupts all off
                movwf       INTCON
                BANKSEL     Bank1           ;BANK1
                movlw       b'00000000'     ;enabling weak pull-ups
                movwf       OPTION_REG      ;put w reg into option register
                movlw       b'00000000'     ;all output
                movwf       TRISA           ;program PORTA
                movlw       b'00000000'     ;no weak pull-ups
                movwf       WPUA
                movlw       b'00000000'     ;all PORTC as outputs
                movwf       TRISC           ;program PORTC
                movlw       b'00000000'     ;all pins digital
                movwf       ANSEL
                BANKSEL     Bank0           ;back to bank0

    ;end MCU initialization
;******************************************************************************
```

Basically the code loads the desired SFR bit pattern configuration into the w-register and the contents of the w-register are moved into the SFR. In this suggested code, the binary representation of the bit pattern is used so that the individual bits can be compared to the documentation for the register. The comments attached to the bit pattern should list the SFR bit switch configuration to make your code more readable and easier to debug. Also note that the memory bank is switched between bank 0 and bank 1 to access the target SFR. You could configure all bank 1 SFRs first and then switch to bank 0 and configure the remainder SFRs in that bank to create some code space savings, but this might sacrifice the logic used to configure the SFRs (there is no real code execution time savings since this section of code is only executed once).

Remember the meaning of the individual configuration bits will be covered later in the associated chapters dedicated to the specific device resource and they were listed in the previous chapter that discusses the SFRs. The following is a general overview of the configuration code.

```
    Init
                BANKSEL     Bank1
                call        0x3FF           ;retrieve factory calibration value
                movlw       OSCCAL
                BANKSEL     Bank0           ;select bank0
```

Init is the label that identifies the start of the initialization of the code. The reset vector section of the code (org 0x00) would contain an instruction goto init to cause a program jump to this location to begin the program execution. The BANKSEL directive switches the memory bank to bank 1. The call opcode retrieves the oscillator calibration code that is stored in memory at the factory (recall the calibration code is part specific and would be lost if you erase the device memory). The memory location 0x3ff actually holds the opcode retlw which loads the calibration code into the w-register and then returns to the calling section of the program with the value in the w-register intact. The calibration value is then loaded into the OSCCAL register before the bank is switched to bank 0.

```
movlw      b'00000000'
movwf      PORTA            ;clear port bus
movlw      b'00000000'
movwf      PORTC
```

The above code sets all I/O pins on the PORTs to zero. This could have been also accomplished by using the clrf opcode. The PORT registers are frequently manipulated within the main code.

```
movlw      b'00000111'      ;turn off comparator module
movwf      CMCON
```

The above code configures the *device comparator resource*, in this case the comparator is disconnected and consumes the lowest power. The comparator is generally configured here and the configuration is not usually changed in the main code.

```
movlw      b'00000000'      ;interrupts all off
movwf      INTCON
```

The above code configures the *interrupt resources*, in this case all interrupts are disabled. The INTCON register is frequently manipulated in the main code to control interrupts.

```
movlw      b'10010001'      ;right justified, Vdd ref RC0 has ADC,
                            ;ADC Stop, ADC on
movwf      ADCON0
```

The above code partly configures the ADC resources. This register is manipulated in the main code if more than one ADC resource is required in your project, otherwise the register is configured only in the initialization section of the code.

```
BANKSEL    Bank1            ;BANK1
movlw      b'00000000'      ;enabling weak pull-ups
movwf      OPTION_REG       ;put w reg into option register
```

The above code switches banks to change the next few registers. The bit pattern for the OPTION_REG is loaded here. You will learn later that the timer 0 will start counting clock cycles (start timing) when this register is loaded. This needs to be considered for the first use of the TMR0 resource.

```
movlw       b'00010000'      ;Fosc/8
movwf       ADCON1
```

The above code completes the configuration of the ADC resources. This register may be manipulated in the main code if more than one ADC resource is required in your project and there is a unique conversion clock required for each resource. If there is only one ADC resource or there is a requirement for only one common conversion clock frequency, this register is configured only in the initialization section of the code.

```
movlw       b'00000000'      ;all output
movwf       TRISA            ;program PORTA
movlw       b'00000000'      ;no weak pull-ups
movwf       WPUA
movlw       b'00000000'      ;all PORTC as outputs
movwf       TRISC            ;program PORTC
```

The above code configures the direction of the I/O resources of PORTA and PORTC. The bit pattern loaded into the WPUA register configures the weak pull-up resistors that are available for the PORTA I/O pins. PORTC does not have internal weak pull-up resistors available so if required, weak pull-up resistors on PORTC pins would have to be external resistors.

```
movlw       b'00000000'      ;all pins digital
movwf       ANSEL
BANKSEL     Bank0            ;back to bank0
```

The above code will set the input I/O pin resources to either digital or analog input. Analog designations are required for those pins assigned to ADC or comparator resources. Failure to configure this register correctly could result in damage to the device. Switching the bank back to bank 0 prepares the memory bank for the main part of the code which follows device initialization.

It is suggested that this initialization code be cut and pasted into the code that you author for your application. The bit patterns are then modified (with associated changes to the comment lines) to configure the device resources as required by the particular application.

Summary

The MCU device resources need to be configured early in the program code as required to meet the needs of the application. The special features of the device can be configured using the *MPLAB IDE* **CONFIGURE** menu pull-down windows or by using the __config directive in the program code. Using the __config directive in code is the preferred method because the program author assumes responsibility through this directive for the proper configuration and it is not left up to the code user. The special function registers are configured in the initialization section of the program code. A generic initialization code was presented in this chapter that could be pasted into the project code being developed and modified to meet the needs of the specific application. Binary numbers are used to represent the bit pattern that is loaded into the SFRs to make the code more readable and easier to debug.

Review Questions

8.1 Write the code segments required to configure PORTA pins 0, 2, 4 and 5 as digital outputs and all other port pins as digital inputs with weak pull-up resistors enabled.

8.2 Write the code segments required to configure PORTA pin 0 as an ADC with a clock frequency of Freq/8 and left hand justified.

8.3 Write the code segments required to disable all weak pull-up resistors.

8.4 Can the direction of a PORT pin be changed after it is initialized in the initialization section of the code? If the direction can be changed, write the code required to change the direction of pin 5 of PORTC.

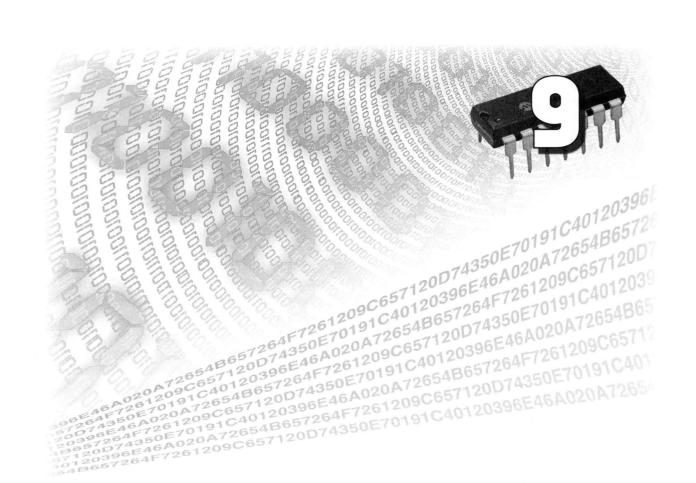

Delay Subroutines
and
MPLAB Simulator

Objective: To learn the code that can be used to create long delays in software and to use *MPLAB Simulator* to evaluate code in detail.

Reading: *PIC16F630/676 Data Sheet*, page 74.

Program: Program Files/Ch 9 Program/Delay Subroutines

Video: "Using *MPLAB SIM*"

Timer Resources

Dedicated timer resources are common among many of the MCU devices. In the PIC16F676 device there are TMR0 and TMR1 resources that can be configured to operate independently of the program code and generate interrupts at specified intervals to stimulate some sort of action. Depending on the prescaler configuration for the individual timers, the TMR0 resource can handle time intervals up to approximately 65 milliseconds (mseconds) and the TMR1 resource can handle time intervals up to approximately 524 mseconds. These timer resources will be covered in detail in later chapters. There may be times when you just want to generate a quick delay without having to configure, or reconfigure the timer resources or you need time delays that far exceed the time interval of the timer resources. These delays might be needed to flash an LED on and off at 1-s intervals or generate a pulse for serial communications of a specified length.

Delay Subroutines

These kinds of delays can be generated by subroutines. Once you build a library of common delays, these subroutines can be cut and pasted into your code without having to recreate the subroutines. You will see a section of code identified as delay subroutines in the code examples used in this text. We will explore these subroutines in this chapter, also use the *MPLAB Simulator* to predict the time delay of the subroutines and learn some programming techniques to fine tune the delays to meet your future application needs.

Before we begin, review the instruction set table that is assigned as reading for this chapter. Take particular note of the column titled "cycles." This column lists the number of instruction cycles required to execute a particular opcode. We are using the on-board oscillator for the clock source of the PIC16F676 which is set to run at 4 MHz. This clock frequency generates an instruction cycle frequency of 1 MHz or a period of 1 μS. You need to keep this period in mind as we explore the delay routines.

Program Files/Ch 9 Program/Delay Subroutines Project

Load the **Program Files/Ch 9 Program/Delay Subroutines** project into *MPLAB IDE* and open the program code window. This project contains the delay subroutines that are used in many of the program examples in the text without the other program code so that you can focus on the delay routines. We will begin this study of delay routines by looking first at a delay subroutine to generate a 1 msecond delay. Scroll down through the code until you find this subroutine listing:

Delay Subroutine to Generate a 1-Millisecond Delay

```
delay1mS
                movlw       .198
                movwf       count
                nop
                goto        $+1
                goto        $+1
dly1mS
                goto        $+1
                decfsz      count, f
                goto        dly1mS
                return
```

Basic Operation of a Delay Subroutine

The following is a brief description of the basic operation of a delay subroutine. A dedicated variable called *count* is defined earlier in the program code. The variable will be used to count down the subroutine iterations that are used to generate the delay, as the name implies. The starting value that is loaded into count is the main control that you have over the delay interval, the higher the value loaded into count, the greater the delay. The value in the count variable is decremented down each time through the *internal loop* until the value is zero. At that point the delay is completed and the program control is returned to the main program.

There is an excellent resource within the *MPLAB IDE* called the *MPLAB Sim Simulator*. This simulator allows you to step through a program and monitor specific registers and variables and also to track the simulated time (based on the number of instruction cycles) for program execution through a *Stopwatch*. You will be using two Stopwatch functions — the *time function* to measure the time required to execute the delay1mS subroutine and the *instruction cycle counter function* to monitor the number of cycles to execute each opcode within the subroutine. You will be using the *Watch window* to monitor the contents of the variable *count* as you step through each line of code. Perform the following steps to setup the *MPLAB Simulator*.

Click on **VIEW** then **WATCH** in the menu bar (**Figure 9-1**). The **WATCH** window will be displayed. Click on the down arrow next to the **ADD SYMBOL** button, scroll down until you find the **VARIABLE LABEL, COUNT**, click on **COUNT**, click on **ADD SYMBOL** (**Figure 9-2**). The **WATCH** window will contain the variable *count* and display its contents in various number formats (**Figure 9-3**). Next, click on **DEBUGGER** then **STOPWATCH** in the menu bar (**Figure 9-4**). The **STOPWATCH** window will appear. Note that the number of instruction cycles and the time of execution are displayed. There is also a **ZERO** button for resetting the stopwatch (**Figure 9-5**). You are now set to explore the delay subroutine in detail.

Figure 9-1

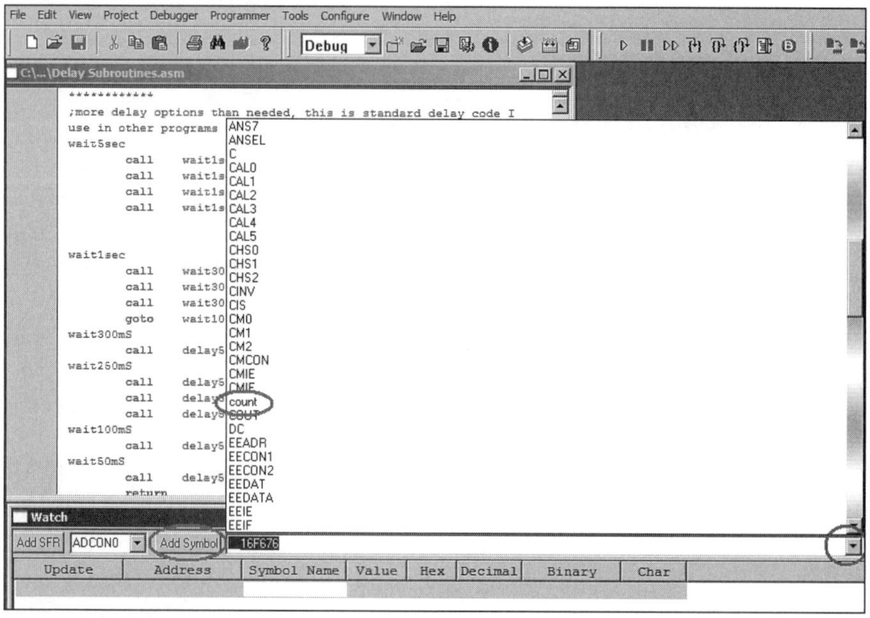

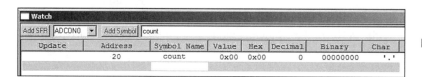

Figure 9-2

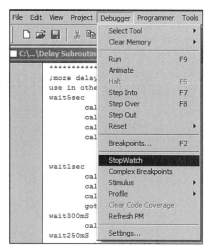

Figure 9-3

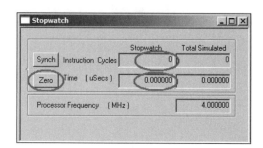

Figure 9-4

Figure 9-5

Delay Subroutine in Detail

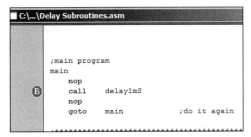

Figure 9-6

Scroll to the main program and set a *break point* at the line `call delay1mS`. Break points are locations that you identify in the code where program execution will stop when the program is run in the simulator. The break points allow you to view the contents of variables and registers and the Stopwatch at that point in time of the program execution, which you will do in just a few moments. You can have numerous break points set at strategic locations within the code. A break point is toggled on or off by double clicking the line of code. The red-bolded B on your screen will indicate the location of the break point (**Figure 9-6**).

Figure 9-7

In a similar manner, set a break point at the end of the `delay1mS` subroutine at the `return` opcode. You have a break point set at the point where the `delay1mS` routine is called in the main program and another break point at the point when the program execution is returned to the main program once the delay subroutine is completed.

Build and then run the program. The program will execute up to the first break point and then stop. The Stopwatch indicates that 39 µS have transpired to this point in the program and 39 instruction cycles were clocked (remember that the clock speed is 4 MHz which gives a 1 µS instruction clock period) (**Figure 9-7**).

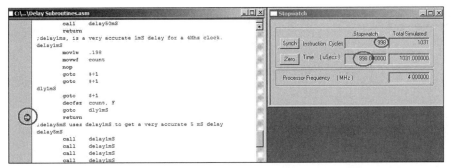

Figure 9-8

Let's see how long it takes to execute the `delay1mS` subroutine. Zero out the Stopwatch by clicking on the ZERO button. Press the RUN button, and the program will continue execution and stop at the next break point (the `return` opcode at the end of the subroutine, **Figure 9-8**). Notice the instruction cycles required are 998 and it took 998 µS to complete the subroutine up to this point. If you now press the F7 key to take a single step through the program and execute the `return` opcode, the program execution returns to the main program, the instruction cycles advance 2 cycles to 1000 and the Stopwatch advances to 1000 µS, or 1 msecond, the desired time interval. You will notice that it took 2 instruction cycles to execute the return opcode. We can use the specific number of instruction cycles to fine tune our delay routines as will be illustrated below.

Now that we have seen the overall time required to execute the delay routine, let's now take a closer look within the routine itself. The delay subroutine has two parts, the first part sets up the delay count variable, and the second part is an internal loop that decrements the count variable to create the delay. This is the code for the internal loop:

```
dly1mS
            goto      $+1
            decfsz    count, f
            goto      dly1mS
```

Table 9-1 – Opcodes and Number of Instruction Cycles Needed

Opcode	Inst. Cycles
call	2
movlw	1
movfw	1
nop	1
goto	2
decfsz	1 (2)
return	2

You can predict the time required to go through this loop one time by looking at the instruction cycle count. **Table 9-1** is an extract of the instruction set for the PIC16F676 and lists the opcode and the number of instruction cycles to execute individual opcodes. The goto opcode is a 2-cycle instruction, the decfsz is a 1-cycle instruction. The total number of instruction cycles required to execute the internal loop is therefore 5 cycles (and at 1 μS per cycle, 5μS). The count variable is loaded with 198 when the delay is set up, so the total time to complete the 198 internal loops is 990 μS. Let's take a look at this section of the delay subroutine and verify this with the simulator.

First, clear the previous break points by double clicking on the lines of code with the break points. Next scroll down into the delay1mS subroutine and set a break point on the goto $+1 line of code. Build and run the program and the program execution will stop at the break point. Zero the Stopwatch. Finally, step through the program using the F7 key and take note of the instruction cycle counter. The goto $+1 instruction requires 2 cycles, the decfsz count, f instruction requires 1 additional cycle (3), and the goto dly1mS instruction requires 2 more cycles (total of 5).

From this test, it should take a total of 990 μS to complete all 198 iterations of the internal loop. Do the following to check this predication. Do not clear the Stopwatch. Clear the break point on the goto $+1 line of code and set a new break point on the return opcode. When you click on RUN, the internal loop will be executed until the count variable is decremented to zero and the decfsz opcode causes a skip to the next opcode return (**Figure 9-9**). Notice that the number of instruction cycles, and therefore time, is only 989, not as predicted 990. What happened to the two cycles? The missing cycles are due to the final execution of the decfsz opcode.

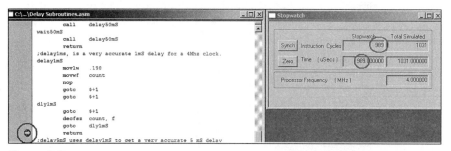

Figure 9-9

When the count variable is zero, the decfsz opcode executes a 2-cycle instruction to skip the next line of code which is the goto opcode. So during the last iteration of the internal loop, there were only 4, not 5, cycles required (the goto opcode is not executed reducing the cycles by 2, but 1 additional cycle was added by the decfsz opcode.) So even though the time required to complete code segments can be predicted by looking at the instruction cycles required for each line of code, things can get a little complicated when branching decisions are involved. This requires the use of some techniques to pad the code to get the desired delay. In this case, we need to add an additional 11 instruction cycles to get the desired delay of 1 msecond.

The whole delay1mS subroutine instruction cycle accounting is listed in **Table 9-2**. The call opcode that jumps the program execution to the delay subroutine uses 2 cycles. The setup section of the code will add 7 instruction cycles, and the return opcode that ends the subroutine adds the final 2 required instruction cycles to give a total of 1000 cycles, 1000 μS, or 1 msecond. Confirm these numbers by setting a break point at the call delay1mS instruction in the main program and stepping

Table 9-2 – Subroutine Instruction Cycle Accounting

Opcode	Opcode (loop)	Inst. Cycles	Cycle Subtotal	Running Total
call delay1mS		2	2	2
delay1mS				
movlw .198		1	1	3
movwf count		1	2	4
nop		1	3	5
goto $+1		2	5	7
goto $+1		2	7	9
	dly1mS			
	goto $+1	2	2	
	decfsz count, f	1 (2)	3	
	goto dly1mS	2	5	
			(5*198)-1=989	998
return		2		1000

through the program from that point.

You may not be able to create the required pad in your code by manipulating variables. There were two techniques used in this subroutine to added instruction cycles without affecting registers or variables, in other words, opcodes that kill time. The first was the nop opcode. This 1-cycle opcode actually performs no operation; it just expends 1 instruction cycle. The second was the goto $+1 instruction. The goto opcode is a 2-cycle instruction. The $ is an assembler reference to the program counter — the +1 simply adds one memory address location to the current program counter represented by the $. The result of this goto opcode then is that the program counter simply advances to the next instruction. The advantage of this programming technique is that it takes two instruction cycles, but requires only one opcode (one word of program memory) to accomplish this delay. You could have used two nop opcodes (two words of program memory), but that would have not been an efficient use of program memory. Keep this technique of using the goto $+# to advance the program counter in mind. It might come in useful later in your programming experience, particularly when you want to increment through a data table.

So far you have looked at programming code to create a very precise delay of 1 msecond. The precision of this delay is only limited by the accuracy of the device clock. You can now use the basic delay interval of 1 msecond to create delays that are multiples of 1 msecond by making sequential calls to the delay1mS subroutine. There are examples of this technique in the program code. The actual development of these more lengthy delays is not that simple. You will need to compensate for the code overhead to make multiple calls to subroutines by "tweaking" your code with delay padding as mentioned above.

The delay routine that you have studied used one 8-bit counter to control the number of iterations of the internal loop. More lengthy delays can be achieved by *nesting counters*. By adding counter variables you can create delays based on increments of 8-bits (16, 32, 64 and so on) to create some very long delays. This is actually the difference between the TMR0 timer resource (8-bit counter) and the TMR1 timer resource (16-bit counter).

Creating Your Own Unique Delay Subroutine

How do you create your own unique delay subroutine? Start out first by writing the internal loop code and calculating the number of instruction cycles or the time required to execute a single loop. Divide that time into the total delay time required to calculate the value that needs to be loaded into the loop counter variable to the nearest integer. Write the delay setup section of the code and calculate the number of instruction cycles required for this overhead section of the code. Don't forget to include the number of cycles required to `call` and `return` from the subroutine. Finally, add padding code to tweak the code to obtain the desired delay.

As you create your own library of delay routines, it is good practice to keep them handy for use in other programs, just as you will see illustrated in the programs in this text. Simply cut and paste the subroutines in your new code. Keep in mind, that in the majority of your applications you will have plenty of memory space available for your programs, however, for larger programs you may have to trim the excess, unused delay subroutines from your code listing to get it all to fit in available memory space.

Summary

There are timer resources available on most MCU devices that operate independently of your program code and can generate interrupts at specific time intervals to jump the program to interrupt service routines to accomplish required tasks. There are times when longer delays are required for an application and these delays can be accomplished through delay subroutines designed for the purpose. A good program habit is to develop a library of delay routines that can be cut and pasted into other code as required. The core of a delay subroutine is an internal loop that is accomplished a set number of times based on the starting value in a loop counter variable. The time required to accomplish one internal loop is used as the base line time that is multiplied by the value loaded into the loop counter variable to get an approximation of the overall delay. Subroutine setup and exit time is added to the loop time and padding instructions are added to the code to tweak the final delay interval. Standardized delays, 1 msecond for example, can be added to create more length delays. Nested loop counter variables also can be used to create longer delays. The *MPLAB Simulator* is a powerful tool that can be used to determine the number of instruction cycles required to execute the delay code. The number of instruction cycles can be translated into the actual time delay by knowing the period of the device system clock. The accuracy of the delay is therefore dependent on the accuracy of the system clock oscillator.

Review Questions

9.1 Serial communications is based on precise timing of pulse widths. The pulse widths can be calculated by the formula $time = \dfrac{1}{baud}$. For 4800 baud, the time interval is .000208 seconds. Write a delay subroutine to generate bit pulses of this duration and test your code using the *MPLAB Simulator* tool.

Basic

Input / Output

Objective: To learn how to configure and use the two PIC16F676 I/O Port pins to send (output) logical states to specific port pins and/or to detect (input) logical states on specific port pins.

Reading: *PIC16F630/676 Data Sheet,* pages 19-21, 27.

Program: Program Files/Ch 10 Program/On Off Button

Configuring Input/Output (I/O) pins for Digital States

Microcontrollers interact with the outside world though collections of pins that make up *input/output* (I/O) ports. In the case of the PIC16F676, there are two I/O ports; PORTA and PORTC. Other MCUs have more or less I/O ports. The individual pins can be configured to interact with the outside world through *digital logic states* (on or off, high or low) or through *analog voltages* (any voltage level between reference extreme voltages). In this chapter on basic input/output, we will examine I/O pins configured for digital states.

Before the ports can be used, they must be configured for either input or output and configured for analog or digital voltages. The individual pins within a port can be configured to output logical states (either high, or +5 V, or low, or 0 V), or they can be configured to sense the logical states on individual pins and return a value of 1 (for high or +5 V) or 0 (for low or 0 V). The port configuration is controlled by specific Special Function Registers (SFRs) that are addressed in the device initialization section of the program code. There are also instances when the configuration of a port or individual pins needs to be changed in the body of the program. To do so, the same SFRs are changed during program execution.

During this discussion and throughout this text, you need to make the distinction between the *resource identifier* as it is listed in the documentation, such as the PORTA pin RA0 or PORTA, 0 and the *physical pin* of the integrated circuit package that is used by the resource. For instance, the I/O pins of PORTA are referred mnemonically in the device documentation as RA0 through RA5. In the actual program to refer to the RA0 I/O pin of PORTA, you will see PORTA, 0. The actual physical IC pin number for PORTA, 0 or RA0 is pin number 13. So for programming purposes you will use the I/O port pin number, for study and documentation you will use the mnemonics, and for project wiring, you will use the physical IC pin number.

Port setup — Special Function Registers

Port setup. There are four SFRs that need to be set up to configure the I/O ports: ANSEL, TRISA, TRISC and WPUA.

Bank1	ANSEL Analog Select Register						
ANS7	ANS6	ANS5	ANS4	ANS3	ANS2	ANS1	ANS0
RC3	RC2	RC1	RC0	RA4	RA2	RA1	RA0

The *Analog Select Register* (ANSEL) assigns individual I/O pins to accept either analog or digital voltage levers. Not all the I/O pins need this kind of flexibility because not all pins can be configured with comparator or ADC resources. If the individual bit within the ANSEL register is SET, then the associated pin is assigned for analog input use. If the individual bit within the ANSEL register is CLEARED, then the associated pin is assigned for digital input use. When a pin is assigned for analog input, other digital input circuitry resources such as weak-pull-up resistors and interrupt-on-change capabilities are automatically disabled.

Bank 1		TRISA PORTA Tri-state Register					
X	X	TRISA5	TRISA4	TRISA3	TRISA2	TRISA1	TRISA0
Unimplemented	Unimplemented	RA5	RA4	RA3	RA2	RA1	RA0

Bank 1		TRISC PORTC Tri-state Register					
X	X	TRISC5	TRISC4	TRISC3	TRISC2	TRISC1	TRISC0
Unimplemented	Unimplemented	RC5	RC4	RC3	RC2	RC1	RC0

The *Tristate Registers* (TRISA and TRISC) are used to configure the appropriate port pin as either an input or output pin. There is a Tristate Register for each port and indicated by the last letter of the mnemonic. SETTING the appropriate bit within the TRIS register will make the I/O pin an input pin, conversely CLEARING the bit will make the pin an output pin.

Bank 1		WPUA Weak Pull-up Register					
X	X	WPUA5	WPUA4	X	WPUA2	WPUA1	WPUA0
Unimplemented	Unimplemented	RA5	RA4	Unimplemented	RA2	RA1	RA0

The last controlling register for port setup is the *Weak Pull-up Register*, (WPUA.) There are weak pull-up resistors tied to all the PORTA I/O pins except RA3. This is because RA3 is used for multiple purposes that are not consistent with an internal weak pull-up resistor. If a weak pull-up resistor is required for a particular application on RA3, this resistor would have to be added externally to the circuit. The purpose of the weak pull-up resistors is to provide a current source when the I/O pin is configured as an input pin which places the pin in the high impedance state. There are no weak pull-up resistors internally attached to PORTC I/O pins and therefore there is no associated WPUA-like register for PORTC. As with pin RA3, or PORTA, 3, weak pull-up resistors would have to be externally connected to PORTC I/O pins if needed. To configure the weak pull-up resistors, the appropriate WPUA bit would be SET. Additionally, the PORTA Pull-up Enable bit (RAPU) in the Option Register (OPTION_REG) would have to be CLEARED. This bit enables all the individually enabled weak pull-up resistors (See Chapter 6). Note that the weak pull-up resistors are automatically disabled if an I/O pin is configured as an output (TRISA associated bit CLEARED) regardless of the WPUA bit or global RAPU bit configuration.

Example Code Segments

Let's take a look as some example code segments that would be included in the Initialization section of the program code to configure the ports. In this first example we want to configure all the port I/O pins as outputs to drive a series of light emitting diodes (LEDs).

```
BANKSEL     Bank1          ;selects BANK1
movlw       b'10000000'    ;load w reg with configuration bits
                           ;for the OPTION_REG, in this case
                           ;disable weak pull-ups
movwf       OPTION_REG     ;put w reg into option register
movlw       b'00000000'    ;load w reg with PORTA I/O pin
                           ;configuration (0 = output, 1 = input)
movwf       TRISA          ;configure register for PORTA
movlw       b'00000000'    ;load w reg with PORTC I/O
                           ;configuration (could also use clear)
movwf       TRISC          ;configure register for PORTC
movlw       b'00000000'    ;load w reg with analog or digital pin
                           ;assignments (0=digital, 1=analog),
                           ;here all digital
movwf       ANSEL          ;configure register for all digital I/O
                           ;pins
BANKSEL     Bank0          ;back to BANK0 for rest of the
                           ;program
```

This program code is not the most efficient use of program memory space and is listed here for illustration. The programming examples used in this text are not necessarily the most efficient and are focused on instruction. In this case, these instructions would be more efficient:

```
clrf        TRISA          ;sets all bits to zero
clrf        TRISC          ;sets all bits to zero
crf         ANSEL          ;sets all bits to zero
```

The clrf opcode sets all the bits in the target register to zero. Another alternative approach is:

```
clrw                       ;load w reg with all zeros
movwf       TRISA          ;sets all bits to zero
movwf       TRISC          ;sets all bits to zero
movwf       ANSEL          ;sets all bits to zero
```

In this code, the W-register is CLEARED and then that value is assigned to each of the following registers to CLEAR each. The first example however is preferred if you are going to cut and paste code between programs.

In the next example of port setup code, let's modify the first code so that pins RA2 and RA 4 (PORTA, 2 and PORTA, 4) and RC0 (PORTC, 0) are inputs, all the other port pins are outputs (except of course RA3, PORTA, 3 which is always an input pin).

```
BANKSEL     Bank1           ;selects BANK1
movlw       b'00000000'     ;load w reg with configuration bits
                            ;for the OPTION_REG, in this case
                            ;disable weak pull-ups
movwf       OPTION_REG      ;put w reg into option register
movlw       b'00010100'     ;load w reg with PORTA I/O pin
                            ;configuration (0 = output, 1 = input)
                            ;RA2 and RA4 input, all others
                            ;output
movwf       TRISA           ;configure register for PORTA
movlw       b'00000001'     ;load w reg with PORTC I/O
                            ;RC0 input, all others output
movwf       TRISC           ;configure register for PORTC
movlw       b'00010100'     ;weak pull-ups enabled on RA2 and
                            ;RA4, (1=enabled, 0=disabled)
movwf       WPUA            ;enabling weak pull-ups
movlw       b'00000000'     ;load w reg with analog or digital pin
                            ;assignments (0=digital, 1=analog),
                            ;here all digital
movwf       ANSEL           ;configure register for all digital I/O
                            ;pins
BANKSEL     Bank0           ;back to BANK0 for rest of the
                            ;program
```

The code above that is bold is changed or added. The changes included clearing
the RAPU bit of the OPTION_REG to enable weak pull-up resistors, SETTING the
appropriate bits for input in the TRISA and TRISC registers, and adding code lines
to enable weak pull-up resistors for pins RA2 and RA4 (remember that there are no
internal weak pull-ups on PORTC and therefore, if required, those resistors would have
to be added to the circuit).

Once the ports have been configured using code contained in the *Initialize* section
of the program code, the individual port I/O pins can be accessed by SETTING or
CLEARING the pins for output or reading the individual pins to sense the applied
voltage for input.

Bank 0	PORTA - PORTA Register						
X	X	RA5	RA4	RA3	RA2	RA1	RA0
Unimplemented	Unimplemented	Pin – 2	Pin - 3	Pin – 4	Pin - 11	Pin12	Pin-13

Bank 0	PORTC - PORTC Register						
X	X	RC5	RC4	RC3	RC2	RC1	RC0
Unimplemented	Unimplemented	Pin –5	Pin -6	Pin –7	Pin –8	Pin-9	Pin - 10

This first program segment simply turns on and off LEDs attached to RA0 (PORTA, 0) and RC1 (PORTC, 1). It is assumed that the ports are initialized as outputs.

```
bcf            PORTA,0         ;start with LED off
bcf            PORTC,1         ;start with LED off
program_loop                   ;this is a label that is used for goto
                               ;and call statements to identify a
                               ;location within the program code.
bsf            PORTA,0         ;turns on LED by setting pin (high or
                               ;5 V on the pin)
bsf            PORTC,1
call           wait1sec        ;calls a delay routine that delays 1
                               ;second, not discussed in this
                               ;chapter.
bcf            PORTA,0         ;turns off LED by clearing pin (low
                               ;or 0 V on the pin)
bcf            PORTC,1
call           wait1sec
goto           program_loop    ;jumps back to the beginning to do it
                               ;again
```

Let's go through this program segment. The first two bcf opcodes make sure the LEDs are turned off. The program_loop statement is called a *label* that identifies a location within the program code to which the goto opcode can jump. This label begins a program segment that will be accomplished over and over again during program execution. The bsf opcode SETS the addressed pin and applies 5 V to that pin. This applied current turns on the LED that is attached (though a current limiting resistor). The call opcode calls a *subroutine* (another code segment that is not defined here, but would be listed in another section of the program code) labeled wait1sec that is designed to delay the program 1 second. The result is that the LEDs will be turned on, then remain on for 1 second before other actions are taken within the code. After this delay of 1 second, the bcf opcode will clear the addressed pins and remove the 5 V which turns off the LEDs. A call again to the wait1sec subroutine causes the LEDs to be off for 1 second. The final goto opcode loops the program back to the program location labeled program_loop to start the process over again. The result is that the LEDs will flash on and off at 1 second intervals. This will continue until the power is turned off.

The following program segment will build upon the LED on and off segment above by assigning a pin as an input and sensing that pin causing a reaction in response to some input. This segment assumes that RA0 and RC1 are outputs and RA2 is an input

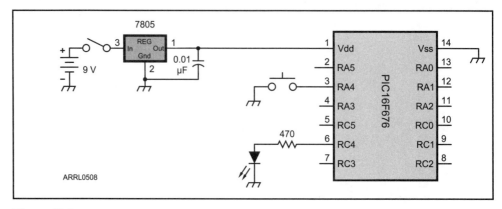

Figure 10-1

with a weak pull-up resistor enabled on that pin. There is a momentary-on push-button switch connected between RA2 and ground. The weak pull-up attached to RA2 will keep the voltage on that pin at 5 V until the push button is pressed which will short RA2 to ground until it is released.

```
bcf      PORTA,0       ;start with LED off
bcf      PORTC,1       ;start with LED off

program_loop           ;this is a label that is used for goto
                       ;and call statements to identify a
                       ;location within the program code.
btfsc    PORTA,2       ;senses the voltage on PORTA,2. If
                       ;the voltage is 0 V, this command
                       ;returns a CLEAR condition and
                       ;the next command is skipped. If the
                       ;voltage is 5 V, this command
                       ;returns a SET condition and the
                       ;next command is executed.
goto     program_loop  ;if the button is not pressed, jump to
                       ;program_loop and continue to do so
                       ;until the button is pressed.
                       ;If the button is pressed the code
                       ;below is executed and the LEDS
                       ;will flash.
bsf      PORTA,0       ;turns on LED by setting pin (high or
                       ;5 V on the pin)
bsf      PORTC,1
call     wait1sec      ;calls a delay routine that delays 1
                       ;second, not discussed in this
                       ;chapter.
bcf      PORTA,0       ;turns off LED by clearing pin (low
                       ;or 0 V on the pin)
bcf      PORTC,1
call     wait1sec
goto     program_loop  ;jumps back to the beginning to do it
                       ;again
```

The added code statements above are in bold. The added btfsc opcode looks at the voltage on pin RA2. If that voltage is 5 V, the instruction returns a SET state on that pin and the next opcode is executed to loop the program back to the label program_loop. If the voltage is 0 V, the instruction returns a CLEAR condition on that pin and the next instruction is skipped causing the program to continue to flash the LEDs before jumping back to the program_loop label. The result is that when the push button is pressed, the LEDs will flash at 1-second intervals (as long as the button is pressed), when the button is released, the program will simply loop and wait for a button press.

Putting it all together, wire up your proto-typing board with the circuit in **Figure 10-1** and shown in **Figure 10-2**. Then load the

Figure 10-2

Program Files/CH 10 Program/On Off Button project into *MPLAB IDE*. While you read the following program description, refer to the code as contained in the On Off Button.asm file and displayed in the *MPLAB IDE* editor window.

The code below is located in the Initialize section of the program and configures PORTA, 4 as an input with the weak pull-up resistor enabled and PORTC, 4 as an output:

```
BANKSEL     Bank1            ;BANK1
movlw       b'00000000'      ;enabling weak pull-ups
movwf       OPTION_REG       ;put w reg into option register
movlw       b'00010000'      ;RA4 as input, all others output
movwf       TRISA            ;program PORTA
movlw       b'00010000'      ;enable weak pull-up on RA4
movwf       WPUA
movlw       b'00000000'      ;all PORTC as outputs
movwf       TRISC            ;program PORTC
movlw       b'00000000'      ;all pins digital
movwf       ANSEL
BANKSEL     Bank0            ;back to bank0
```

The code below is located in the main section of the program and senses the voltage on PORTA, 4 waiting for you to press the button. Once you press the button to short PORTA, 4 to ground, the program continues to flash the LED. Release the button and the LED is off and the program waits for the next button press.

```
main
    btfsc     PORTA,4        ;check if button pressed (0)
    goto      main           ;if 0 then skip this goto

    bsf       PORTC,4        ;turn on LED tied to RC4
    call      wait1sec       ;wait for 1 second
    bcf       PORTC,4        ;turn it off LED
    call      wait1sec       ;wait another second
    goto      main           ;do it again
```

If you scroll down to where the delay routine code below is listed, you will find the code for the wait1sec subroutine that is called by the main program. The wait1sec subroutine is actually made up of additional calls to other subroutines. The wait1sec subroutine calls the wait300 mS subroutine three times. The wait300 mS subroutine will cause a delay of 300 milliseconds for each call. Then the wait1sec subroutine ends with a call to a wait100mS subroutine that causes a delay of 100 milliseconds. The sum of these delays adds up to 1 second.

Summary

This chapter has focused on the setup and the basic use of the I/O port pins of the MCU. The setup of the ports in the program Initialization section included using the ANSEL register to dictate if a port pin is configured for digital or analog level voltages, the TRIS registers to dictate if a port pin resource is an input or an output and the WPUA and OPTION_REG registers to enable weak pull-up resistors internally attached to PORTA resources. We learned a hardware nuance that the weak pull-up resistors are disabled on an associated pin when that pin is configured as an output. Once the I/O resources are configured for digital input/output you learned that the bsf and bcf opcodes will either SET or CLEAR the operand pin. Finally you learned that the state of an input pin can be sensed and appropriate action taken by the program. For instance `btfsc` will sense the state on the appropriate pin and if the state is CLEAR, the next statement is skipped, if it is SET, the next instruction is executed. As an example:

```
btfsc       PORTA, 1
goto        somewhere
continue_with_program
```

Review Questions

10.1 List the code that would be required to configure the I/O resources of the MCU so that RA0, RA3, RA4, RC1 and RC2 are digital inputs, the rest of the pins are digital outputs and Weak pull-up resistors are enabled on the PORTA input pins.

10.2 List the I/O restrictions on RA3.

10.3 You have a pin in PORTA configured as an input with the weak pull-up resistor enabled for that pin. Inside the main program, you would like to momentarily change the direction of that pin to an output. What command(s) would you need to include to do the switching from input to output and back again?

10.4 Write a command line that is an alternative to:
```
movlw       b'00000000'
movwf       PORTA
```

10.5 The following command segment will toggle the status on pin PORTA, 4, which means if the pin is SET, the program will CLEAR the pin, and vice versa:
```
btfsc       PORTA,4
bcf         PORTA,4
btfss       PORTA,4
bsf         PORTA,4
continue_with_program
```

Write a tighter (more efficient code) that will accomplish the same task. (Hint: look at the `xorwf` command.)

10.6 Switches are notorious for contact bouncing, which means that when the contacts within a switch are opened or closed, there is not an instantaneous make or break of the switch contacts. When the switch closure or opening is sampled fast enough with a computer, multiple closures or openings could be detected with potentially disastrous results. Write a code segment that would help to alleviate the switch contact bounce issue.

10.7 Write out the default configuration for the ANSEL, TRISA, TRISC, OPTION_REG, and WPUA registers. Under what resource configuration conditions would the default configurations of these registers be okay, meaning you would not have to address these registers in the Initialization segment of your program? Would it be advisable to use the default configuration instead of deliberately configuring these registers, why or why not?

10.8 Adjust the code that you used during this chapter to flash an LED when the switch was pressed so that two LEDs flash but alternately (when one LED is on, the other is off and vice versa).

10.9 Adjust the same code so that the LED is flashing when the switch is open and stops flashing when the switch is closed.

10.10 Adjust the same code to make a stop light simulation. In this simulation, the red LED is on until the switch is pressed. Then like the operation of a stop light, there is a pause, then the red light goes out and the green LED comes on for a short period. After the green period, the yellow LED comes on, the green goes out for a short period. Finally, the red LED is turned on and the yellow is turned off and the program awaits for the next switch press (the car).

Analog to Digital Converter

Objective: To learn how to configure and use the eight PIC16F676 analog to digital converter (ADC) resources to sense variable voltages applied to an I/O pin and display the digital value that is proportional to the applied voltage relative to a reference voltage.

Reading: *PIC16F630/676 Data Sheet*, pages 43-48.
Program: **Program Files/Ch 11 Program/ADC**

The Analog to Digital Converter (ADC) — Powerful MCU Resource

The most powerful resources contained in MCUs are analog to digital converters (ADC). An analog to digital converter is a circuit that takes an instantaneous sample of an applied voltage, compares the level of the sensed voltage to a reference voltage and using a mathematical algorithm (commonly a binary search algorithm is used) returns a digital value that represents the proportional relationship between the two voltages. ADCs are typically used with peripheral sensors that measure an environmental factor and report that measurement as a voltage that in turn is sensed by an MCU to take some action. For instance, the sensor might be a temperature sensor, one of the most common sensors. The temperature sensor measures the temperature of the device that is being monitored. The value of the temperature is returned as some calibrated voltage level that is proportional to the degrees of temperature. The MCU in turn would monitor the output voltage of the temperature sensor using an ADC and waits for a specified voltage level before taking some action, for instance, turning off or on a heating element.

ADC Level of Accuracy

The level of accuracy for measuring this relative difference between the two voltages is indicated by the bit resolution of the ADC. In the specific case of the PIC16F676, there are 8 10-bit ADCs available. Ten-bit resolution means that the resolution of the ADC could detect 1024 incremental steps of the reference voltage (b'1111111111'= 1023 decimal). If the reference voltage is 5 V, then the ADC could resolve voltage changes of 4.9 mV [(1/1023) × 5 V = 4.9 mV]. This level of resolution does not take into account the influences of various kinds of noise injected into the system from electronics and conversion schemes that in reality reduce the practical resolution (a discussion beyond the scope of this text, but the limitation that needs to be considered in the most stringent applications). Continuing with this discussion, if the voltage being measured by the ADC is 3.9 V and the reference voltage is 5 V, it would be anticipated that the ADC would return a value of 798, [(3.9/5) × 1023] = 798). The MCU would be programmed to take some action based on this ADC value.

ADC Limitations

There are some ADC limitations to consider. It takes a finite amount of time to sense the voltage being measured before the conversion can be accomplished. There actually is a small value capacitor that is charged by the applied current and enough time needs to be allowed for this capacitor to charge up and reach the voltage level being measured. Additionally, it takes some time for the MCU to perform the ADC algorithm. The amount of time required depends on the algorithm scheme and the clock speed of the particular device. In the more critical, high speed applications, the circuit designer will have to study the specifications of the MCU device that is going to be used to take these limitations into consideration.

ADC setup

Before you set up the ADC resources for use you will need to do some preplanning.

First, you will need to define what *reference voltage* you will use. You have two choices — use the internal V_{dd} (5 V) voltage or some external variable reference voltage (up to the value of V_{dd}) that is applied to I/O port pin RA1. Using V_{dd} as your reference voltage may be limiting, but many of the external sensors that you will be using use V_{dd} as the reference. Using an external voltage will give you a lot of flexibility and may improve the measurement accuracy but at the expense of tying up one of the I/O resources for the purpose. In the program example of this chapter, you will be using V_{dd} as the reference voltage.

Second, you will need to determine which I/O port pins will be used for ADC. You can assign up to 8 pins to ADC resources, but only one ADC measurement can be made at a time since each of the ADC-assigned pins (called channels) share some common circuitry.

Third, you will need to research the minimum conversion time required for the device and determine the appropriate clock speed for the ADC to meet that minimum time. The PIC16F676 requires 11 clock cycles to complete the conversion algorithm and 1.6μS according to the documentation. There are operating frequencies for the device and various V_{dd} voltage levels possible. All interact to affect the ADC performance. Fortunately there is a selection chart that provides some guidance on selecting the appropriate ADC clock frequency on page 44 of the device documentation. In the exercise of this text, you will be using the internal device clock that runs at a frequency of 4 MHz. Cross referencing that clock frequency with the minimum conversion time required of 1.6 μS returns an ADC to system clock ratio of 1 to 8, so plan on using a bit setting in the ADCON1 register to set the ADC conversion clock to Fosc/8 (more on this will follow).

Finally, you will need to determine the justification of the ADC output data. The ADCs on the PIC16F676 are 10-bit resources which means that the ADC value will require 2-bytes to hold the output value, but only 10 of the 16 available bits. This means that 6 bits go unused. Often, you will want to shift bits out of the registers that hold the ADC output values, or you will want to truncate either the upper or lower bits depending on the application. This will determine if you want the ADC output value to be right- or left-hand justified within the two ADC output registers. In the exercise of this text, you will be using right-hand justified data in the ADC output registers meaning the lower byte of the 10-bit ADC output will be held in the lower ADC output register (ADRESL) and the remaining upper 2-bits will be held in the upper ADC output register (ADRESH).

Special Function Registers to Be Configured to Use the ADC Resources

There are three SFRs that need to be configured to use the ADC resources of the 16F676. These registers are configured in the Initialization section of the program.

ADCON0 — The A/D Control Register

The state of the ADFM bit within ADCON0 determines the ADC output format. The 10-bit output of the ADC is placed in two registers, the high byte in ADRESH and the low byte in ADRESL. If ADCON0, ADFM is SET, the output is right justified with the lower 8-bits of the ADC output placed in ADRESL and the upper 2-bits placed in the lower portion of the ADRESH. If ADCON0, ADFM is CLEARED, the result is left justified with the high 8-bits of the ADC output placed in ADRESH and the lower 2-bits placed in the upper portion of ADRESL. The voltage reference used by the ADC is determined by the VCFG bit. If ADCON0, VCFG is SET, the reference voltage is an external voltage applied to pin RA1, if ADCON0, VCFG is CLEARED, V_{dd} is used as the reference voltage. The ADC channel setting is determined by configuring the CHS2, CHS1, and CHS0 bits as appropriate for the channel desired. These bits along with the next bit, GO/DONE, are frequently changed during the main part of the program. The GO/DONE bit of the ADCON0 register is used to start the ADC conversion by SETTING this bit in software. Upon the completion of the ADC conversion, this bit is CLEARED by the PIC16F676 hardware. You can pole this bit during the ADC conversion to check to see if the conversion is in progress or completed. The final bit, ADON, is SET to turn on the ADC module or CLEARED to turn off the ADC module. In the off state, the module draws no current.

Bank 0	ADCON0 A/D Control Register						
ADFM	*VCFG*	*X*	*CHS2*	*CHS1*	*CHS0*	*GO/DONE*	*ADON*
A/D Result Formed Select bit	Voltage Reference bit	Unimplemented	Analog Channel Select bit	Analog Channel Select bit	Analog Channel Select bit	A/D Conversion STATS bit	A/D On/ Off bit

ADCON1 — The A/D Control Register 1

This register has only three bits implemented. The ADCS2, ADCS1, and ADCS0 bits are used to determine the ADC conversion clock rate. These bits are SET or CLEARED as outlined in the device documentation for the appropriate clock rate. The examples in this text will use a conversion clock rate of Fosc/8 which equals a bit pattern of b'001'.

Bank 1	ADCON1 Control Register 1						
X	*ADCS2*	*ADCS1*	*ADCS0*	*X*	*X*	*X*	*X*
Unimplemented	A/D Conversion Clock Select bits	A/D Conversion Clock Select bits	A/D Conversion Clock Select bits	Unimplemented	Unimplemented	Unimplemented	Unimplemented

ANSEL — The Analog Select Register

You have seen the final ADC associated register before. The ANSEL register assigns individual I/O pins to accept either analog or digital voltage levers. Because the ADC will be measuring analog voltages, the pin resource associated with the ADC need to be configured for analog input by SETTING the appropriate bit in ANSEL.

Bank 1	ANSEL Analog Select Register						
ANS7	*ANS6*	*ANS5*	*ANS4*	*ANS3*	*ANS2*	*ANS1*	*ANS0*
RC3	RC2	RC1	RC0	RA4	RA2	RA1	RA0

Code to Configure the ADC Resources

Now let's take a look at some code that would be placed in the Initialize section of the program to configure the ADC resources. The following examples are extracted from the example program that you will use later in this chapter (**Program Files/Ch 11 Program/ADC**). The following lines will configure the PIC16F676 so that RC0 is an analog input assigned to the ADC, right justified and V_{dd} as the reference voltage.

```
        movlw    b'00000111'    ;non inverted, comp with output
        movwf    CMCON
        movlw    b'00000000'    ;globals, peripherals, RA2 int, clear INTF
        movwf    INTCON
        movlw    b'10010001'    ;right justified, Vdd ref RC0 has ADC,
                                ;ADC stopped, ADC resource connected

        movwf    ADCON0
        BANKSEL  Bank1          ;go to Bank1
        movlw    b'00000000'    ;load w reg
        movwf    OPTION_REG     ;put w reg into option register
        movlw    b'00010000'    ;Fosc/8
        movwf    ADCON1
        movlw    b'00000000'    ;load w reg with PORTA I/O
        movwf    TRISA          ;program PORTA
        movlw    b'00000001'    ;load w reg with PORTC I/O (RC0 input all
                                ;others output)
        movwf    TRISC          ;program PORTC
        movlw    b'00010000'    ;RC0 analog, all other digital
        movwf    ANSEL
        BANKSEL  Bank0          ;back to Bank0
```

Now more closely examine the bolded lines of code. Those are the ones specifically associated with the ADC. The bit pattern b'10010001' sets up the ADCON0 register with right justified (ADFM=1), voltage reference V_{dd} (VCFG=0), the next bit unimplemented, ADC channel AN4 (RC0) selected (CHS2=1, CHS1=0, CHS0=0), ADC stopped (GO/DONE=0), and ADC connected and operating (ADON=1). This bit pattern is loaded into the w-register and then in turn loaded into the ADCON0 register in memory Bank 0.

The fastest ADC conversion clock that will give reliable conversions with the 4 MHz clock frequency used with the device and still be within the minimum conversion time of 1.6 µS specified for this device is Fosc/8. The bit pattern b'00001000' sets up the ADCON1 register with ADCS2=0, ADCS1=0 and ADCS0=1. This bit pattern is loaded into the w-register and then in turn loaded into the ADCON1 register. Note that ADCON1 is in memory Bank 1 and therefore that Bank 1 has to be selected before actions can address ADCON1.

Finally, the RC0 pin needs to be designated as an analog pin. The bit pattern b'00010000' sets up the ANSEL register with bit ANS4=1, the other bits CLEARED. This bit pattern is loaded into the w-register and then in turn loaded into the ANSEL register. This register is also with Bank 1.

All that is left to do to use the ADC on RC0 is to start the conversion, then read and act upon the result. That is what is accomplished in the following code extracted from the ADC program.

```
        bsf      ADCON0,GO      ;set GO bit to begin ADC conversion
wait_ADC
        btfsc    ADCON0,GO      ;check if ADC complete (cleared bit)
        goto     wait_ADC       ;if not, loop and wait until clear

        BANKSEL  Bank1          ;switch to Bank 1 to access ADC low
                                ;byte
        movfw    ADRESL
        BANKSEL  Bank0          ;go back to Bank 0 to access l_byte
                                ;variable
        movwf    l_byte
        movfw    ADRESH         ;get ADC high byte
        movwf    h_byte         ;put in h_byte
```

The ADCON0 GO/DONE bit is assigned the mnemonic GO in the PIC16F676.inc file and that is how that bit is referred to in this code example. The bsf opcode SETS the ADCON0, GO bit and starts the ADC conversion. It takes a finite amount of time for the PIC16F676 to complete the conversion. Once the conversion is complete, the device hardware will CLEAR the GO bit. The next three lines of code will sense the value of ADCON0, GO bit with btfsc. If that bit is SET, the conversion is not completed and the program jumps back to the label wait_ADC until the conversion is completed and the GO bit is CLEARED. Once the ADC conversion is completed, the 10-bit right-justified result is loaded into SFRs reserved for the ADC result ADRESL (which is in Bank 1) and ADRESH (which is in Bank 0). The memory bank is switched to Bank 1 so that the low 8-bits of the ADC result in ADRESL can be accessed and loaded into the W-register. Once the value is in the W-register, the bank is switched back to Bank 0 where the l_byte variable space is reserved and the contents of the W-register is loaded into l_byte. It is not necessary to switch banks at this specific location in the code of this example to access the l_byte variable location because in the 16F676 the General Purpose Registers, memory locations 0x20 to 0x5f, are mapped across the both banks. However it is a good habit to consider — being in the appropriate bank — because other MCUs that you might use may not have the same cross mapping architecture. In any event there is no code savings because you still need to switch banks to access ADRESH. Finally the high 2-bits of the ADC result in ADRESH are moved into the variable space h_byte. The code that follows this segment would take some action based on the ADC result.

Putting It into Practice — Build Up the Circuit

Now it is your turn. Build up the circuit as depicted in **Figure 11-1** and as illustrated in the picture in **Figure 11-2**. This circuit places a 10K Ω variable resistor on RC0 (IC pin 10). The top side of the potentiometer is connected to V_{dd} (which is the reference voltage) and the bottom side to ground. The LCD display is set up so that the ADC value can be displayed. Load the ADC project located at **Program Files/Ch 11 Program/ADC** into *MPLAB IDE*, build the program and install it into the PIC16F676.

If you review the code in the program (file ADC.asm) you will see program lines that are associated with working with the LCD display. Do not be concerned if you do not fully understand these lines of code at this time. They will be covered in later chapters of this text. The following gives just a brief explanation of the purpose of these lines simply to put them in context for the main focus of this exercise.

The following lines send the characters "RC0" to subroutines that in turn send these

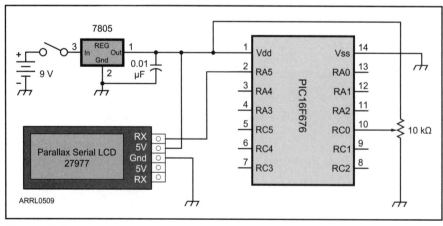

Figure 11-1

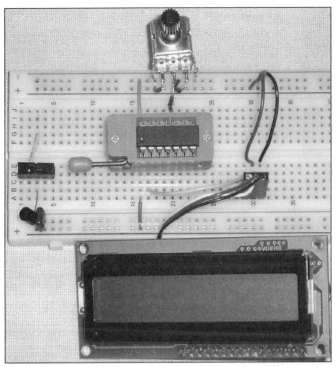

Figure 11-2

characters to the LCD for display. The subroutine sends the characters serially to the
LCD:

```
movlw      LCD_LINE0      ;sends text to LCD display
call       LCDOutput
movlw      "R"
call       LCDOutput
movlw      "C"
call       LCDOutput
movlw      "0"
call       LCDOutput
```

The following two lines move the cursor on the LCD to a position where the ADC
value will be displayed:

```
movlw      LCD_LINE0+4    ;moves LDC display location
                          ;to line
                          ;0 position 4
call       LCDOutput
```

Finally, the call to the LCDOutput subroutine converts the 4-digit decimal ADC
value into a format that can be displayed on the LCD and then displays the value.

The main body of the program that does the ADC conversion should look familiar.
It was discussed in detail above.

Applying Power to the Circuit

When you apply power to the circuit, the LCD will display RC0 and then the ADC
value (**Figure 11-3**). If you adjust the variable resistor, the value of the ADC will change

Figure 11-3

Table 11-1

Voltage	ADC	Predicted ADC
0.03	4	6
0.5	100	101
1	201	203
1.5	304	304
2	403	406
2.5	508	507
3	608	609
3.49	707	708
4	809	812
4.5	911	913
5.04	1022	1023

proportionally to reflect the digital value of the voltage applied to RC0. If you take a close look at the 1's digit of the ADC value, you will see it rapidly change +/– some value. This is due to the noise injected into the circuit by electronic and computational limitations.

Next, using a voltmeter, measure the voltage applied to RC0 (the center post of the variable resistor) and record the ADC value from one extreme (0 V) to the other (V_{dd} or 5 V). Next, calculate the predicted ADC value based on the applied voltage relative to the reference voltage using the formula (voltage/Vref) × 1023 (on my board, Vref was measured to be 5.04 V). Record these data points next to the observed ADC values for comparison. The data in **Table 11-1** was collected. This data was then graphed using Excel graphing utilities and shows good linear ADC conversion (**Figure 11-4**).

Summary

Analog to Digital Converters are very powerful resources on MCUs. The PIC16F676 has up to 8 10-bit ADCs available. The special function registers ADCON0, ADCON1, and ANSEL are used to select and configure these available ADC resources. The output of the ADC is stored in two SFRs ADRESH and ADRESL. The ADCs have good conversion linearity and therefore have a predictable outcome.

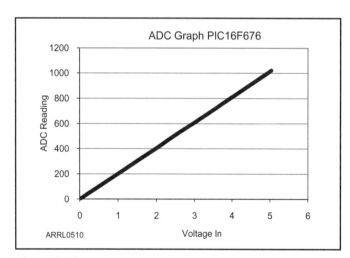

Figure 11-4

Review Questions

11.1 The ADC resources of the PIC16F676 share common input circuitry. What considerations must be taken because of this common circuitry?

11.2 Which register and bit are used by the PIC16F676 hardware to signal that the conversion is still in progress?

11.3 Which register and bit can be used to disable the ADC circuits (this also would reduce chip power consumption)?

11.4 Can you read both the ADRESH and ADRESL registers while operating in memory Bank 0?

11.5 Is bank switching required in this code snippet? Explain your answer.

```
BANKSEL     Bank1
movfw       ADRESL
BANKSEL     Bank0
movwf       1_byte
```

11.6 What could you do if you wanted to reduce the noise present on the LSB of the ADC output by changing the ADC output from 10-bits to 8-bits? Write a short code segment to efficiently accomplish this change. (Hint: look at left justifying the ADC data.)

11.7 What would happen to the contents of the ADRESH and ADRESL registers if you clear the ADCON0, GO bit before the ADC conversion is completed?

Comparator

Objective: To learn how to configure and use the PIC16F676 analog comparator resource to sense the relative difference between two input voltages and program an appropriate response.

Reading: *PIC16F630/676 Data Sheet,* pages 40-44.
Programs: **Program Files/Ch 12 Program/Comparator_1**
Program Files/Ch 12 Program/Comparator_2
Program Files/Ch 12 Program/Comparator_3

The Comparator Circuit

As the name implies, a *comparator circuit* compares the relative value of two input voltages and returns either a high or low state based on the comparison. The comparator has two different inputs, one *non-inverting* (+) and one *inverting* (-). When the comparator is configured in the non-inverting mode, if the voltage applied to the non-inverting input is less than the voltage applied to the inverting input, the comparator output will be low and vice versa. Alternatively, when the comparator is configured in the inverting mode, the outcome would be reversed. The PIC16F676 has one comparator circuit that can be configured eight different ways. The alternative configurations include *inverting/non-inverting outputs*, the *output tied to one of the I/O pins* in addition to a *flag bit in a special function register*, *internal reference voltage* tied to the *non-inverting input*, and *toggling between I/O pins* tied to the *inverting input.* During this exploration of the comparator resource, you will focus on just two of these configurations.

Setting up the Comparator

The comparator resource needs to be set up in the Initialization section of the program code. Configurations that need to be considered when setting up the comparator include non-inverting/inverting output, connecting the output to an I/O pin along with the special function register flag available, and/or if the internal reference voltage ladder will be used on the non-inverting input. In previous program examples, the comparator was configured in the off mode which internally grounded the inputs to the comparator circuit to provide the lowest power consumption.

The Comparator Control Register (CMCON)

The Comparator Control Register is in memory Bank 0. The CMCON, COUT bit is the *comparator output flag*. In the non-inverting mode, COUT will be SET if the non-inverting input voltage is greater than the inverting input voltage. In the inverting mode, the COUT bit state will be reversed. The CINV bit if SET will invert the comparator output, CLEARING the bit will place the comparator in the non-inverting mode. The *CIS bit* is the comparator input switch when the comparator is placed in the modes represented by the *CM2:CM0 bit patterns* b'110' or b'101'. The bits CM2, CM1, and CM0 set one of the eight comparator modes.

Bank 0	CMCON Comparator Control Register						
X	COUT	X	CINV	CIS	CM2	CM1	CM0
Unimplemented	Comparator Output bit	Unimplemented	Comparator Output Inversion bit	Comparator Input Switch bit	Comparator Mode bit	Comparator Mode bit	Comparator Mode bit

As was required in previous examples, the Analog Select Register, ANSEL needs to be loaded with the bit pattern that assigns RA0 and RA1 as analog inputs because the comparator inputs are analog and tied to those I/O pins.

Bank 1	ANSEL Analog Select Register						
ANS7	ANS6	ANS5	ANS4	ANS3	ANS2	ANS1	ANS0
RC3	RC2	RC1	RC0	RA4	RA2	RA1	RA0

The Voltage Reference Control Register (VRCON)

The *Voltage Reference Control Register* uses the *internal voltage reference* and configuring this SFR is not a trivial exercise. The PIC16F676 documentation provides detailed instructions on the voltage range and step resolution of the internal reference voltage and the instructions require solving a few algebraic algorithms to set the desired reference voltage. *The reference voltage is based on a proportion relative to V_{dd}.* In this discussion, it is assumed that V_{dd} is 5 V. The reference voltage is divided into two ranges, the *low range* will allow 16 voltage steps between 0 and 3.125 V — steps of approximately .2 V; the *high range* will allow 16 voltage steps between 1.25 and 3.59 V — steps of approximately .15 V. The *VREN bit* enables the internal voltage reference if SET, disables and powers down if CLEARED. The VRR bit determines the *voltage reference range* used — SET for the low range, CLEAR for the high range. The VR3:VR0 bits set the proportional value of the selected range as calculated in the documented algorithms (0 to 15, b'0000' to b'1111'). The following are two examples of using the algorithms.

For the low range, the algorithm is: $V = \dfrac{VR3:VR0}{24} \times V_{dd}$. Substituting VR3:VR0 = 10 (b'1010') and 5 V for V_{dd}: $2.08V = \dfrac{10}{24} \times 5$ The reference would be 2.08 V.

For the high range, the algorithm is: $V = \dfrac{V_{dd}}{4} + \left(\dfrac{VR3:VR0}{32} \right) \times V_{dd}$. Substituting VR3:VR0 = 12 b'1100' and 5 V for V_{dd}: $3.125V = \dfrac{5}{4} + \left(\dfrac{12}{32} \right) \times 5$ The reference would be 3.125 V.

Bank 1	VRCON Voltage Reference Control Register						
VREN	X	VRR	X	VR3	VR2	VR1	VR0
CVref Enable bit	Unimplemented	CVref Range Selection bit	Unimplemented	CVref Value Selection	CVref Value Selection	CVref Value Selection	CVref Value Selection

Initialization Segment of the Program Code for Setting Up Comparator

The following is a portion of the Initialization segment of the program code that you will be using in this chapter's exercise. The entire Initialization segment of the code can be reviewed and studied in *MPLAB IDE*, only the relevant lines of code associated with setting up the comparator are reproduced here.

```
        movlw       b'00000001'     ;non inverted, comp with output
                                    ;comparator with non inverted output, +/- inputs
                                    ;connected CM2:CM0 = 001,COUT connected to
                                    ;RA2 - use in step one of exercise

;       movlw       b'00010001'     ;inverted, comp with output
                                    ;comparator with inverted output, +/- inputs
                                    ;connected CM2:CM0 = 001, COUT connected to
                                    ;RA2 - use in step two of exercise

;       movlw       b'00000010'     ;non-inverted, comp without output
                                    ;comparator with non inverted output, +/- inputs
                                    ;connected CM2:CM0 = 010, COUT not connected
                                    ;to RA2, must be read in
                                    ;software - use in step three of exercise

        movwf       CMCON           ;

        BANKSEL     Bank1           ;BANK1
        movlw       b'00000011'     ;RA0, RA1 is analog, all other digital
        movwf       ANSEL
        BANKSEL     Bank0           ;back to bank0
```

The setup code contains code for three different comparator configurations, two are "commented" out to facilitate exploring the comparator during the exercises. Review again the comparator modes that are graphically summarized on page 41 of the *PIC16F630/676 Data Sheet* for the following discussion. The comparator is configured by the bit pattern that is loaded into the CMCON special function register. The bit pattern is first loaded into the W-register and then the contents of the W-register are transferred into the CMCON register.

movlw   b'00000001' The COUT bit (comparator output bit) works in concert with the CINV bit (comparator inversion bit) to determine the reaction of the comparator relative to the input voltages. If the comparator is non-inverting, the comparator output will be SET if V_{in+} is greater than V_{in-} and CLEAR if V_{in-} is greater than V_{in+} If the comparator is inverting, the comparator output will be the opposite. The bit pattern b'00000001' CLEARS CINV and therefore makes the comparator non-inverting.

The CM2:CM0 bits of CMCON determine the comparator mode. Within the bit pattern b'00000001' the lowest 3 bits set up the comparator with the output connected to I/O pin RA2. This allows the COUT bit to drive an external component connected to the I/O pin as well as allow the program to access the comparator output.

movlw b'00010001' This bit pattern SETS the CINV bit of CMCON which configures the comparator as inverting. The comparator mode remains unchanged.

movlw b'00000010' This bit pattern CLEARS the CINV bit which configures the comparator as non-inverting. The last three bits of the pattern change the comparator mode so that the COUT bit is disconnected from the RA2 I/O pin freeing that resource for other uses.

Analog Select Register

The final SFR that needs to be addressed in setting up the comparator is the *Analog Select Register* or ANSEL register. The inputs to the comparator are analog voltages. The output if connected to RA2, is at digital levels, therefore, the associated I/O pins must be configured appropriately. The bit pattern b'00000011' sets up RA0 and RA1 as analog inputs and RA2 (an all other port I/O pins) as digital resources.

Three Programming Exercises to Explore the Comparator

You will now be doing three programming exercises to explore the use and capabilities of the comparator. Wire up your proto-board with the circuit illustrated in **Figure 12-1**. An example of the wired circuit is shown in the picture in **Figure 12-2**. This circuit applies approximately 2.5 V on the RA0 (the inverting input to the comparator) through a voltage divider, a variable voltage on RA1 (the non-inverting input to the comparator) through a variable resistor, and an LED through a current limiting resistor on RA2. Load the program project **Program Files/Ch 12 Program/Comparator** into *MPLAB IDE* and open the .asm file for study. This program will be used for three exercises to illustrate specific points about the comparator.

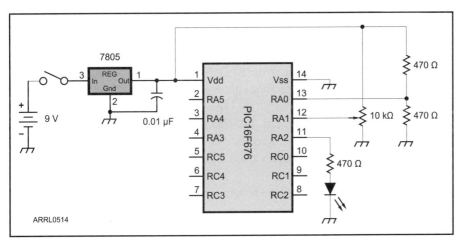

Figure 12-1

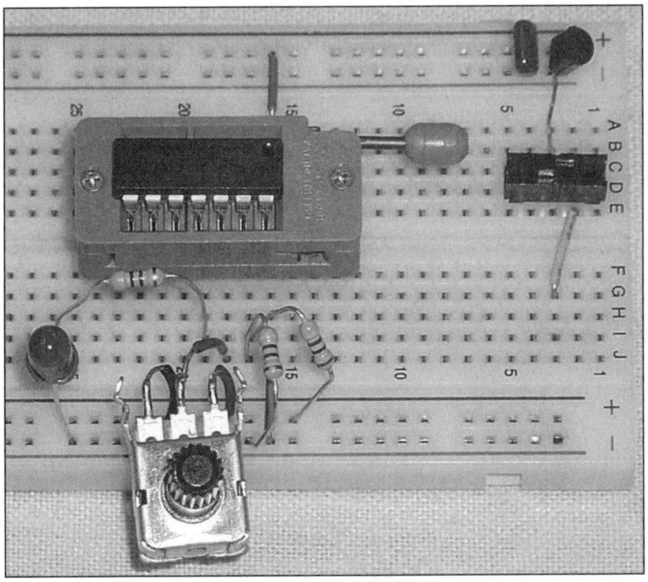

Look in the Initialize segment of the code with particular attention to these lines of code (comments have been removed):

```
        movlw       b'00000001'
;       movlw       b'00010001'
;       movlw       b'00000010'
        movwf       CMCON
```

The first movlw opcode is active, the other two are commented out and are inactive. These lines will sequentially be commented in an out during the exercises. The first movlw instruction loads the bit pattern b'00000001' into the W-register and the movwf opcode in turn transfers this bit pattern into the CMCON register to configure the comparator with RA1 and RA0 inputs as inputs with the COUT bit tied to RA2 for output. In this configuration, the comparator is actually a stand-alone resource that operates regardless of what is going on with the program.

Figure 12-2

Build and load this program into the PIC16F676. When the program is running in the circuit, adjust the value of the variable resistor through its range. At some point, the LED tied to RA2 will illuminate. Reversing the variable resistor rotation will extinguish the LED. What is happening is that when the voltage on RA1 (C_{IN-}) is greater than the voltage on RA0 (C_{IN+}), the LED will be off; when the voltage on RA1(C_{IN-}) is less than the voltage on RA0 (C_{IN+}), the LED will be illuminated. That is the basic function of a comparator. The following is the truth table for the non-inverted configuration.

Using a VOM, measure the voltage on RA0. The voltage should be approximately half V_{dd} or 2.5 V. Now attach the VOM to RA1. Observe the voltage on RA1 while you adjust the variable resistor through its range and while observing the LED. Slowly adjust the variable resistor and stop when the LED just turns on. The voltage measured at this point should be very close to the voltage applied to RA0. If you are very careful with the resistor adjustment and observe the LED very closely, you should be able to detect the LED dim from full on to full off over a very short range of resistor adjustment. The measurable voltage range on RA1 during this transition is probably beyond the resolution of most common voltmeters. This illustrates a characteristic of comparator devices; there is some level of uncertainty in determining the difference between the two input voltages when those voltages are very close together.

Table 12-1

Truth Table for the Non-Inverted Configuration

Input Conditions (non-inverted)	COUT
RA1(C_{IN-}) > RA0(C_{IN+})	0
RA1(C_{IN-}) < RA0(C_{IN+})	1

Now take a look at the main part of the program code:

```
main
      goto main
```

This code is simply a loop and accomplishes very little except keep the MCU busy. The point here is that the comparator is actually a separate resource that is operating simultaneously and separately from the MCU program code. In a later exercise, the program code will access the comparator and take some action based on the status of the comparator output, but for now we will be looking specifically at the comparator as a stand-alone resource.

The next exercise takes a look at the comparator behavior when it is configured to have an inverted output. In the Initialization segment of the code, comment out the first `movlw` instruction and remove the comment on the second movlw opcode lines as illustrated below:

```
;   movlw       b'00000001'
    movlw       b'00010001'
;   movlw       b'00000010'
    movwf       CMCON
```

This change simply SETS the CINV bit of the CMCON register to make the comparator output inverted. The comparator in this configuration will follow this truth table:

Table 12-2

Truth Table for the Comparator Inverted

Input Conditions (inverted)	COUT
RA1(C_{IN-}) > RA0(C_{IN+})	1
RA1(C_{IN-}) < RA0(C_{IN+})	0

Build the Modified Code

Build the modified code and load it into the PIC16F676. Now when you adjust voltage on RA1, the output conditions that drive the LED will be inverted from the output of the previous exercise when the comparator was non-inverting.

In the final part of this exercise, modify the code in the Initialization segment of the code as indicated below:

```
;       movlw    b'00000001'
;       movlw    b'00010001'
        movlw    b'00000010'
        movwf    CMCON
```

Build the Changed Code

This code change reconfigures the comparator as non-inverting but also changes the comparator mode so that the output COUT bit is no longer connected to the RA2 I/O pin. Build the changed code and load it into the PIC16F676. Now when you adjust the variable resistor, there will appear to be no response because the LED does not turn on. In reality, the comparator is still functioning; however, in this configuration the comparator output is not available on the I/O pin and is only available through the COUT bit of the CMCON register. This will be demonstrated in the next exercise.

Build Up Circuit

Build up the circuit that is illustrated in **Figure 12-3** and depicted in the picture in **Figure 12-4**. This circuit moves the LED from RA2 to RC3 and adds another LED to **RC4**.

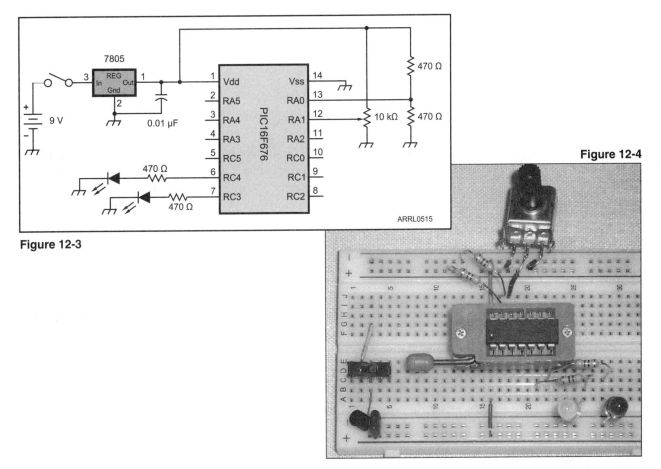

Figure 12-3

Figure 12-4

Load the program project **Program Files/Ch 12/Comparator_2** into *MPLAB IDE* and open the .asm file for study.

Take a look at the Initialization segment of the code and take note of these lines of code:

```
        movlw       b'00000010'
;       movlw       b'00010010'
        movwf       CMCON
```

This code should look familiar from the previous exercises. The first `movlw` opcode will load the bit pattern to configure the comparator as non-inverting with RA0 and RA1 connected to the comparator inputs and the comparator output is not connected to an I/O pin (not connected to RA2). In this configuration, the program needs to access the comparator output via the COUT bit of the CMCON register.

Now scroll down and review the main part of the program:

```
main
        btfsc       CMCON,COUT      ;sense CMCON,COUT bit, if clear skip next
        goto        flash_RC3       ;if set do this goto
        goto        flash_RC4

        goto main
```

In the main program, the `btfsc` opcode senses the status of the COUT bit of CMCON and makes a decision branch. If the bit is SET the next command is executed; if the bit is CLEAR the next instruction is skipped and the following opcode is executed. Those subsequent instructions that follow the `btfsc` opcode are goto instructions that cause a jump to the program sections identified by the assigned labels `flash_RC3` or `flash_RC4`. These labels are descriptive of what is being accomplished by the associated code.

```
flash_RC3
        bsf         PORTC,3
        call        wait250mS
        bcf         PORTC,3
        call        wait250mS
        goto        main
```

The `flash_RC3` code first SETS the I/O pin PORTC, 3 to turn on the attached LED, calls a subroutine that will delay the program for 250 milliseconds, CLEARS the I/O pin to turn off the LED and then wait again for 250 ms. The `flash_RC4` code does the same thing except the delay period between turning the LED on and off is 50 ms.

Build this program

Build the program, load it into the PIC16F676 and install the MCU into the circuit. When power is applied and you adjust the variable resistor through its range, the LEDs will flash in turn depending on the output of the comparator. This exercise illustrates how a program can be developed to respond to the status of the comparator output which is dependent on the relative values of the input voltages.

Now adjust the code in the Initialization section of the program to reconfigure the comparator as inverting:

```
;       movlw       b'00000010'
        movlw       b'00010010'
        movwf       CMCON
```

Build and load this program

Build and load the program into the MCU. Now when you adjust the variable resistor, the flashing LEDs will be opposite as in the previous exercise as you would expect with an inverting comparator.

Up to this point, we have been using an external reference voltage connected to RA0 (C_{IN+}). This reference voltage is developed across the voltage divider circuit comprised of two, series 470 Ω resistors that applied ½ V_{dd} on pin RA0. In this last exercise, you will use and explore an *internal voltage reference* that is developed by a *resistance ladder module* that is a resource within the PIC16F676.

Internal Voltage Reference Developed by a Resistance Ladder Module

The voltage reference module can output 32 distinct reference voltages that are accessed in two voltage ranges, high and low, as detailed previously in this chapter. The voltage reference module is connected to RA0 (C_{IN+}) by selecting the appropriate comparator mode. The value of the reference voltage is selected by loading the appropriate bit pattern into the VRCON special function register. You should go through the calculation of the reference voltages using the algorithms that are documented in the PIC16F676 reference manual as an academic exercise. You can compare your calculations to the results calculated and provided in **Table 12-3**. In Table 12-3 you will find the calculated voltage for the associated VR3:VR0 bit pattern for both the high and low voltage ranges. There are also columns for the measured reference voltages. You will be performing your own measurements in the final exercise and you can compare your measured values to those in Table 12-3.

Table 12-3
CM3:CM0 = 011
Comparator with Output and Internal Reference

VR3:VR0		Low Range	b'1010####'	High Range	b'1000####'
Dec.	Binary	Calculated	Measured	Calculated	Measured
0	0000	0	.02	1.25	1.25
1	0001	.208	.22	1.41	1.40
2	0010	.417	.42	1.56	1.57
3	0011	.625	.63	1.72	1.73
4	0100	.833	.83	1.875	1.88
5	0101	1.04	1.03	2.03	2.02
6	0110	1.25	1.24	2.1875	2.19
7	0111	1.46	1.45	2.34	2.35
8	1000	1.67	1.66	2.5	2.50
9	1001	1.875	1.87	2.66	2.65
10	1010	2.08	2.07	2.81	2.81
11	1011	2.29	2.28	2.98	2.97
12	1100	2.5	2.49	3.125	2.13
13	1101	2.71	2.70	3.28	3.29
14	1110	2.92	2.92	3.44	3.46
15	1111	3.125	3.13	3.59	3.61

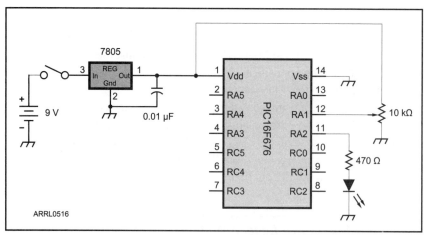

Figure 12-5

Build the circuit as detailed in Figure 12-5

Build the circuit as detailed in **Figure 12-5**. Load the program project **Program Files/Ch 12 Program/Comparator_3** into *MPLAB IDE* and open the .asm file for study. In this exercise, you will be configuring the comparator so that the internal reference voltage will be applied to the C_{IN+} comparator input. Then you will change the value of the reference voltage by making code adjustments. With each change in the reference voltage, you will manipulate the other input voltage to the comparator to determine when the input voltage you control matches the reference voltage (by the status of the indicator LED) and make voltage measurements to verify the applied reference voltage.

Display the .asm file and focus on the Initialization section of the code. This code segment configures the comparator with the COUT bit connected to RA2, RA1 connected to the comparator C_{IN-} input, and connects the internal voltage reference to the comparator C_{IN+} input:

```
movlw      b'00000011'
movwf      CMCON
```

Control of the internal reference voltage is via the VRCON SFR. The following code loads the appropriate bit pattern into the W-register and then transfers that bit pattern into the VRCON register:

```
;   movlw      b'10101111'    ;Vref on, low range, #### value
    movlw      b'10001111'    ;Vref on, high range, #### value
    movwf      VRCON
```

SETTING the VREN bit powers-up the internal voltage reference resistance ladder. SETTING the VRR bit selects the low reference voltage range, CLEARING the VRR bit selects the high reference voltage range. The four lowest bits of VRCON determine the actual reference voltage within the selected range as determined by the algorithms. The instruction movlw b'10001111' selects the high range and a reference voltage of 3.59 V (for a V_{dd} of 5 V).

During this portion of the exercise, you will be tasked to start with the lowest reference voltage of the high range (b'0000'), build and load the program into the PIC16F676, adjust the variable resistor until the LED just comes on, measure the voltage on pin RA1, and record and compare that measured voltage to the reference voltage (change movlw b'1000####' to the appropriate bit pattern). Then go on to the next reference voltage step in the high range (b'0001'), and so on, to complete the 16 voltages available within the high range.

Once you complete that portion of the exercise, re-comment the code lines to change over to the low range of reference voltages and repeat the process for the low range:

```
    movlw    b'1010####'
;   movlw    b'10001111'
```

At the completion of the exercise compare your measured reference voltages with those listed in Table 12-3. Your voltages should be similar.

The use of the internal voltage reference has its positives and negatives. On the positive side, using the internal voltage reference frees up an I/O pin resource that can be used for other purposes. On the negative side, you have limited control over the reference voltage used and are limited to the 32 discrete values as determined by the internal resistance ladder.

Summary

There is one comparator circuit available within the PIC16F676. This circuit operates simultaneously and independently of the program that is running in the MCU. The comparator can be configured in eight different modes with various configurations for the comparator inputs, outputs and reference voltages. The CMCON special function register configures the comparator, the VRCON register configures the internal resistance ladder to a high or low voltage range and also sets the reference voltage to one of 32 discrete values. The ANSEL register must also be addressed so that the I/O pins connected to the comparator inputs are configured appropriately.

Review Questions

12.1 What comparator mode configures the comparator to consume the lowest power?

12.2 Which comparator mode connects the C_{IN-} and C_{IN+} comparator inputs to RA0 and RA1 and does not connect the COUT bit to RA2? Does the use of this mode create a conflict if your application does not even use the comparator circuit?

12.3 What is the value of the internal reference voltage applied to comparator input $C_{IN}+$ in the mode dictated by CM2:CM0 loaded with b'011' and VREN loaded with b'10001011'?

Interrupts

Objective: To learn how to configure and use the interrupt capabilities of the PIC16F676 that allow the MCU to perform multiple tasks simultaneously. This chapter will introduce the concept of the interrupt and use the interrupt from the RA2/INT External Interrupt resource of the PIC16F676 to illustrate the concept. Using additional resource interrupts will be covered in subsequent chapters.

Reading: *PIC16F630/676 Data Sheet*, pages 5-7 and 65-68.
Program: Program Files/Ch 13 Program/Interrupt
Video: "Studying Interrupts"

Operations of an Interrupt

Interrupts are very powerful capabilities that are included in most common MCUs including the PIC16F676. As the name implies, an interrupt suspends the execution of the main program and a jump is executed to an interrupt service subroutine that takes some action in response to the interrupting condition and then returns control of the MCU back to the main program that picks up where it left off at the time of the interrupt. The interrupt can be triggered by external or internal MCU resources.

The interrupt capable resources are monitored by the MCU for specific criteria to be met and when those criteria are met an interrupt signal is generated by the hardware within the MCU. Once an interrupt is generated:

•The program that is being executed by the MCU is suspended.

•The next line that would have been executed had the interrupt not occurred is identified by *the program counter* (PC) and stored in a temporary memory location called the *Stack*.

•The PC is replaced with memory location 0x04 that is reserved for interrupt service code and the program jumps to that location.

•The program code beginning at 0x04 is generally a call to the interrupt service subroutine where actions required by the interrupt conditions are accomplished.

•When the interrupt has been serviced, the *return instruction* that ends the interrupt service subroutine "pops" the PC from the Stack and the execution of the main program resumes at the code location identified by the recovered program counter.

•The MCU then continues to monitor for another interrupt to occur while it continues executing the main program.

External and Internal Interrupt Capable Resources

The interrupt capable resources within the PIC16F676 can be divided into the two broad categories, those generated by external devices that are monitored by the MCU and internal resources. The external devices might include switches or sensors (temperature, pressure, magnetic, light, etc.) that are connected to I/O port pins, ADCs, or the comparator. The internal resources that can generate interrupts include TMR0 and TMR1 timer resources and write operations to internal Electrically Erasable Programmable Read-Only Memory (EEPROM.) There are a number of special function registers involved in working with interrupts that are configured in the device initialization section of the program code and these SFRs are also monitored and manipulated during program execution to manage interrupts. During device setup, the special function registers include enable bit "flags" that are SET to enable or CLEARED to disable the specific interrupt resources. During program execution, the special function registers include interrupt occurred "flags" that are hardware SET when a specific interrupt has been generated by a resource and software CLEARED to enable additional interrupts. Additionally there are overall interrupt enable bits that are SET or CLEARED to globally control the interrupts during program execution.

Seven Interrupt Resources

There are seven interrupt resources with the PIC16F676:

1. *External Interrupt RA2/INT-* an interrupt is generated when there is a state change on PORTA I/O pin RA2.

2. *TMR0 Overflow Interrupt-* an interrupt is generated when there is an overflow in the `TRM0` register from 0xff to 0x00.

3. *PORTA Change Interrupts -* an interrupt is generated when any of the PORTA enabled I/O pins change state.

4. *Comparator Interrupt -* an interrupt is generated when the comparator output state changes.

5. *ADC Interrupt-*an interrupt is generated when the ADC conversion is completed.

6. *TMR1 Overflow Interrupt -* an interrupt is generated when there is an overflow in the TMR1 registers TMR1H and TMR1L increments and overflows from 0xffff to 0x0000.

7. *EEPROM Data Write Interrupt -* an interrupt is generated when a write to an EEPROM location is completed.

Control of Interrupt Resources

These resources are controlled by individual flags or bits within three SFRs (INTCON, PIR1, and PIE1) which can get a bit confusing. The RA2/INT, TMR0, and PORTA Change Interrupts can be considered basic interrupt resources managed through the INTCON register. The remaining interrupts can be grouped into a category of interrupts generated by peripheral resources of the PIC16F676 managed by the PIR1 and PIE1 registers. The peripheral interrupts are globally controlled as a group by the PEIE bit within the INTCON register. All interrupts are globally controlled by the GIE bit within the INTCON register. Therefore, to enable the peripheral interrupts, both the PEIE and GIE bits need to be SET. To enable just the basic interrupt resources, only the GIE bit needs to be SET. There will be more detail on the use of the interrupt control bits later so be patient and follow closely during the next discussion on configuring the controlling registers.

Bank 0-1	INTCON Interrupt Control Register						
GIE	PEIE	T0IE	INTE	RAIE	T0IF	INTF	RAIF
Global Interrupt Enable bit	Peripheral Interrupt Enable bit	TMR0 Overflow Interrupt Enable bit	RA2/INT External Interrupt Enable bit	Port Change Interrupt Enable bit	TMR0 Overflow Interrupt Flag	RA2/INT External Interrupt Flag bit	Port Change Interrupt Flag bit

INTCON. *The Interrupt Control Register* is used to setup and control the different interrupt resources of the device. SETTING the individual bits will enable the interrupt, CLEARING the individual bits will disable the interrupt.

GIE. *The Global Interrupt Enable bit* is like the master switch for all the different interrupts. SETTING this bit will enable all the interrupts to function, CLEARING this bit will disable all the interrupts.

PEIE. *The Peripheral Interrupt Enable bit* allows interrupts from the peripheral resources of the PIC16F676 including interrupts from the ADC, Comparator, Timer1, and EEPROM Data Write. SETTING this bit will allow peripheral interrupts, CLEARING this bit will disable the interrupts.

T0IE. *The TMR0 Overflow Interrupt Enable bit* allows an interrupt when the TMR0 counter overflows from 255 (0xff) to 0 (0x00). SETTING this bit allows the TMR0 interrupt, CLEARING this bit will disable the interrupt.

INTE. *The RA2/INT External Interrupt Enable bit* allows an interrupt from a clocking signal applied to pin RA2. Whether the interrupt occurs on the rising or falling edge of this clocking signal is determined by the state of the INTEDG bit in the OPTION_REG. SETTING the INTE bit allows an interrupt from the signal on RA2, CLEARING; this bit disables the interrupt.

RAIE. *The Port Change Interrupt Enable bit* allows an interrupt when there is a change of state on any of the authorized I/O pins on PORTA. Whether an individual PORTA I/O pin is authorized to generate an interrupt when the pin state changes is determined by setting the appropriate pin in the Interrupt-On-Change PORTA Register (IOCA) that will be covered later. Consider the RAIE bit as a switch that turns on or off all port change interrupts, while the individual pin change interrupts are turned on or off by the IOCA register bits. SETTING the RAIE bit will allow the PORTA change interrupts; CLEARING this bit disables the interrupts.

T0IF. *The TMR0 Overflow Interrupt Flag* bit is used by the device to indicate if the interrupt was the result of a TMR0 overflow. As you may have noticed, an interrupt code will be triggered by any of the different resources available on the MCU. It is up to you, the programmer, to determine through your software code which of the resources generates the interrupt. Flag bits allow you to make that determination. In this case, when a TMR0 overflow interrupt occurs, the T0IF flag bit is SET. Early in the interrupt service routine (the subroutine program that you will write to deal with an interrupt), a check of the various flags is accomplished — in this case, the T0IF flag, and if it is SET, a TMR0 interrupt occured and the program will take the desired action. You reset the TMR0 interrupt by CLEARING the T0IF bit. If you fail to reset the T0IF bit, additional TMR0 interrupts will occur immediately once the interrupt service routine has completed.

INTF. *The RA2/INT External Interrupt Flag* bit is used by the device to indicate if the interrupt was the result of a clocking signal on the RA2 pin. As previously discussed, you will check the state of INTF in the interrupt service routine to determine if the interrupt occurred because of a clock signal on RA2. At completion of the interrupt service routine, the INTF pin must be CLEARED to prevent unintended interrupts.

RAIF. *The Port Change Interrupt Flag* bit is used likewise by the device to indicate if the interrupt was the result of a change on authorized I/O pins of PORTA. At the completion of the interrupt service routine, the RAIF pin must be CLEARED to prevent unintended interrupts.

Bank 1	PIE1 Peripheral Interrupt Enable Register						
EEIE	ADIE	X	X	CMIE	X	X	TMR1E
EE Write Complete Interrupt Enable bit	A/D Converter Interrupt Enable bit	Unimplemented	Unimplemented	Comparator Interrupt Enable bit	Unimplemented	Unimplemented	TMR1 Overflow Interrupt Enable bit

PIE1. *The Peripheral Interrupt Enable Register* is used to allow interrupts from specific peripheral resources including the EEPROM write, ADC, Comparator, and Timer1. The INTCON, PEIE bit allows all authorized peripheral interrupts when SET, the PIE register bits allow interrupts from specific peripheral resources.

EEIE. *EE Write Complete Interrupt Enable* bit allows an interrupt to occur when a write operation to the EEPROM has completed. This interrupt may be required in your programs because it takes time for a write operation to EEPROM to complete. This interrupt capability allows the program to do other things instead of halting while the write operation is accomplished.

SETTING the EEIE bit allows an interrupt when the write to EEPROM operation is complete, CLEARING the bit disables the interrupt. This bit will not be used during exercises in this text.

ADIE. *The A/D Converter Interrupt Enable bit* allows an interrupt to occur when an ADC conversion is completed. It takes a finite amount of time for the ADC within the PIC16F676 to complete a conversion. The amount of time is not fixed and is dependent on the supply voltage, device temperature and other factors. Therefore the interrupt, if enabled, allows the program to continue with other tasks while the ADC conversion process proceeds independently. Though the ADIE will not be used during the exercises in this text, the associated ADIF, A/D Converter Interrupt Flag bit will be polled to see if the conversion is completed. SETTING the ADIE bit will enable an interrupt when the ADC conversion is completed, CLEARING the bit will disable the interrupt.

CMIE. *Comparator Interrupt Enable bit* allows an interrupt to occur when there is a difference between the two input voltages to the comparator circuit. The voltage differences between the input voltages are relative and the relationship that will generate an interrupt is set by the bits in the COMCON register that is covered later. SETTING the CMIE bit will enable an interrupt when a voltage difference is detected by the comparator, CLEARING the bit will disable the interrupt.

TMR1IE. *Timer 1 Overflow Interrupt Enable bit* allows an interrupt to occur when the Timer 1 counter registers overflow to 0x0000 (TMR0 is an 8-bit timer, TMR1 is a 16-bit timer). SETTING the TMR1IE bit will enable an interrupt when a TMR1 overflow occurs, CLEARING the bit will disable the interrupt.

Bank0	PIR1 Peripheral Interrupt Register 1						
EEIF	ADIF	X	X	CMIF	X	X	TMR1IF
EEPROM Write Operation Interrupt Flag bit	A/D Converter Interrupt Flag bit	Unimplemented	Unimplemented	Comparator Interrupt Flag bit	Unimplemented	Unimplemented	TMR1 Overflow Interrupt Flag bit

PIR1. *The Peripheral Interrupt Register 1* contains the interrupt flags for the EEPROM Write Operation, A/D Converter, Comparator, and Timer1 Overflow peripheral resources. When these flags are SET by the microcontroller, the enabled resource has completed its assigned task and generates an interrupt. The interrupt flags will be SET no matter if the interrupt for the specific resource has been enabled or not (by setting the appropriate bit in the PIE1, Peripheral Interrupt Enable register, and setting the GIE bit in the INTCON register), therefore these flags can be checked in your program before the output of the resource is queried for the outcome of its operation. For instance, instead of using interrupts, you could monitor the status of the ADC by checking the interrupt flag and wait for the conversion to complete before shifting the results of the conversion into a variable space for further computation or action by the program. You should use care to CLEAR the appropriate interrupt flag with software after you finished with the peripheral resource so that additional operations can be performed with that resource if desired, and particularly before enabling an interrupt with the resource. Failing to do so in the latter case will result in continuous interrupts being triggered by the resource.

EEIF. *EEPROM Write Operation Interrupt Flag* will be SET when an EEPROM write has been completed. The flag will remain CLEAR until the operation is completed. You need to CLEAR this bit to enable another write operation or interrupt involving an EEPROM write operation.

ADIF. *A/D Converter Interrupt Flag* will be SET when the ADC has completed the conversion of an analog voltage value to digital number. The flag will remain CLEAR until the operation is completed. You need to CLEAR this bit to enable another ADC conversion or to allow an interrupt once the ADC conversion is completed.

CMIF. *Comparator Interrupt Flag* will be SET when the assigned comparator condition is reached. The flag will remain CLEAR until that assigned comparator condition is true. For instance, if you program the comparator to trigger when voltage on pin RA0 is greater than the voltage applied to RA1, the CMIF flag will remain CLEARED until that condition is present, immediately upon that condition being present on the two pins, the CMIF flag will SET and an interrupt will be generated (if enabled). You need to CLEAR this bit to enable the Comparator and to allow an interrupt generated by the Comparator.

TMR1IF. *Timer 1 Interrupt Flag* will be SET when the timer 1 has overflowed the counter registers to 0x0000 (when running). The amount of time of this overflow condition depends on the starting count that you assign when the timer is turned on. The flag will remain CLEAR until the overflow condition has occurred. You need to CLEAR this bit before you enable and start the TMR1 resource to get an accurate time delay from an interrupt generated by the TMR1 overflow.

Bank 1		IOCA Interrupt-On-Change PORTA Register					
X	X	IOCA5	IOCA4	IOCA3	IOCA2	IOCA1	IOCA0
Unimplemented	Unimplemented	RA5	RA4	RA3	RA2	RA1	RA0

IOCA. T*he Interrupt-On-Change PORTA* Register contains the enable bits for the individual PORTA I/O pins to generate an interrupt when the state on the enabled pins change. SETTING the bit enables the interrupt, CLEARING the bit disables the interrupt.

The EEPROM associated register will not be covered in this text. Readers are encouraged to explore using the EEPROM capabilities after they have become more familiar with the basic operation of MCUs.

Exploring Basic Operation of Interrupts Using the RA2/INT Interrupt Resource

In this chapter, the basic operation of interrupts will be explored by using the RA2/INT interrupt resource. The operation of the timer interrupts will be explored in the next chapter.

Build the circuit for this exercise as depicted in **Figure 13-1** and as pictured in **Figure 13-2**. A momentary switch is connected to PORTA, 2 (RA2) and will serve as the source of an interrupt signal when pressed. The LCD will be used to display the number of times the switch is pressed (the number of interrupts generated). The LED will be flashed on and off by the main program as an indicator that the MCU is accomplishing some programmed task.

Load the project Interrupt located in the folder **Program Files/Ch 13 Program/ Interrupts** folder into *MPLAB IDE* and display the Interrupt.asm file.

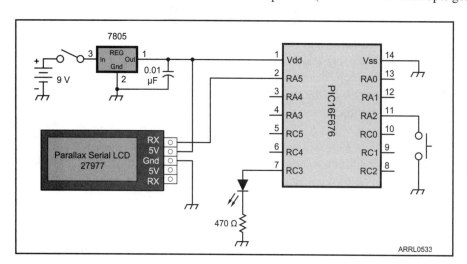

ARRL0533

Figure 13-1

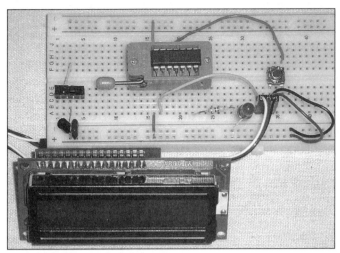

Figure 13-2

The PIC16F676 is configured with I/O pin PORTA, 2 as a digital input with weak pull-up attached, all other I/O pins are digital outputs. The interrupt control registers are configured in the Initialization section of the program code to enable the RA2/INT interrupt. With this interrupt enabled, the MCU will monitor the state on PORTA, 2 for a change in state. As configured with the weak pull-up attached, the static state of this I/O pin is SET, when the switch is pressed the state momentarily goes CLEAR. Therefore, the RA2/INT is configured so that the interrupt is generated when the RA2/INT pin goes low. Scroll down to the Initialization section of the code and follow along as the register setup is discussed.

```
BANKSEL     Bank1
call        0x3FF               ; retrieve factory calibration value
movwf       OSCCAL

BANKSEL     Bank0               ;select bank0
clrf        PORTA               ;clear port bus
clrf        PORTC
movlw       b'00000111'         ;comparator disconnected
movwf       CMCON               ;
movlw       b'00010000'         ;globals off, peripherals off, RA2 external
                                ;interrupt enabled,
                                ;interrupt flags cleared
movwf       INTCON

BANKSEL     Bank1               ; Bank 1 selected
clrf        OPTION_REG          ;enable weak pull-ups

movlw       b'00000100'         ;weak pull-up on RA2
movwf       WPUA
movlw       b'00000100'         ;RA2 set as input, others output
movwf       TRISA               ;program PORTA
movlw       b'00000000'         ;all output
movwf       TRISC               ;program PORTC
movlw       b'00000000'         ;all digital I/O
movwf       ANSEL
BANKSEL     Bank0               ;back to Bank 0
```

There are two registers that are configured in the Initialization section of the code to set up the RA2/INT interrupt. The RA2/INT is one member of the basic interrupt group and there are no peripheral interrupts used in this exercise. Consequently, to enable the RA2/INT specifically, only the associated enable bit in the INTCON register, bit INTE, is SET. To ensure that the RA2/INT interrupt will not be generated until we want it to, all interrupts (including the RA2/INT interrupt) are globally disabled by CLEARING the GIE bit in the INTCON register. The bit pattern b'00010000' CLEARS bit GIE and SETS bit INTE. (Later in the code, the GIE bit will be SET to globally enable the interrupt.) This bit pattern is loaded into the W-register and then transferred into the INTCON register:

```
movlw       b'00010000'
movwf       INTCON
```

Now that the interrupt is specifically enabled, the pin state change that will generate the interrupt is configured. This is accomplished by ensuring the OPTION_REG, INTEDG bit is CLEARED so that the interrupt is generated on the falling edge (high to low transition) on the PORTA, 2 pin. If the INTEDG bit is SET, the interrupt would be generated on the rising edge (low to high transition) on the pin. The default configuration of the OPTION_REG is b'00000000', which enables the weak pull-up resistors and sets the interrupt on the fall edge transition so the following code is actually redundant. It however is good practice to deliberately configure the OPTION_REG in the event that the initialization code is copied from one program to another where the default configuration of the register is not appropriate. The clrf OPTION_REG instruction CLEARS all bits within the OPTION_REG.

```
clrf            OPTION_REG
```

To connect a weak pull-up resistor on PORTA, 2, the following bit pattern would be loaded into the WPUA register to enable the resistor:

```
movlw           b'00000100'
movwf           WPUA
```

Finally, the PORTA, 2 pin is configured as an input pin by loading the following bit pattern into the TRISA register:

```
movlw           b'00000100'
movwf           TRISA
```

Now scroll down to the main part of the program.

```
        bsf             INTCON,GIE
main
        movlw           b'00001000'
        xorwf           PORTC
        call            wait250mS
        goto            main
```

This program segment will flash the LED attached to PORTC, 3. Notice that the instruction before the main program label SETS the INTCON, GIE bit to globally enable interrupts. Then within the main program, the bit 3 is SET (this bit will refer to the PORTC, 3 I/O pin) and loaded into the w-register. The xorwf opcode exclusively ORs the bit pattern in the w-register with the bit pattern of PORTC and puts the result back into the PORTC register. Remember, an exclusive OR Boolean logic follows the truth table (Table 1). This is a simple way to toggle an I/O pin on and off. If PORTC, 3 was SET, it is CLEARED and vice versa. The call to the delay subroutine will cause a delay of 250 mseconds before the process is repeated.

Table 13-1
Truth Table Exclusive OR

A	B	Output
0	0	0
1	0	1
0	1	1
1	1	0

Now scroll up to the beginning of the program where the reset and interrupt vectors are declared:

```
;****************************************************************
;Reset Vector
;****************************************************************
```

```
        ORG         0x000                   ;processor reset vector
        nop                                 ;required by in circuit debugger
        goto        Init                    ;go to beginning of program
;********************************************************************
;Interrupt Vector
;********************************************************************
        ORG         0x004
        goto        interrupt_service
        return                              ;interrupt trap - returns without re-enabling
```

Hardware Considerations

A short discussion of hardware is warranted here. It is hard-wired in the PIC16F676 that when the device is first powered-up or if a reset of the device is triggered, that the program counter jumps to memory location 0x000 to start the program. This is called the *reset vector*. This section of the code is where you tell the program to jump to the label that identifies where your actual program code begins, in this case the label Init is used (short for Initialize). It is also hard-wired in the PIC16F676 that if an interrupt is generated, the program counter jumps to memory location 0x004 to go to the interrupt service routine. This is called the *interrupt vector*. In this section of the code you tell the program to go to the label interrupt_service which identifies the beginning of the code that is run in the event of an interrupt. The memory locations 0x000 and 0x004 are dedicated for the specific purpose of holding jump vectors to appropriate sections of code.

Handling Interrupts

The following will be a fairly lengthy and detailed discussion on handling interrupts. To begin this discussion we need to revisit the Stack.

The Stack

The Stack is a small amount of memory where the program counter is temporarily held during calls to subroutines. The Stack is 8-levels deep and 13-bits wide. This means that the Stack can hold up to eight 13-bit program counter addresses. When a call to a subroutine is executed, the program counter address for the next instruction to be executed upon the return from the subroutine is "pushed" onto the Stack. Upon the return, the last program counter is "popped" off the top of the Stack and the calling program resumes. The programmer must use care because of the limited size of the Stack. If more than 8 "pushes" of program counter addresses occur before addresses are "popped", some information will be lost. Then if subsequent returns from subroutines are executed, the associated program counter information will not be there and your program will crash. This situation can occur when the programmer uses nested calls to subroutines, calls to subroutines within subroutines. This can be a particular problem because interrupts generate asynchronous calls to the interrupt service subroutine that might occur when the main program itself calls subroutines.

Conflict Precautions

There are also common working registers (the W-register and STATUS) that might be used by the main program and subroutines at the same time which can cause conflicts and program crashes. Programmers must use care that the contents of the w-register and STATUS register are preserved and recovered when called subroutines could potentially change the values within the registers.

With these precautions fresh in your mind, scroll down to the interrupt_service routine in the code:

```
interrupt_service
    bcf         INTCON,INTE
    movwf       w_temp
    swapf       STATUS,w
    BANKSEL     Bank0
    movwf       status_temp

    movlw       LCD_LINE0+.6
    call        LCDOutput
    incf        RA2_counter
    movfw       RA2_counter
    movwf       l_byte
    call        display_DEC

    swapf       status_temp,w
    movwf       STATUS
    swapf       w_temp,f
    swapf       w_temp,w
    bcf         INTCON,INTF
    bsf         INTCON,INTE
    retfie
```

When an interrupt is generated, the PIC16F676 is hard-wired to jump to address 0x004, this is where you program a call to the interrupt_service subroutine. Upon this call, the PC is pushed onto the Stack for later recovery on the return from the subroutine. This jump to address 0x004 also CLEARS INTCON, GIE to prevent subsequent interrupts. Normally the first thing that you would do in the interrupt_service routine is to determine the source of the interrupt by checking the individual interrupt flags to see which is SET, and therefore the source of the interrupt. However, in this program, only the RA2/INT interrupt is being used and it can be the only source of the interrupt.

Even though the interrupts are globally disabled by CLEARING the GIE bit, interrupt attempts will continue to be generated by the enabled interrupt resources when the interrupt conditions are met. For instance, if an RA2/INT interrupt is generated by a low condition on PORTA, 2 and the interrupt_service subroutine is in progress, subsequent, rapid low conditions on PORTA, 2 will SET associated flags, even though actual jumps to address 0x004 will be prevented. To prevent these attempted interrupts from causing problems when the interrupts are globally enabled, the interrupts should be disabled early in the subroutine, this is accomplished by CLEARING the appropriate enable bit in INTCON register:

```
    bcf         INTCON,INTE
```

In this case, the RA2/INT interrupt is disabled.

The program counter was automatically preserved on the Stack when the interrupt occurred, however, it is a good programming habit to preserve the contents of the w-register and STATUS register before those registers are changed within the interrupt_ service subroutine. The following lines of code save the contents of the w-register and STATUS register in temporary variables in memory:

```
movwf      w_temp
swapf      STATUS,w
BANKSEL    Bank0
movwf      status_temp
```

The movwf, w_temp instruction stores the current contents of the w-register into w_temp. The swapf STATUS, w instruction is an elegant way to store the contents of the STATUS register with a single command. The swapf opcode swaps the nibbles within the target register and stores the result in the w-register. (Later at the end of the subroutine, the nibbles will be re-swapped to return them to the original sequence before being returned to the STATUS register.) The alternative would be:

```
movfw      STATUS
movwf      status_temp
```

Then to recover STATUS:
```
movfw      status_temp
movwf      STATUS
```

The BANKSEL Bank0 directive ensures that Bank 0 is the operative memory bank regardless of the bank selected at the time the interrupt occurred. Because the BANKSEL directive modifies the STATUS register, it is put at this location in the code (after the contents of STATUS is preserved).

Now that the contents of the w-register and STATUS register are preserved, the actions of the subroutine can be accomplished.

```
movlw      LCD_LINE0+.6
call       LCDOutput
incf       RA2_counter
movfw      RA2_counter
movwf      l_byte
call       display_DEC
```

Here the LCD cursor is moved to the end of the line, a temporary variable RA2_counter is incremented by 1 and the new RA2_counter value is displayed on the LCD. The result is that each time the switch button is pressed, RA2_counter is incremented and displayed.

After the LCD display is changed, the w_register and STATUS register contents are recovered:

```
swapf      status_temp,w
movwf      STATUS
swapf      w_temp,f
swapf      w_temp,w
```

The nibble content of memory location status_temp are swapped by swapf and placed into the w-register (remember that the STATUS register nibbles were swapped before they were stored in status_temp, now they are re-swapped to return the nibble sequence to the original state). The w-register contents are then stored back into the STATUS register.

The next two `swapf` opcodes swap the memory nibbles into and out of the W-register to recover the original W-register contents. This could have been accomplished by using `movfw` and `movwf` opcodes, however, the `movfw` opcode will affect the Z bit of the STATUS register and could corrupt the just recovered STATUS register contents. The `swapf` does not affect the STATUS register.

With the interrupt serviced and the W-register and STATUS register returned to the starting conditions, the interrupts need to be re-enabled before the program control is returned to the main program:

```
bcf     INTCON,INTF
bsf     INTCON,INTE
retfie
```

Figure 13-3

CLEARING the INTF flag resets the RA2/INT interrupt flag to allow a new interrupt. If this flag were not cleared by software, an interrupt condition would immediately be present when the RA2/INT interrupt is enabled regardless of the state on PORTA, 2. SETTING the INTE bit then enables future RA2/INT interrupts. There is one last step, that is to enable interrupts globally. That is accomplished by SETTING the INTCON, GIE bit (remember that bit was automatically CLEARED when the interrupt was generated). The `retfie` opcode will cause the program counter to 'pop' off the Stack to jump back to the calling program and at the same time SET the INTCON, GIE bit.

The Interrupt in More Detail

Let's use the debugging capabilities of the *MPLAB* simulator to further explore the interrupt in more detail. Follow along using the text and figures to set up the *MPLAB* simulator and step through the program as we monitor the program behavior and the state of the register bits while we inject an interrupt signal as if we pressed the switch attached to PORTA, 2.

Click on **VIEW WATCH** in the *MPLAB IDE* menu bar (**Figure 13-3**). This displays the **Watch Window** where we can display contents of selected registers and memory locations. For this interrupt exploration, we are interested in the contents of the INTCON register. This register is an SFR, so click on the down arrow adjacent to **ADD SFR,** click on **INTCON**, and then click on the **ADD SFR** button (**Figure 13-4**). A watch for the INTCON register will be added to the list of watches. Note that the contents of the register can be displayed in various formats at once. We are interested in the individual enable and flag bits within INTCON, so our main interest is the binary representation of the register contents (**Figure 13-5**).

Next we will set up the features that will allow us to inject a simulated input that will generate an interrupt, in this case, cause the voltage on PORTA, 2 to momentarily drop from 5 V to 0 V as if we closed the attached switch. Click on **DEBUGGER/STIMULUS/NEW WORKBOOK (Figure 13-6)**. This will display the **Stimulus** dialog box. Here we will enter the types of actions that are needed as stimuli and the pins associated with each stimulus. Click on the down arrow under **Pin/SFR (Figure 13-7)**. Highlight **RA2** which refers to PORTA, 2 (**Figure 13-8**). Similarly enter another stimulus (**RA2**) in the second line. Click on the **ACTION** box on the first stimulus line and select Set High, and select Pulse Low for the second stimulus action (**Figure 13-9**). Just for clarification of these two stimuli, the simulator is not capable of simulating an enabled weak pull-up resistor, therefore the first stimulus will be "Fired" to SET the PORTA, 2 pin high to manually simulate the weak pull-up resistor. The second stimulus when "Fired" will momentarily pull the voltage on PORTA, 2 low to simulate the switch closure.

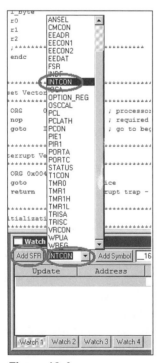

Figure 13-4

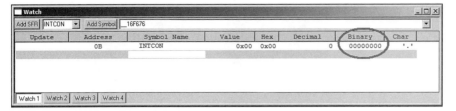

Figure 13-5

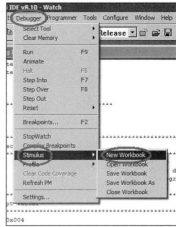

Figure 13-6

Figure 13-7

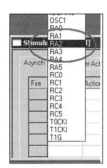

Figure 13-8

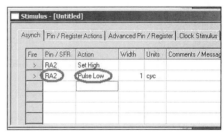

Figure 13-9

Break points

Break points will now be inserted in the code to stop the program execution at strategic locations that will allow study. Double click on the line of code call interrupt_ service (**Figure 13-10**) and a **B** will be displayed in the left margin. Likewise set break points as illustrated within the main program and in the interrupt_service subroutine (**Figure 13-11**).

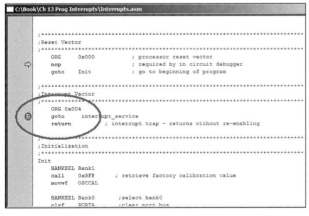

Figure 13-10

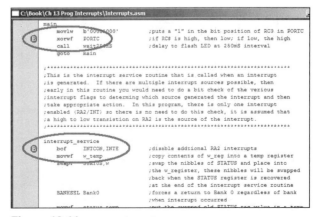

Figure 13-11

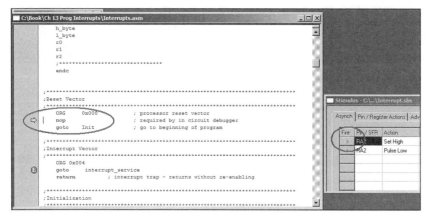

Figure 13-12

Build and Explore the Program

The *MPLAB* simulator is now ready to explore the program. Build the program and click on the **RUN** button. The program will run up to and stop at the first break point. This illustrates the point that the hardware of the PIC16F676 is set to jump to memory location 0x00 on initial power-up and upon an MCU reset (**Figure 13-12**). This is a good opportunity to simulate the weak pull-up on PORTA, 2, click on the "**FIRE**" button in the **Stimulus** dialog window.

Press the f7 key on the keyboard to step through the program from the first break point until you reach the line in the Initialize section of the code where the INTCON register is configured. In this area of the code, the RA2/INT interrupt will be enabled by setting the associated bit (bit 4) as pointed to by the arrow in **Figure 13-13**. When you f7 step through the movwf INTCON instruction, notice that the RA2/INT Enable bit in INTCON is SET (**Figure 13-14**). The next line of code switches to memory bank 1. Press the **RUN** button again on the menu bar to continue with normal program execution, the program will stop at the next break point. Notice here that the INTCON, GIE bit has been SET to globally enable the device interrupt resources, in this case the RA2/INT interrupt (**Figure 13-15**). Continuing the program execution will cause the program to loop through the main program and simply flash the LED attached to PORTC, 3 on and off.

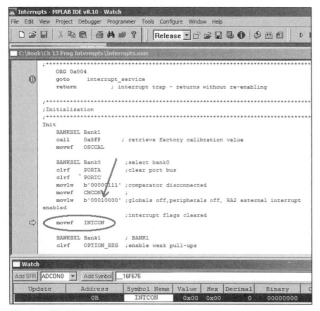

Figure 13-13

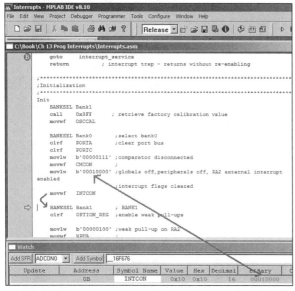

Figure 13-14

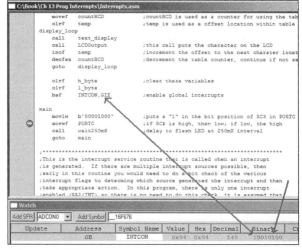

Figure 13-15

Simulate an Interrupt

It is time now to simulate an interrupt. Click on the "**FIRE**" button in the **Stimulus** dialog window as illustrated in **Figure 13-16**. This simulates the momentary closure of the switch attached to PORTA, 2. Click on the **RUN** button on the menu bar to continue program execution and notice that the program stops at the break point at 0x04, the jump to the interrupt_service subroutine. This illustrates the hard wiring of the PIC16F676 to jump to 0x04 when an enabled interrupt occurs. Also notice that the INTCON, GIE bit

Figure 13-16

is automatically CLEARED by the hardware to prevent additional interrupts and that the INTF flag bit is SET to indicate that an interrupt from RA2/INT has occurred (**Figure 13-17**). Accomplish an f7 step though the program and notice that the program jumps into the interrupt_service subroutine. The first line of the interrupt_ service routine CLEARS the INTCON, INTE bit to disable additional interrupts from RA2/INT (**Figure 13-18**). Continue to f7 step through the program and notice that after the interrupt has been serviced by the interrupt_service routine (in this case the interrupt counter variable is incremented and displayed on the LCD) and before the program execution is returned to the main program, the INTF flag bit is CLEARED

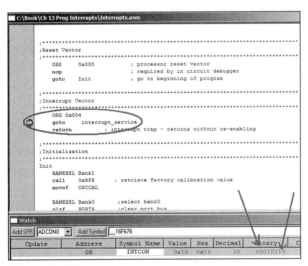

Figure 13-17

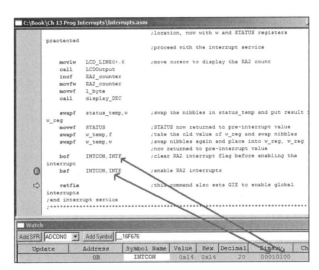

Figure 13-19

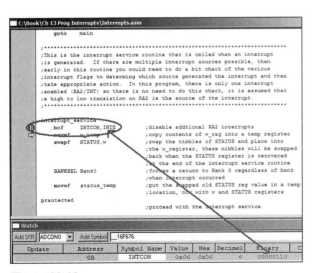

Figure 13-18

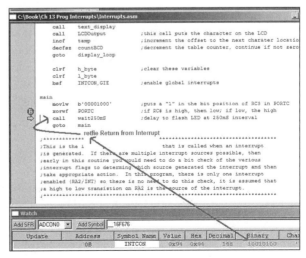

Figure 13-20

(so that the old interrupt event does not trigger a false interrupt) and the INTE bit is SET to re-enable RA2/INT interrupts (**Figure 13-19**).

Finally, continue to do f7 program steps and the program returns to the main program at the point after where the interrupt occurred. Notice here that the `retfie` opcode closed the interrupt_service subroutine and automatically SET the INTCON, GIE bit to globally re-enable interrupts (**Figure 13-20**). Try going through the process again to generate another interrupt to make sure you are comfortable with what happens during the interrupt process.

Actually Run the Program

It is time now to actually run the program. Build and load the program into the PIC16F676. Install the device into the circuit you built on the proto-board. When you apply power, the LED should flash on and off indicating that the main program is running. The LCD will display the RA2 label and the count (probably 0000) of the number of interrupts that have been generated by pressing the switch. Now press the switch and you will see the result of generating an interrupt by momentarily setting the voltage on PORTA, 2 pin to 0 V, the counter will advance by one count for each switch closure and then return to the main program to continue flashing the LED.

Summary

Interrupts provide a powerful resource that allows the MCU to accomplish multiple tasks at once. When an external device or internal MCU resource senses a specified condition, an interrupt signal is generated that causes the main program to cease operation and a jump is made to an interrupt service subroutine that is designed to respond to the interrupting condition. Upon completing the interrupt service call, the main program resumes. The interrupt resources of the 16F676 are primarily controlled by three special function registers, INTCON, PIR1, and PIE1 which are configured in the Initialization section of the program code but can be manipulated in the run time area of code to manage interrupts.

Review Questions

13.1 What would happen if an interrupt "flag" is not reset before the interrupt service subroutine returns control back to the main program?

13.2 Describe the difference between globally enabling interrupts (SETTING the INTCON, GIE bit) and enabling a specific interrupt, for instance TMR0 (SETTING the INTCON, T0IE bit).

13.3 Does an interrupt have to be enabled for the associated interrupt flag to be SET by the interrupt condition?

13.4 What is the depth (number of bytes) of the Stack? What precautions must be considered when working with the Stack?

13.5 What precautions must be considered when using interrupts and other subroutine calls that deal with the w-register and the STATUS register?

13.6 How can "break points" be used in program debugging?

Timer 0 (TMR0) and Timer 1 (TMR1) Operation

Objective: To learn how to configure and use the TMR0 and TMR1 resources of the PIC16F676 for timed event interrupts and accurate time delays. This chapter will build on the previous chapter that introduced the concept of the interrupt. Timer interrupts will be explored through programming examples.

Reading: *PIC16F630/676 Data Sheet*, pages 31 - 36.
Program: **Program Files/Ch 14 Program/TMR0 Basic Operation**
Program Files/Ch 14 Program/TMR0
Program Files/Ch 14 Program/TMR1
Video Files: "TMR0_1"
"TMR0_2"

Additional, More Elegant Timer Resources

Previously you learned how to use delay subroutines to create delays of standardized length. These delay subroutines are commonly included in a library of subroutines that are used in different programs by cutting and pasting the code. Though functional, there are other more elegant timer resources available in most MCU devices including the PIC16F676 that can function as stand alone timers or counters that operate independently of other MCU activities, can be started and stopped as needed and can generate interrupts. The two timer resources in the PIC16F676 are identified by the mnemonics TMR0 for Timer 0 and TMR1 for Timer 1.

The two timers have similar operating characteristics. The timers can be set up to operate in either a counter mode or timer mode. In the counter mode, the dedicated timer registers will increment on state changes (either high to low or low to high transitions) on specific I/O pins. In the timer mode, the timer registers will increment on the internal MCU clock or an externally applied clock signal. The main difference between the two timers is in the magnitude of the interval or number of counts that can be handled. TMR0 can be considered a short duration timer; TMR1 can handle significantly longer durations. These timer durations are all relative. However, neither can handle the lengthy durations that are required by some applications, therefore TMR0 or TMR1 cannot always easily replace the use of delay subroutines.

The dedicated timer registers mentioned determine the number of counts or the time interval that can be handled by the timers. TMR0 has an 8-bit working register labeled TMR0. Alternatively TMR1 has two 8-bit working registers labeled TMR1L containing the low byte and TMR1H containing the high byte for an overall total 16-bit register size. The basic timer operation involves incrementing the associated register on either clock pulses or count pulses. When the associated register increments through 0xff for TMR0 or through 0xffff for TMR1 to roll over to 0x00, a timer overflow flag is set and an interrupt is generated if enabled. The duration of the timer or the number of counts required to generate the overflow condition is controlled by the starting point that is programmed into the timer register before the timer is enabled and starts running. For instance if you are using TMR0 and want to reduce the timer duration to half the maximum value, you would load 127 into the TMR0 register before CLEARING the TMR0 overflow flag. With these starting conditions, the TMR0 register would increment on each clock cycle starting at 127 until the register reaches 0xff. The very next increment of the register will overflow the register to 0x00, would SET the TMR0 overflow flag and an interrupt would be generated if enabled. Likewise, the duration of TMR1 can be controlled by the starting values loaded into the 16-bit register TMR1L and TMR1H.

Using Pre-Scalers to Control the Duration of the Timers

The duration of the timers can be further controlled by the use of pre-scalers. The pre-scaler circuits associated with the timers can be configured and inserted between the controlling clock or counter signal source and the timer input. The pre-scaler actually divides the clock rate by predefined factors or ratios which lengthens the duration of the timers. For instance, if the TMR0 pre-scaler is configured to divide the clock rate by 16 (a ratio of 1:16), the pre-scaler will deliver a single clock pulse to TMR0 for every 16 clock pulses it receives from the clock thereby lengthening the time duration of TMR0 by a factor of 16. Alternatively in the counter mode, the TMR0 could count up to 256 counts without the pre-scaler, with the pre-scaler configured for a ratio of 1:16, the TMR0 could count up to 4096 counts.

TMR0 Setup. There are three special function registers that control TMR0.
In the OPTION_REG, T0CS bit, *TMR0 Clock Source Select*, determines if the clocking source for the timer comes from the internal clock of the MCU or from an external clocking source connected to the PORTA, 2 (RA2). SETTING T0CS configures TMR0 to use an external clock source (putting the resource in the counter mode), CLEARING T0CS configures TMR0 to increment on the internal clock. OPTION_REG, T0SE bit, *TMR0 Source Edge Select*, configures the TMR0 to increment on the high-to-low transition of the external clocking source if SET or to increment on the low-to-high transition of the external clocking source if CLEAR. OPTION_REG, PSA bit, *the Pre-scaler Assignment,* inserts the pre-scaler between the clocking source and TMR0 if the bit is CLEAR or assigns the pre-scaler to the Watch Dog Timer (this resource is not covered in this text) if SET. Lastly, OPTION_REG, PS2:PS0 bits, the *Pre-scaler Rate Select* (PS2, PS1, and PS0), are used to select from the available pre-scale ratios as detailed in the device documentation. For instance a bit pattern loaded into the Pre-scaler Rate Select bits of b'000' would select a pre-scale ratio of 1:2 while a bit pattern of b'111' would select a pre-scale ratio of 1:256.

The actual register TMR0 is loaded with a value that determines the number of increments before the register overflow occurs which in turn SETS the TMR0 interrupt flag and generates an interrupt. After each overflow condition, the TMR0 register needs to be reset to its initial value if equal time intervals or counts are required. Failing to re-set the TMR0 register will result in the full delay or count of 255 to be used. It is interesting to note that the TMR0 interrupt flag is SET upon the overflow condition regardless of whether the interrupt is enabled or not. This allows the programmer to pole the status of the interrupt flag and take desired actions without having to generate an interrupt. Of course the interrupt flag needs to be CLEARED because once it is SET by the TMR0 register overflow hardware, the flag can only be CLEARED by software and will remain SET after the first overflow regardless of subsequent overflow conditions.

If the TMR0 is to be used to generate an interrupt, the interrupt from the resource must be enabled by SETTING INTCON, T0IE as well as enabling global interrupts by SETTING INTCON, GIE. TMR0 is considered a basic MCU resource and therefore is not controlled by the peripheral interrupt enable bit in INTCON. Make sure that the TMR0 Interrupt Flag (INTCON, T0IF) is CLEARED before enabling the TMR0 interrupt or an automatic, unintended interrupt will immediately be generated. The OPTION_REG and INTCON setup for TMR0 can be accomplished in the Initialization section of the program code or in the main body of the code depending on the application.

Bank 0 & 1	Interrupt Control Register - INTCON						
GIE	PEIE	T0IE	INTE	RAIE	T0IF	INTF	RAIF
Global Interrupt Enable	Peripheral Interrupt Enable	TMR0 Overflow Interrupt Enable	RA2/INT External Interrupt Enable	Port Change Interrupt Enable	TMR0 Overflow Interrupt Flag	RA2/INT External Interrupt Flag	Port Change Interrupt Flag

Bank 1	Option Register - OPTION_REG						
RAPU	INTEDG	T0CS	T0SE	PSA	PS2	PS1	PS0
PORTA Pull-up Enable	Interrupt Edge Select bit	TMR0 Clock Source Select bit	TMR0 Source Edge Select bit	Prescaler Assignment bit	Prescaler Rate Select bit	Prescaler Rate Select bit	Prescaler Rate Select bit

The following code snippets illustrate setting up the TMR0 resource in the Initialization section of the code:

```
BANKSEL         Bank1
movlw           b'00000001'
movwf           OPTION_REG
movlw           b'00000000'
movwf           TRISA
movlw           b'00000000'
movwf           TRISC
movlw           b'00000000'
movwf           ANSEL
BANKSEL         Bank0
bcf             INTCON, T0IF
movlw           b'10100000'
movwf           INTCON
```

The bit pattern b'00000001' that is loaded into the OPTION_REG assigns the internal clock as the TMR0 clock source T0CS, assigns the pre-scaler to TMR0, PSA, and sets the pre-scaler rate to 1:4 (bits2:0 PS2:PS0) to configure TMR0. The TMR0 register will begin incrementing as configured following the loading of the bit pattern into the OPTION_REG. You need to keep this in mind because incrementing the TMR0 register at this point may corrupt the first interrupt and produce unwanted consequences. Deliberately CLEARING the TMR0 interrupt flag, INTCON, T0IF, prevents unintended interrupt consequences when the interrupt resource is finally enabled and is a good programming habit. The bcf statement CLEARS the T0IF flag bit. Finally the bit pattern b'101000000' is loaded into the INTCON register from the w-register by the movwf statement to SET the GIE and T0IE bits to specifically enable the TMR0 overflow interrupt and globally enable all enabled interrupts (in this case, only the TMR0 interrupt is enabled). Because the TMR0 register begins incrementing immediately upon configuring the TMR0 with the OPTION_REG, a better programming choice would be to enable the TMR0 interrupt just prior to its need in the program. An alternative Initialization code might be:

```
BANKSEL         Bank0
movlw           b'00000000'
movwf           INTCON


main
   ;main program lines of code
movlw           b'10100000'
movwf           INTCON
movlw           b'00000000'
movwf           TMR0

   ;the rest of the main program
goto            main
```

In the above code, the Initialization segment of the code is changed so that the bit pattern b'00000000' CLEARS the GIE and T0IE bits disabling interrupts and also CLEARS the T0IF interrupt flag. (Remember the TMR0 register is still incrementing after the OPTION_REG is configured.) At the appropriate point in the main program, the TMR0 interrupt is enabled with the bit pattern b'10100000' being loaded into the INTCON register to SET the T0IE and GIE bits. The TMR0 register is still being incremented during the execution of these lines of code, so to start the TMR0 from the beginning, the appropriate starting point is loaded into the register, in this case b'00000000'. [This could have been more efficiently accomplished simply by using clrf TMR0, however the listed code is intended to emphasize the setting of the TMR0 register to a starting point.]

TMR1 Setup. TMR1 is a peripheral resource and therefore is controlled by a different set of SFRs. The main differences between TMR0 and TMR1 include:

Table 14-1

TMR0	TMR1
8-bits (TMR0 Register)	16-bits (TMR1L, TMR1H registers)
Max time: 65536 µs (@ 4MHz Clk)	Max time: 524280 µS (@ 4MHz Clk)
Prescale up to 1:256	Prescale up to 1:8
Basic resource	Peripheral resource
Starts when OPTION_REG loaded	Starts when TR1ON SET
External clock on PORTA, 2	External clock on PORTA, 5
Set-up and operating registers:	Set-up and operating registers:
INTCON, OPTION_REG,	INTCON, T1CON, PIR1, PIE1,
TMR0	TMR1L, TMR1H

Bank 0	Timer1 Control Register - T1CON						
X	TMR1GE	T1CKPS1	T1CKPS0	T1OSCEN	T1SYNC	TMR1CS	TMR1ON
Unimplemented	Timer1 Gate Enable bit	Timer 1 Input Clock Prescale Select bit	Timer 1 Input Clock Prescale Select bit	Timer 1 Oscillator Enable Control bit	Timer 1 External Clock Input Sync Control bit	Timer 1 Clock Source Select bit	Timer 1 On bit

T1CON. *Timer 1 Control Register*. This SFR configures the clock source for TMR1 and turns on the timer. The T1CKPS0 and T1CKPS1 bits select the pre-scale ratio for the clock as detailed in the device documentation. The TMR1CS bit configures the clock source for TMR1 to the internal clock when CLEAR or to an external clock source on pin PORTA, 5 if SET. There are three clock options available for TMR1, in the exercises in this text we will work only with the internal clock oscillator of the device therefore the TMR1GE, T1OSCEN, and T1SYNC bits will be CLEARED. The TMR1ON bit when SET starts TMR1, when CLEAR, TMR1 is off. The TMR1 registers will start incrementing after TMR1ON is SET.

Bank 0	Peripheral Interrupt Register 1 - PIR1						
EEIF	ADIF	X	X	CMIF	X	X	TMR1IF
EEPROM Write Operation Interrupt Flag bit	A/D Converter Interrupt Flag bit	Unimplemented	Unimplemented	Comparator Interrupt Flag bit	Unimplemented	Unimplemented	TMR1 Overflow Interrupt Flag bit

PIR1. *The Peripheral Interrupt Register 1*, contains the TMR1 *Overflow Interrupt Flag*, TMR1IF. When the TMR1 registers TMR1H and TMR1L overflow from 0xffff to 0x0000, the TMR1IF flag is set by hardware and must be CLEARED by software to allow further interrupts. If this flag is not CLEARED before the TMR1 interrupt is enabled, an immediate and probably unintended TMR1 interrupt will occur.

Bank 1	Peripheral Interrupt Enable Register - PIE1						
EEIE	ADIE	X	X	CMIE	X	X	TMR1E
EE Write Complete Interrupt Enable bit	A/D Converter Interrupt Enable bit	Unimplemented	Unimplemented	Comparator Interrupt Enable bit	Unimplemented	Unimplemented	TMR1 Overflow Interrupt Enable bit

PIE1. *The Peripheral Interrupt Enable Register* is used to enable the interrupts for the individual peripheral resources of the PIC16F676. When TMR1E is SET, the TMR1 Overflow Interrupt is enabled, but remember that two additional interrupt control bits also need to be SET to enable peripheral interrupts, the PEIE and GIE bits in the INTCON register.

The following code snippets illustrate setting up the TMR1 resource in the Initialization section of the code:

```
movlw       b'00000000'
movwf       INTCON
movlw       b'00110000'     ;TMR1 pre-scale 1:8, internal clock,
                            ;TMR1 stopped
movwf       T1CON
bcf         PIR1,TMR1IF     ;clear TMR1 interrupt flag

BANKSEL     Bank1           ; BANK1

movlw       b'00000001'     ;TMR1 interrupt enabled
movwf       PIE1
BANKSEL     Bank0           ;back to bank0
```

The bit pattern b'00000000' when loaded into the INTCON register ensures that all interrupts are disabled until needed. This could have been more efficiently accomplished with the single instruction clrf INTCON. The bit pattern b'00110000' when loaded into the T1CON register configures the TMR1 pre-scaler to a 1:8 ratio and ensures that TMR1 is off. The bcf PIR1, TMR1IF CLEARS the TMR1 interrupt flag to prevent an unintended TMR1 interrupt. The bit pattern b'00000001' when loaded into PIE1 will enable the TMR1 interrupt. Alternatively this could have been more efficiently accomplished with bsf PIE1, TMR1IE. There are other lines of code that configure resources that are required in the Initialization section of the code, but those lines are not listed above for clarity. All that is left to be done within the main program is to preload the TMR1 registers TMR1H and TMR1L, turn on TMR1 and enable the interrupt:

```
main
            movlw           b'########'
            movwf           TMR1H
            movlw           b'########'
            movwf           TMR1L
            movlw           b'11000000'
            movwf           INTCON
            bsf             T1CON, TMR1ON
;rest of the main program
```

In the first four lines of code, the w-register is loaded with the bit pattern of the values that are in turn loaded into the TMR1 registers. The TMR1 registers will increment up from these values when the timer is turned on and an interrupt will be generated when the 16-bit value overflows to 0x0000. The bit pattern b'11000000' enables the individually enabled peripheral resource interrupts and globally enables all interrupts when this value is loaded into INTCON. Finally, bsf T1CON, TMR1ON SETS T1CON to turn on TMR1.

Basic Operation of TMR0

Now let's take a look at the operation of these timers. We will turn our attention first to TMR0. Load the project **Program Files/Ch 14 Program/TMR0 Basic Operation** into *MPLAB IDE*. This project as stored on the resource CD-ROM will come up with simulator windows that will be used to monitor the contents of selected registers and the stop watch to monitor the times for interrupts. The project will also have breakpoints set that will be used to stop the program at specific lines during execution so that the contents of the selected registers can be viewed. This first program example is looking at the very basic operation of TMR0. To do this exploration, TMR0 will be configured to generate an interrupt using various pre-scaler settings and TMR0 register starting values. The main program enables the TMR0 interrupt and enters a holding loop to await TMR0 interrupt. The interrupt service subroutine CLEARS the interrupt condition, resets the TMR0 register value, returns control back to the main program.

Scroll into the Initialization section of the code in the TMR0 Basic Operation.asm file to these lines of the code that will be used to configure TMR0:

```
    BANKSEL     Bank1            ;BANK1
    movlw       b'00001000'      ;pre-scale assigned to WDT,
                                 ;no pre-scale on TMR0
;   movlw       b'00000000'      ;TMR0 set-up: pre-scale TMR0,
                                 ;pre-scale 1:2
;   movlw       b'00000011'      ;TMR0 set-up: pre-scale TMR0,
                                 ;pre-scale
                                 ;1:16
;   movlw       b'00000111'      ;TMR0 set-up: pre-scale TMR0,
                                 ;pre-scale
                                 ;1:256
    movwf       OPTION_REG       ;put w-register into option register,
                                 ;this starts TMR0
```

The commented lines will be used to change the pre-scaler assignment during the exercise. The first time through the exercise, the bit pattern b'00001000' that is loaded into the OPTION_REG assigns the pre-scaler to the Watch Dog Timer with no pre-scaler assigned to TMR0.

Continue to scroll down into the main section of the program:

```
;main program
            movlw       b'00000000'      ;preload TMR0 for a count that
                                        ;will generate an interrupt of length
            movwf       TMR0             ;determined by this value

            bcf         INTCON,T0IF      ;clear TMR0 interrupt flag
            bsf         INTCON,T0IE      ;enable TMR0
            bsf         INTCON,GIE       ;enable global interrupts

self        goto        self             ;keep the main program busy doing
                                        ;something while waiting for an
interrupt
                                        ;from TRM0
```

The bit pattern b'00000000' is loaded into the TMR0 register to establish the starting point for that register. This value will be adjusted during the exercise to see how the starting point of the TMR0 register affects the time delay of the TMR0 interrupt. In this case, the TMR0 register will have to increment through the full 8-bits (255) before an interrupt is generated. The bit manipulation of the INTCON bits CLEAR the T0IF interrupt flag, enables the TMR0 interrupt by SETTING the T0IE bit and globally enables the TMR0 interrupt by SETTING the GIE bit.

Build and Run the Program

Build and run the program. The program executes from the starting point at 0x00 through the device Initialization section of the code, through the beginning of the main program that enables the TMR0 interrupt and halts at the first breakpoint which is located at the point where the interrupt_service subroutine is called (**Figure 14-1**). In other words, the first TMR0 interrupt has occurred. Take note in the **WATCH** window that INTCON, T0IF (bit 3) is SET which indicates that the TMR0 overflow interrupt has occurred. The hardware of the 16F676 is set so that when an interrupt is generated, the GIE bit of the INTCON is automatically CLEARED to disable further interrupts. This is indicated by inspection of the INTCON register in the **WATCH** window. Also take note of the value in the TMR0 register, in this case 2. This number reflects that the TMR0 register has incremented 2 times since the TMR0 register was reset to the starting value, in this case reset to 0. The significance of this number will be covered a bit later. The numbers in the **STOPWATCH** window at this stage are of little interest because there has been program time required to run the overhead section of the code. Click on the **ZERO** button to clear these values.

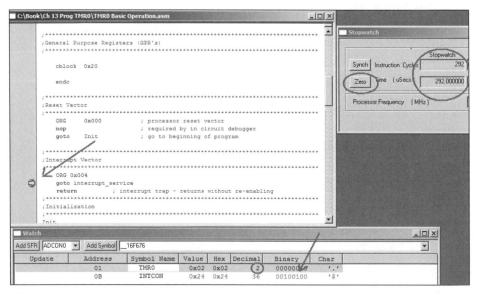

Figure 14-1

Step Through the Program

Step through the program from the breakpoint by pressing the f7 key on the computer keyboard.

Interrupt_Service Subroutine

The first step executes the `goto` jump into the interrupt_service subroutine (**Figure 14-2**). Note that two instruction cycles were required to make this jump but more importantly note that the TMR0 register also incremented by 2 (starting at 2 and ending at 4 at this point in the program execution), an equal number of changes as the instruction cycles. With no pre-scaler attached to TMR0, as is the case for this first exercise, the TMR0 register increments in step with the number of instruction cycles.

Continue to f7 step through the program to the `nop` statement (**Figure 14-3**). Note that the increment in the TMR0 register matches the number of instruction cycles for these two steps. Also note that the `bcf` statements CLEARED the T0IE TMR0 Interrupt Enable bit to disable further TMR0 interrupts and also the T0IF flag bit to get ready for

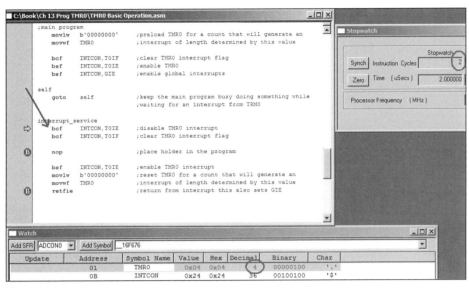

Figure 14-2

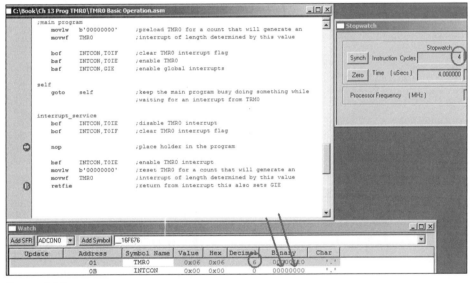

Figure 14-3

the next interrupt. The T0IF flag is SET by hardware when a TMR0 overflow interrupt occurs and must be CLEARED in software just as is done in this example. Failure to do so will result in an immediate, unintended TMR0 interrupt when the interrupt is subsequently enabled.

Click the **RUN** button in the menu bar to continue the program execution to the next breakpoint which is at the end of the interrupt_ service subroutine (**Figure 14-4**). Take note that it took 8 instruction cycles to complete this portion of the interrupt_ service subroutine, the TMR0 register has been cleared to zero and the T0IE bit has been SET to enable the next TMR0 interrupt.

Let's take a moment and discuss the significance of where it is in the interrupt service subroutine that the TMR0 register is reset to its initial value. Clearly it takes some finite

amount of time and instruction cycles to accomplish the tasks to service the interrupt. In this most simple of examples, it took 8 µs and 8 instruction cycles. If the programmer wants this amount of time to be included in the time interval between interrupts, then the TMR0 register would need to be reset at the beginning of the routine so that it would be incremented while the subroutine is being executed. If the programmer wants the next interrupt to occur a specified time after the previous is serviced, then the TMR0 register would be reset at the end of the subroutine as was done here. There may be critical timing issues when this difference could be significant.

Continue with an f7 step to complete the interrupt_service subroutine (**Figure 14-5**). There are a couple of things to note here. First, the `retfie` command automatically SETS the INTCON, GIE bit to enable interrupts globally. Second, note that the instruction cycles have advanced by 2, but the TMR0 register values remains 0. In other words the register did not increment as would be expected. This illustrates a hardware nuisance that once the TMR0 register is written, the register will not increment

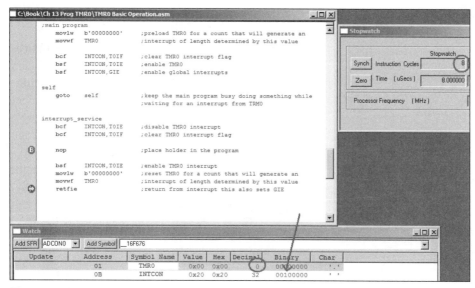

Figure 14-4

during the next two instruction cycles. This might cause a problem for the most critical timing issues and the program can compensate by making appropriate adjustments to the starting values loaded into the TMR0 register.

The interrupt has now been serviced and the program is back into the main loop. As you continue to f7 step through the program you will see the instruction cycles and TMR0 register to advance in step. You can continue to do this until the TMR0 register approaches 255 then slowly step though the program to observe that indeed, when the TMR0 register overflows from 0xff to 0x00, the next interrupt is generated. Alternatively, press the **RUN** button to continue normal program execution to the next breakpoint (**Figure 14-6**). Remember that the timer was zeroed at the end of the previous interrupt, now take note of the time

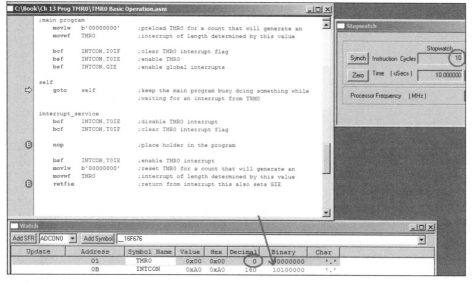

Figure 14-5

to complete the next interrupt, 268 μs. The instruction cycle time interval with the device clock at 4MHz is 1 μs, and in this configuration, the TMR0 register increments in step with the instruction cycle. It should therefore take 256 instruction cycles to generate a TMR0 overflow interrupt, or 256 μs. But there is a difference of 12 μs from what would be expected. During our study of the TMR0 interrupt, you noted that it took 8 instruction cycles to complete the interrupt service routine, 2 cycles to return program control to the main program, and 2 cycles after a write to the TMR0 register before the register continues to be incremented, that is where the 12 μs difference comes from.

TMR0 Register and Time Interval Between Interrupts

Next, let's take a look at how the starting value of the TMR0 register affects the time interval between interrupts. Remember that the TMR0 register increments in step with the

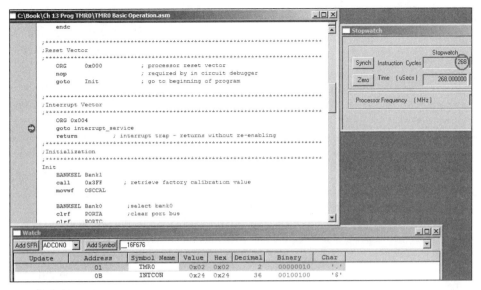

Figure 14-6

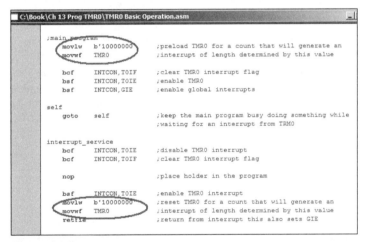

Figure 14-7

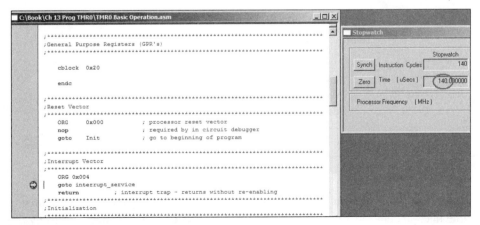

Figure 14-8

internal clock of the device and an interrupt is generated when the TMR0 register overflows to 0x00. In the previous exercise, the TMR0 register was loaded with 0x00 which caused the timer to delay the maximum amount between interrupts. To explore the TMR0 register starting point, you need to change the starting value. Scroll to the main program and find the two locations in the code where the TMR0 register is loaded. Change the value of the literal that is loaded into the TMR0 register to 128 or b'10000000' (**Figure 14-7**). Build and run the program, when the program stops at the first breakpoint (at the goto interrupt_service instruction), zero the **STOPWATCH**, and press **RUN** again. If there are remaining breakpoints from the previous exercise, press **RUN** until the program stops again at the goto statement in the interrupt vector section of the code. Note that the time to complete the TMR0 interrupt with the register loaded with 128 is 140 μs, significantly less than the time required with the TMR0 register beginning from 0x00 of 268 μs (**Figure 14-8**). The time is not half, this is due to the instruction cycle overhead required to execute an interrupt. Do additional explorations using various values from 0 to 255 loaded into the TMR0 resister and take note of the time differences.

Pre-Scaler Effect on TMR0 Interrupt Time

Return the bit pattern that is loaded into the TMR0 register to b'00000000' for the next exercise that compares the effect that the pre-scaler has on the TMR0 interrupt time.

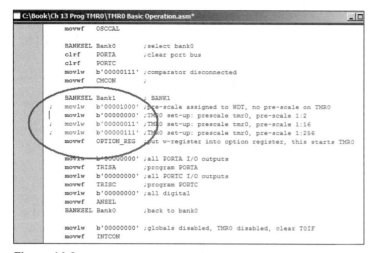

```
■ C:\Book\Ch 13 Prog TMR0\TMR0 Basic Operation.asm*                    _ □
          movwf   OSCCAL

          BANKSEL Bank0        ;select bank0
          clrf    PORTA        ;clear port bus
          clrf    PORTC
          movlw   b'00000111'  ;comparator disconnected
          movwf   CMCON        ;

          BANKSEL Bank1        ; BANK1
;         movlw   b'00001000'  ;pre-scale assigned to WDT, no pre-scale on TMR0
          movlw   b'00000000'  ;TMR0 set-up: prescale tmr0, pre-scale 1:2
;         movlw   b'00000011'  ;TMR0 set-up: prescale tmr0, pre-scale 1:16
;         movlw   b'00000111'  ;TMR0 set-up: prescale tmr0, pre-scale 1:256
          movwf   OPTION_REG   ;put w-register into option register, this starts TMR0

          movlw   b'00000000'  ;all PORTA I/O outputs
          movwf   TRISA        ;program PORTA
          movlw   b'00000000'  ;all PORTC I/O outputs
          movwf   TRISC        ;program PORTC
          movlw   b'00000000'  ;all digital
          movwf   ANSEL
          BANKSEL Bank0        ;back to bank0

          movlw   b'00000000'  ;globals disabled, TMR0 disabled, clear T0IF
          movwf   INTCON
```

Figure 14-9

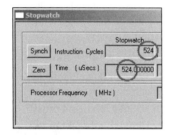

Figure 14-10

The pre-scaler assignment and the ratio of the pre-scaler is configured in the Initialization section of the code. Scroll up to that section and find the commented lines of code that will be loaded into OPTION_REG in the following exercises (**Figure 14-9**). Comment the first movlw command and remove the comment from the second movlw command as illustrated (comment lines are disregarded during the program build process, a semi-colon (;) indicates a comment line). The bit pattern b'00000000' when loaded into OPTION_REG assigns the pre-scaler to TMR0 and sets the ratio to 1:2 which means that the TMR0 register will increment once for every 2 instruction cycles. As you did in the previous exercise, build, **RUN**, zero the **STOPWATCH**, and **RUN** and note the amount of time required to generate a TMR0 overflow interrupt with the pre-scaler assigned with a ratio of 1:2 (**Figure 14-10**). The time required is 524 µs versus 268 µs when there was no pre-scaler; this is approximately twice the time (the difference again is due to the interrupt code overhead.) Because the TMR0 register increments only once for every two instruction cycles, it takes twice as long to overflow the TMR0 register and generate an interrupt. You can verify the increment interval of the TMR0 register by f7 stepping through the program and watching the change in the TMR0 register as displayed in the **WATCH** window and compare that interval with the coincident change in the instruction cycle count in the **STOPWATCH** window.

Change the Pre-Scaler Ratio

Continue this exercise by changing the pre-scaler ratio to 1:16 and 1:256 with adjustments to the commented lines in the Initialization section of the code. Run the exercise and take note of the change in the TMR0 register increment interval and in the interrupt time. The following table reflects the data that you should expect. Note that the maximum time for a TMR0 interrupt is 65.5 mseconds.

Table 14.2
TMR0

Pre-scale	TMR0 Increment	Interrupt Time
None	Each Instruction Cycle (IC)	268 µs
1:2 (b'000')	every 2-IC	524 µs
1:16 (b'011')	every 16-IC	4108 µs
1:256 (b'111')	every 256-IC	65548 µs

There are a few important points to remember about controlling the TMR0 resource. The time interval between TMR0 Overflow Interrupts is determined in macro terms by the pre-scaler ratio and refined by the value loaded into the TMR0 register. Also there are a few lines of code and associate instruction cycle overhead required to generate the interrupt, these variables complicate the calculation of the actual interrupt time interval. However, by using the *MPLAB* Simulator, you can determine the predicted interrupt time interval with good accuracy, the actual interrupt interval will depend on the accuracy of the device clock circuit.

TMR0 Resource Exploration Exercise

You will use the **Program Files/Ch 14 Program/TMR0 project** for the next exploration exercise. Load the project into *MPLAB IDE,* construct the circuit that is depicted in **Figure 14-11** and pictorially illustrated in **Figure 14-12**. In this circuit, an LED is tied to PORTC, 4 through a current limiting resistor and a speaker is connected to PORTC, 5. The program sets up the TMR0 resource to generate an interrupt every 500 µs and toggle the PORTC, 5 pin to generate a 1000 Hz audio tone in the speaker. The main program will flash the LED at 1 s intervals. This program demonstrates the multitasking capabilities of an MCU by the use of interrupts. Build the program and load it into the PIC16F676. Install the device into the circuit and apply power to verify the program is operating correctly.

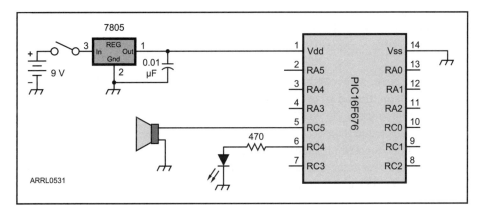

Figure 14-11

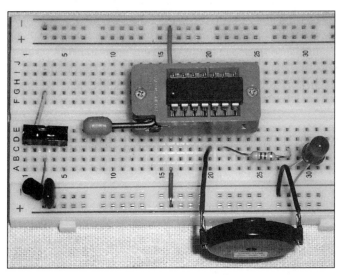

Figure 14-12

The TMR0 interrupt is used to toggle the pin connected to the speaker to generate a square wave with a period of 1 millisecond. This square wave is formed by SETTING the pin for 500 µs, then CLEARING the pin for 500 µs, therefore we are looking for an interrupt of the main program at 500 µs intervals. From the previous exploration you found that a pre-scaler ratio of 1:4 and setting the TMR0 register to 0x00 will generate interrupts at 524 µs intervals. All that you need to do is refine the starting value loaded into the TMR0 register to reduce the interval to the desired 500 µs. To help determine this starting value, a constant called TMR0_scale is defined in the program and an initial value (which turns out to be the correct value) of 14 is assigned to that constant label. Scroll up in the TMR0.asm file after the build to the Defines section of the code and you will see that constant definition:

```
#define Bank0        0x00
#define Bank1        0x80
#define TMR0_scale   .14      ;TMR0 preload factor, this value gives
                             ;1000Hz toggle
```

As in the previous exercise, a breakpoint has been set inside the Interrupt vector section of the code. Follow along in with your *MPLAB* Simulator as we test the value of 14 as the starting point for the TMR0 register. Press Run and the program will execute and stop at the breakpoint after the first interrupt is generated. Zero the **STOPWATCH** and press **RUN** again (**Figure 14-13**). Note that the time to generate the interrupt is 499 µS, that is about as close as you can get. Continue the exercise by changing the value of TMR0_scale and see how it affects the interrupt interval and how you can use this technique to refine the interrupt interval to meet the program demands. Also f7 step through the program to observe the program behavior, particularly in the main loop of the program and what happens when the interrupt is generated. The project as supplied on the CD that accompanies this text is set up with the TMR0 register in the **WATCH** window so that you can monitor the incrementing of that register as you step through the program. Take note of the starting value which will equal the value that is assigned to the TMR0_scale constant. As the TMR0 register approaches 0xff, slow down and observe the program behavior as the register overflows from 0x00 to 0x00.

In the next exercise, we'll combine the use of TMR0 and TMR1. The TMR0 interrupt will be set up to send a 1000Hz tone to the speaker as in the previous exercise. The TMR1 interrupt will use the ADC reading of the voltage on the wiper of the variable resistor that is connected to the ADC resource as the TMR1 register starting point which in turn will determine the TMR1 interrupt interval. The TMR1 interrupt will turn on or off the TMR0 interrupt with the result that the generated tone would toggle on and off at a period determined by the variable resistor.

TMR1 Resource

Build the circuit as depicted in the picture in **Figure 14-14** and illustrated in **Figure 14-15**. Load the project **Program Files/Ch 14 Program/TMR1** into *MPLAB IDE*. The project includes appropriate **WATCH** and **STOPWATCH** windows if you want to explore the program code in detail by using the *MPLAB* Simulator. Take this opportunity to scroll through the TMR1.asm file to the Initialization section of the code and find those lines of code that configure the TMR0 and TMR1 interrupt resources with the following:

TMR0 - TMR0 disabled, TMR0IF CLEAR, pre-scaler assigned to TMR0, pre-scale ratio 1:2

```
movlw    b'00000000'    ;globals disabled, peripherals disabled,
movwf    INTCON         ;TMR0 disabled, TOIF cleared
  :
  :
  :
movlw    b'0000000'     ;TMR0 set-up: pull-ups enabled, X, internal clk, X,
movwf    OPTION_REG     ;pre-scale tmr0, pre-scale 1:2
```

TMR1 – TMR1 pre-scale ratio 1:8, TMR1 stopped, TMR1 interrupt flag CLEAR, TMR1 interrupt enabled

```
movlw    b'00110000'
movwf    T1CON
bcf      PIR1, TMR1IF
movlw    b'00000001'
movwf    PIE1
```

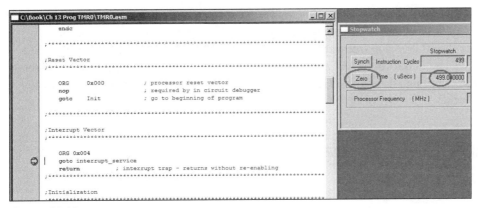

Figure 14-13

At the completion of the Initialization section of the code, the ADC is configured and ready for use and the TMR0 and TMR1 interrupt resources are ready with the appropriate values to be loaded into the associated incrementing registers, for TMR1 to be turned on, and for the interrupts to be globally enabled, all done within the main program.

Scroll down to the main program. The first part of the program accomplishes the tasks described above and then enters a holding loop waiting for interrupts from TMR0 and TMR1.

```
call     get_adc
movfw    h_byte
movwf    TMR1H
movlw    b'11100000'
movwf    INTCON
movlw    TMR0_scale
movwf    TMR0
bsf      T1CON,TMR1ON

self goto self
```

One subtle point needs to be explained in this code. The TMR1 interrupt interval is determined by the overflow of the 16-bits of TMR1H and TMR1L bytes that make up that register. In this program segment, only the upper byte of the register is adjusted with varying starting values because only this byte produces interrupt interval changes that are perceptible by the human ear, the lower bytes only contribute interval increments of a few mseconds. The source of the starting values for the TMR1 16-bit register is the 10-bit ADC value as determined by the variable resistor setting. Only the upper 8-bits of the ADC value is used and loaded into TMR1H that sets the

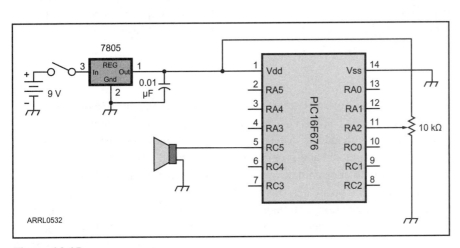

Figure 14-14

Figure 14-15

TMR1 interrupt interval. The shifting of the ADC bits to eliminate the lower two bits is accomplished within the get_adc subroutine by having the ADC resource set to left justify the 10-bit value when it is placed into the ADRESH and ADRESL registers. The upper 8-bits of the 10-bit ADC value are loaded into the ADRESH register that is in turn is transferred into the TMR1H register. The contents of TMR1L is automatically set to 0x00 when the overflow occurs.

There are two interrupt sources, TMR0 and TMR1, however, each interrupt requires different actions. Scroll into the interrupt_service subroutine to learn how this is handled.

```
interrupt_service
        btfss       PIE1, TMR1IF
        goto        tone
        call        get_adc
        movfw       h_byte
        movwf       TMR1H
```

The first step in the interrupt_service subroutine checks the TMR1IF interrupt flag. Since there are only two sources of interrupts allowed with this setup, the interrupt will either occur from TMR1 or TMR0. The btfss opcode checks the TMR1IF bit and if it is SET, the next instruction is skipped, if it is CLEAR, the next instruction is executed. In this case, if the TMR1IF is SET (in other words the TMR1 is the source of the interrupt), the goto instruction is skipped. The code that services the TMR1 interrupt resets the TMR1 register using the ADC value. It determines if the tone is on or off and toggles to the opposite state, and prepares the TMR1 resource for another interrupt by CLEARING the interrupt flag with the following code:

```
bcf         PIR1, TMR1IF
retfie
```

Remember, the retfie command automatically re-enables interrupts globally when the program counter jumps back to the main program.

Load the program into the PIC16F676, install the device into your circuit, power it up, and you should hear a continuous stream of tone dashes. If you vary the value of the resistor, the tone dash length changes in step. The tone is generated by TMR0 interrupts, the tone dash lengths are generated by TMR1 interrupt intervals that are determined by the ADC value that is adjusted by the variable resistor. Remember, the value of interrupts is to allow the MCU to multitask. In this program, the actual main program is a simple infinite loop, the tones are generated by interrupts. The main loop could just as easily have been programmed to do other, more meaningful tasks.

Summary

There are two internal timer resources available within the PIC16F676 device, Timer 0 (TMR0) and Timer 1 (TMR1). The timer resources can be configured as timers or as counters, this chapter focused on using the resources as timers. TMR0 is an 8-bit timer. Using an optional and programmable pre-scaler, this timer can generate interrupts at intervals up to approximately 65 ms. TMR1 is a 16-bit timer. Using the optional and programmable pre-scaler, this timer can generate interrupts at intervals up to approximately 524 ms. Longer time interval delays are possible by nesting timer interrupts or by the use of delay subroutines. The interrupts generated by these timer resources are stimulated by the overflow of associated timer registers that are incremented though the maximum (0xff or 0xffff) back to 0x00. The time interval between interrupts is determined on the macro level by the configuration of the associated pre-scaler, and on the micro level by the starting value loaded into the associated timer register. There is some level of code and instruction cycle overhead associated with the use of the interrupts that contribute to the end interrupt time interval. This overhead is a function of the code technique used. The interrupt interval time can be predicted by the use of the *MPLAB* simulator before the code is loaded into the device and run in circuit. The actual interrupt interval is ultimately dependent on the accuracy of the clock source for the device. The timer interrupt resources can be used simultaneously in a program, the actual source of an interrupt can be identified by checking the interrupt flags in the interrupt service routine and taking appropriate action.

Review Questions

14.1 At what rate (in instruction cycles) does the TMR0 register increment when there is no pre-scaler assigned to the resource. Alternatively, at what rate does the TMR1 register increment when a pre-scaler ratio of 0:0 is assigned?

14.2 What command begins the incrementing of the TMR0 register? When does the TMR1 register begin to increment?

14.3 Do the timer resources operate even if their interrupt function is not enabled?

14.4 Can you monitor the progress of the timer resources between interrupts? If so, how?

14.5 Why is it important to CLEAR the associated interrupt flag in the interrupt service subroutine before returning control back to the main program?

14.6 In the programming exercises in this chapter, the interrupt service subroutines did not contain code designed to temporarily store the w-register and STATUS register contents while servicing the interrupt and then reload the pre-interrupt values into these registers when returning to the main program as was recommended in the chapter on interrupts. Why was this not a problem during the execution of the exercise programs? Amend the exercise code to take these precautions.

14.7 You can very accurately determine the interrupt time interval due to program code execution. What factor other than code determines the actual interrupt time interval? How might you measure the actual interrupt time interval?

14.8 Thinking in general terms of the resources available in the PIC16F676, how would you configure the resources to build a basic frequency counter?

Asynchronous
Serial
Communication

Objective: To learn how to configure and use resources of the PIC16F676 for basic Asynchronous Serial Communications. This chapter will describe in detail the serial programming techniques used in the exercises and programs in previous chapters that used serial communication techniques to send and display data on the LCD display.

Reading: *Serial LCD(#27977) Data Sheet*, pages 1-11.
Program: Program Files/Ch 16 Program/Serial.

Asynchronous Serial Communication

Asynchronous serial communication is a common communication *protocol* to send and receive data between a MCU and an external device as a series of data bits. "Asynchronous" means that the data can be sent at any time without regard to synchronizing the individual clocking signals of the MCU and the external device. To accomplish the sending of data asynchronously there must be agreement between the devices as to the configuration of a "start" signal that identifies the start of the data stream, the number of bits that make up the data, the order the bits will be sent (LSB first or MSB first), the rate at which the data bits will be sent, and a "stop" signal that identifies the end of the data stream. This *data package* consists of a *start bit*, a number of *data bits*, and a *stop bit*. The advantage of this form of sending data is that only one line (or MCU pin) is needed to send the data. The disadvantage is that timing is critical. From this point on, a reference to serial communication will mean asynchronous serial communication.

How Serial Communication Works

In serial communication, the receiving device is connected to the MCU through a *data line connection*. The receiving device monitors the data line waiting for the start bit. Once the start bit is detected, the receiving device verifies the validity of the start bit by checking that it is the proper length (time interval). If the start bit is determined to be invalid, the receiving device continues to wait for another, and valid, start bit. If the start bit is valid, the receiving device will wait ½ bit period and monitor the data line for the first data bit. The data bit will either be high or low and the appropriate bit value of 1 or 0 will be loaded into a data register. The receiving device will then wait 1 bit period and detect the next and subsequent bits. The first delay of ½ bit period puts the bit detection at the center of the bit interval, subsequent delays of 1 bit period keep the bit detection at the center of the subsequent bit intervals. After the correct number of data bits are received (usually 8, or multiples of 8, or sometimes 7) the receiving device may look for a stop bit. The stop bit length is verified, and if it is the correct length, the data is considered valid and is accepted. Many times the protocol does not require a stop bit and the data is assumed to be correct, this is usually the case for hardwired data connections. There are also other more complicated protocols that include parity bits which are used as a simple check-sum to verify the accuracy of the received bits. In the exercise program in this chapter we will be using the simplest form of serial communications using only the start bit, 8 data bits with the LSB bit sent first as depicted in **Figure 15-1**. The oscilloscope view of a byte of transmitted data is shown in **Figure 15-2**.

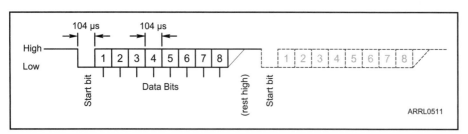

Figure 15-1

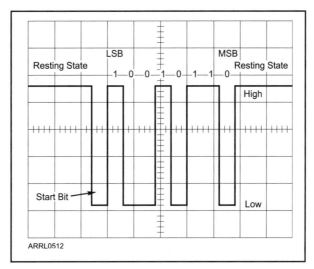

Figure 15-2

Serial Communication is Accomplished in Software in the PIC16F676 Device

There are a number of MCU devices that include specialized resources, instructions, and registers for dealing with serial communications, for instance the PIC16F688. In these parts, special function registers are loaded with values for baud rates, number of bits, number of stop bits and parity bits (if used), and have receive and transmit registers where data is stored. Once the SFRs are configured and loaded, the serial resources are enabled and the serial communication is accomplished in parallel with other MCU operations. The PIC16F676 device used in this text does not have these serial communications resources and therefore the serial communications will be accomplished in software. This allows you to fully explore serial communications to see how it is accomplished in software and thereby better understand what is involved if and when you elect to use the more capable MCUs that include dedicated serial communications resources.

Baud Rates

With the number of data bits defined, the baud rate (the length, in time, of the bit interval) needs to be defined. There are standard baud rates for serial communications as listed in **Table 15-1**. The time interval of an individual bit is calculated by taking the reciprocal of the baud rate. The bit intervals listed in Table 15-1 are rounded.

Table 15-1

Baud	Bit length ($\frac{1}{baud}$)
2400	416 μs
4800	208 μs
9600	104 μs
19200	52 μs

Port Resource Used as Data Line

The LCD unit recommended in the parts list that accompanies this text has switch selectable baud rates of 2400, 9600 and 19200 baud. The 19200 baud rate will stretch the limits of the PIC16F676, therefore the 9600 baud rate will be used in the exercises. To accomplish serial communications in software, the port resource to be used as the data line is configured as a digital output pin, delay subroutines that are the length of a bit for the desired baud rate are authored, the data bits are shifted out of the data byte variable in the required direction (in this case LSB first) and checked for either a high or low state and the data pin is SET or CLEARED for the bit period. Review the code block diagram in **Figure 15-3** before we go over the code segment for sending serial data.

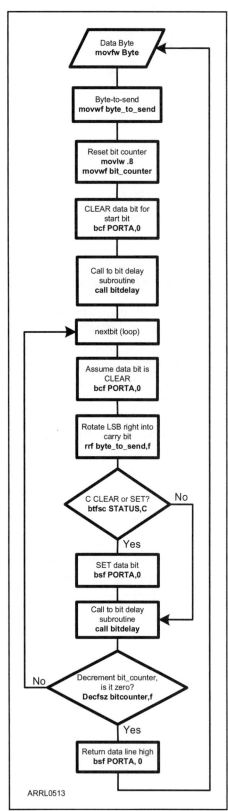

Figure 15-3

Program Exercise

Open *MPLAB IDE* and load the project **Program Files/Ch 15 Program/Serial**. This project as stored on the CD-ROM includes a **WATCH** window with the W-register, the **STOPWATCH** window, and *break points* assigned at specific locations in the code. These windows and break points will be used as we explore the serial communications routine with the *MPLAB Simulator*. The program in this exercise simply sends the word "Hello" by 9600 baud, LSB first, serial communications to the LCD for display. Scroll down into the main part of the program and take note of these lines of code:

```
;main program
     movlw     LCD_LINE0
     call      LCDOutput
     movlw     "H"
     call      LCDOutput
     movlw     "e"
     call      LCDOutput
```

The characters or LCD display command codes are loaded into the W-register and the subroutine LCDOutput is called. The real work of sending the serial data stream is accomplished in the subroutine. The first movlw command loads the value 0x80h which is the command value recognized by the LCD hardware to move the cursor to the first line of the display, far left column. The LCD command constants are defined in the program and assigned descriptive labels. These LCD command constants are listed in the LCD documentation. The LCDOutput subroutine then takes the value that was passed to it in the W-register and sends it to the LCD via a serial stream. On return to the main program, the next character "H" is loaded into the W-register and it is sent to the LCD and so on.

Scroll down and display the LCDOutput subroutine. Let's focus at the beginning of the code in the subroutine:

```
LCDOutput
     movwf     byte_to_send
     movlw     .8
     movwf     bitcounter
     bcf       PORTA,5
     call      bitdelay
```

W-Register

The w-register contains the value that we want to send to the LCD. It was loaded before the call to LCDOutput. The w-register is manipulated and used in virtually all parts of the program so it is important to keep in mind that the contents of the w-register will probably be changed often, consequently, the value contained in the w-register is first moved into a working variable location, in this case byte_to_send. To keep track of the number of bits as they are being sent to the LCD via the serial stream, a variable called "bitcounter" is loaded with the number of bits to be sent, in this case 8. As depicted in the oscilloscope illustration of the serial stream in Figure 15-1, the resting state for the serial data line is high (traditionally called the Mark, the low state is called the Space). Earlier in the code, the data pin PORTA, 5 was SET to establish the Mark state. The bcf PORTA, 5 instruction brings the data pin low to start the start bit. Finally the call to bitdelay which will generate a delay of approximately 100 µs, the delay required for 9600 baud. The next section of the LCDOutput subroutine code will send the 8 data bits. Turn your attention now to the remainder of the subroutine code and the internal loop:

```
nextbit
        bcf         PORTA,5
        rrf         byte_to_send,f
        btfsc       STATUS,C
        bsf         PORTA,5
        call        bitdelay
        decfsz      bitcounter,f
        goto        nextbit
        bsf         PORTA,5
        call        delay5mS
        return
```

The loop begins by assuming that the next bit to be sent in the serial stream is CLEAR. This assumption is arbitrary. It could just as easily have been assumed to be SET (with requisite code changes). In the serial protocol used by the LCD, the least significant bit is sent first. The rrf instruction rotates the LSB of the target register into and through the carry bit which is STATUS, C and stores the result back into the target register as illustrated in **Figure 15-4.**

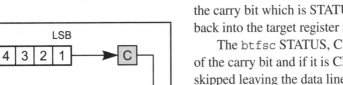

Figure 15-4

The btfsc STATUS, C instruction checks the state of the carry bit and if it is CLEAR, the next instruction is skipped leaving the data line pin CLEAR. If the carry bit is SET, the next instruction is executed making the data line pin SET. The data line state now matches the state of the data bit to be sent. The call to the bitdelay subroutine maintains that state for the desired bit length. The decfsz command decrements the value stored in the variable bitcounter (the first time through the value goes from 8 to 7, and so on) and the decremented value is stored back into the variable. If the decremented value is not zero, meaning there are more bits to be sent, the next bit is sent. If all 8 bits have been sent, the goto statement is skipped over. The data line pin is returned to the resting state, SET, by bsf PORTA, 5 and a call to a short delay subroutine to allow the LCD hardware to respond to the new data received completes the serial transmission of the value passed to the LCDOutput subroutine.

Build the Program

Let's see how this all works in the software. Build the program and press **RUN**. The program will stop at the first breakpoint in the LCDOutput subroutine and zero the

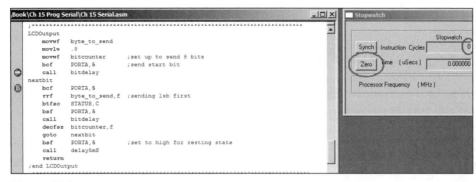

Figure 15-5

Figure 15-6

Figure 15-7

Stopwatch (**Figure 15-5**). Run the program to the next breakpoint and note the time required to complete the call to the bitdelay subroutine (**Figure 15-6**). This portion of the code sends the start bit, which for a baud rate of 9600 baud, the bit length should be 104 µs, the delay of this routine is 100 µs. This difference is a tradeoff as you will see in a minute and produces acceptable timing for this application. Zero the Stopwatch again and run the program again — this will take you through the sending of the first data bit in the stream (**Figure 15-7**). Note that the time required to send the data bit is 107 µs, or 3 µs longer than required for 9600 baud. This is due to the code overhead required to access the bit to be sent, determine its state, set the data pin state to match, check the bit count, and return for the next bit to be sent. Consequently, the data bits will not be exactly time centered at the receiving end, but the timing is well within tolerances for this application, particularly when sending only 8 bits. Sending more bits, or at a higher baud rate (shorter bit time interval), the time delay created by the code overhead might be significant and require a different program architecture to keep within timing tolerances. Continue to run the program through the next and subsequent bits and the time required remains static. Load the program into the PIC16F676.

Putting It Together

Connect the LCD to the PIC16F676 as depicted in the circuit in **Figure 15-8.** The LCD data line is connected to PORTA pin 5. Insert the device in circuit and power it up. You will see "Hello" displayed. Before we leave serial communications, let's take a closer look at those values that are sent to the LCD to display characters.

Remove the two breakpoints in the LCDOutput subroutine and scroll up to the main part of the program. Set a new breakpoint as illustrated in **Figure 15-9** and run the program to this new breakpoint. Look down at the **WATCH** window and note the

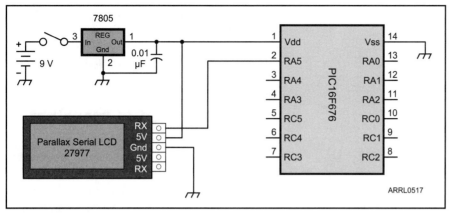

Figure 15-8

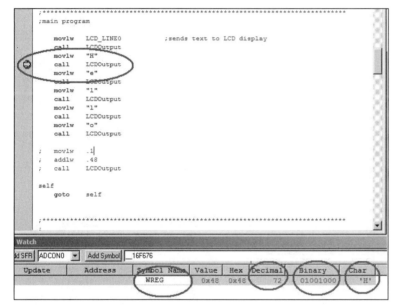

Figure 15-9

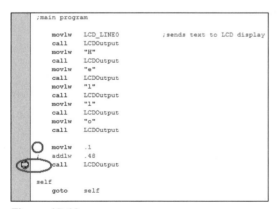

Figure 15-10

contents of the W-register in the various numerical forms. The code loaded the letter "H" into the W-register. The numerical value actually loaded is the ACSII value that represents the letter "H," in this case 72 decimal. *The ASCII code* is a standardized code of numerical values that are used to display alpha numeric characters or to control video displays. If you set additional breakpoints to skip over the calls to the LCDOutput subroutines and view the W-register contents for each letter, you will see the ASCII value for "e" is 101, for "l" is 108, and "o" is 111.

Next remove any breakpoints that you inserted. Remove the comments from the two lines of code that will load the value 1 into the W-register and send that value for display, and set a breakpoint on the call to the LCDOutput subroutine as illustrated in **Figure 15-10**. Build the program, load it into the PIC16F676, install the device into your circuit, and power it up. You would expect to see "Hello1" displayed, but in reality you see "Hello~". Return to the code in *MPLAB IDE* and run the code to the breakpoint (**Figure 15-11**). Note that the W-register contains the decimal value of 1 as commanded, but notice that the character representation of the number 1 is "." not the character "1". What the program sent to the LCD was the numerical value 1 which is the ASCII code for the Start of Heading command. The LCD hardware apparently cannot decode that ASCII command and in turn displayed the character "~" instead. You will need to keep in mind when working with display devices that you need to send the ASCII code representation of numbers, not the numbers themselves. To determine the ASCII code representation of the numbers 0 through 9, simply add 48 to the number value to come up with the ASCII code for that number. So the number 1 is actually the value 49 in ASCII code.

Go back to the code in *MPLAB IDE* and remove the final comment as illustrated in **Figure 15-12**, build the program and run the program to the breakpoint as before. The opcode addlw adds the literal 48 to the contents of the W-register (1) and places the result back into the W-register. This instruction converted the number 1 into the ASCII code representation for "1" and this

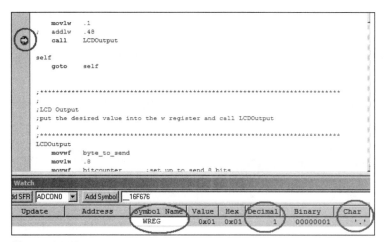

Figure 15-11

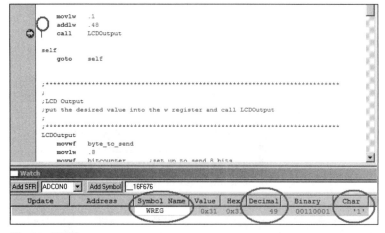

Figure 15-12

is the value that is sent to the LCD for display. Load this modified program into the PIC16F676, install the device in circuit, and power it up. Now you will see "Hello1" displayed.

Data Format Is Important

I am emphasizing the point about ASCII code for a good reason. Frequently data is passed back and forth between devices in ASCII code and not the actual numerical values. It is important to keep track of the format that is being used if you are going to do any mathematical manipulation of the data. For instance, if the devices are using ASCII code to pass numbers, then before any mathematic operations can be done on those numbers, the data must first be converted into the numbers that the ASCII values represent by subtracting 48 from the ASCII value. Then when the mathematics is completed, the results must be converted back into ASCII by adding 48 to the number before the results are sent back to the device.

Pluses and Minuses of Using Delay Subroutines

One final note needs to be addressed. The delay subroutine that is used to generate the bit length in the exercise generated a delay of 100 μs instead of 104 μs. This delay interval was a compromise so that one delay subroutine could be used to generate an "acceptable" data stream that is recognized by the receiving device, in this case the LCD. The start bit was deliberately shortened to compensate for the lengthened data bits that follow (due to the code overhead to detect the state of the individual bits being sent). The final compromise was determined by trial and error. At increased baud rates (shorter bit intervals) the amount of room for compromise would be reduced and more accurate bit lengths required. The delay subroutine was used here specifically for learning about serial communications but more accurate bit lengths can be generated by using the TMR0 or TMR1 interrupt resources. If properly configured and programmed, the overhead code needed for bit manipulation could be accomplished simultaneously while the appropriate starting value is assigned to the timer resource register that is incremented to create the desired bit interval. Additionally, the main program could be accomplishing other tasks while also using the interrupts to manage the serial communications. The code required for the interrupt-based program architecture, however, is not as transparent as the code used in the exercise here. Additionally, if the timing requirements are that critical, the developer might consider using those MCU devices that have serial hardware resources to save development time.

Summary

Asynchronous serial communications involve sending data between devices using a single data line. The advantages of using a serial communications protocol is that only one pin resource is required and the data can be sent as needed without regard for synchronization. The disadvantage is that timing is critical and that specific data packaging criteria must be followed so that the data is received correctly. Those criteria include the sequence that the data bits will be sent (MSB or LSB first), the number of bits, the bit length (baud rate), if a stop bit is used and its duration, and if an additional check sum bit (parity) will be used. This chapter focused on a common serial communications protocol of a start bit, 8 data bits sent LSB first, no stop or parity bits, and a baud rate of 9600 baud. Some MCU devices have dedicated hardware for handling serial communications in parallel with other MCU operations. Other devices, such as the PIC16F676 which is used for this text, require that serial communications be handled in software and those techniques were detailed in this chapter.

Review Questions

15.1 In looking at the bitdelay subroutine in the example code, what value would be loaded into the count variable to produce a delay appropriate for 2400 baud serial communications?

15.2 What code adjustments are required if the data stream was increased from 8-bits to 16-bits? What else must be considered if there is a significant increase in the number of data bits that are transmitted at one time (hint: think about the bit time interval produced by the delay routines and the code overhead contribution to the delay)?

15.3 The *MPLAB Simulator* can be used to predict the length of a delay produced by code, what other factor also contributes to these timing delays? How can you determine the actual timing of a serial data stream?

15.4 What is(are) the ASCII code(s) required to send the number 127 to the LCD?

15.5 What is the code that you would send to the LCD to clear the display and move the cursor to the upper left corner?

15.6 What adjustment to the exercise code would be required if the LCD used data sent with the MSB sent first?

15.7 In the previous chapter on Interrupts, the temporary storage of the contents of the w-register and the STATUS registers was emphasized. Why would that strategy be important if the timer interrupt resources are used to generate the bit interval delays?

15.8 In the program exercise, the individual bit being sent was rotated through the carry bit that is included in the STATUS register. What code alternative might be used to determine the state of the bit to be transmitted?

Serial Peripheral

Interface

Communications

Objective: To learn how to configure and use the resources of the PIC16F676 for basic Serial Peripheral Interface Bus communications. This chapter will describe in detail the serial programming techniques used in the SPI™ communications protocol to communicate with and control external SPI based devices. The programming exercise will use the MCP41010 Digital Potentiometer to practically illustrate SPI communications.

Reading: *MCP41XXX/42XXX Single/Dual Digital Potentiometer with SPI™ Interface Data Sheet*, pages 1, 6, 12-14 and 17-19.
Program: Program Files/Ch 1a6 Program/SPI

Alternative Serial Communication Protocol

This chapter covers an alternative serial communication protocol that allows for duplex communications between a master and one or more slave devices. Though the Motorola named *Serial Peripheral Interface Bus* (SPI) communications scheme may not be an official industry standard, it is widely used. The SPI protocol requires up to four signal lines between devices to make the communication connection versus the one line required for asynchronous serial communications. These signal lines include a chip (or device) select, a transmitting data line, a receiving data line, and a clock line. The collection of the four signal lines make up the communication bus specified by SPI.

The MCP41010 Digital Potentiometer

The exercises in this chapter will use the MCP41010 Digital Potentiometer which uses basic SPI communications for MCU control of the device. The digital potentiometer has an internal wiper with 256 possible positions that taps a 10K Ω resistor ladder. The position of the wiper is dictated by the data byte that is shifted into the controlling register of the device, and thereby setting the resistance at the *wiper output pin* between 0 and 10K Ω (in 256 steps). The resistance increment is approximately 40 Ω (but there is also some resistance in the wiper connection itself, specified at 52 Ω). The device documentation details not only the hardware specifications of the potentiometer but also details the hardware for communication with the device. There are three required signal lines for controlling the device; a *chip select line*, CS, a *serial clock line*, SCK and a *serial data input line*, SI. These three lines will be connected to PORT I/O pin resources on the PIC16F676. (Because the communications with this particular device is one-way only, the fourth signal line specified by SPI is not needed.) When selecting an SPI based peripheral device to be controlled by an MCU, you must consider the signal line specifications of the device hardware.

The CS Line

The CS line is used to signal the external device that the clock and associated data on the SI line are intended for the device. This allows single clock and data lines to be shared with multiple devices (as long as those device pins are in tri-state when the device is not selected, otherwise a digital high or low state would conflict with signals sent to parallel devices). The documentation must be reviewed to determine if the device is selected when the CS line is high or low — both arrangements are used by SPI based devices. In the case of the MCP41010 device, it is selected when the CS line is low — the associated clock and data lines go to tri-state when the CS line is high.

The Clock

Next, you need to consider at what point during the clock cycle (either on the rising or falling edge) that the data bit presented on the SI line is clocked into the data register of the device. The resting state of the clock, either high or low, also may be a factor. In some devices, the data may be clocked-in on the rising edge of the clock, and clocked-out on the falling edge, or vice versa. This arrangement allows for daisy-chaining devices. For the MCP41010 device, the data is clocked-in on the rising edge of the clock signal. The resting state of the clock signal can be either high or low, but this must be considered in software to make sure that the first bit of data is on the data line when the first rising edge of the clock occurs. In the sister device of the MCP41010, the dual potentiometer MCP42010, the hardware alternatively allows for daisy-chaining devices and the data is presented on the device data output line on the falling edge of the clock signal (so that the data will be properly clocked in a second device by the master clock signal).

Notice that there is no mention of frequency or period of the clock signal, there is no baud rate to consider in SPI because the clock synchronizes and drives the process, not timing. The only clock frequency specification that needs to be considered is the hardware limitations of the MCU to produce a clock signal and limitations of the device to respond to the clock signal. Often there are response time limitations that must be considered. In the case of the MCP41010, the maximum clock frequency is specified at 10 MHz which is not a factor for the exercises in this chapter.

Sequence of Bits

Finally, you must determine the sequence of bits that is required by the device, either MSB or LSB first. In previous exercises dealing with the LCD, the sequence was LSB first, in the case of the MCP41010 device, data needs to be sent MSB first.

MCP41010 Device Summary

In summary, for the MCP41010 device the resting state of the clock signal is low, the device is selected when the CS signal is low, the data is clocked in on the rising edge of the clock signal — MSB first — and the data is latched into the internal register of the device when the CS signal returns to high.

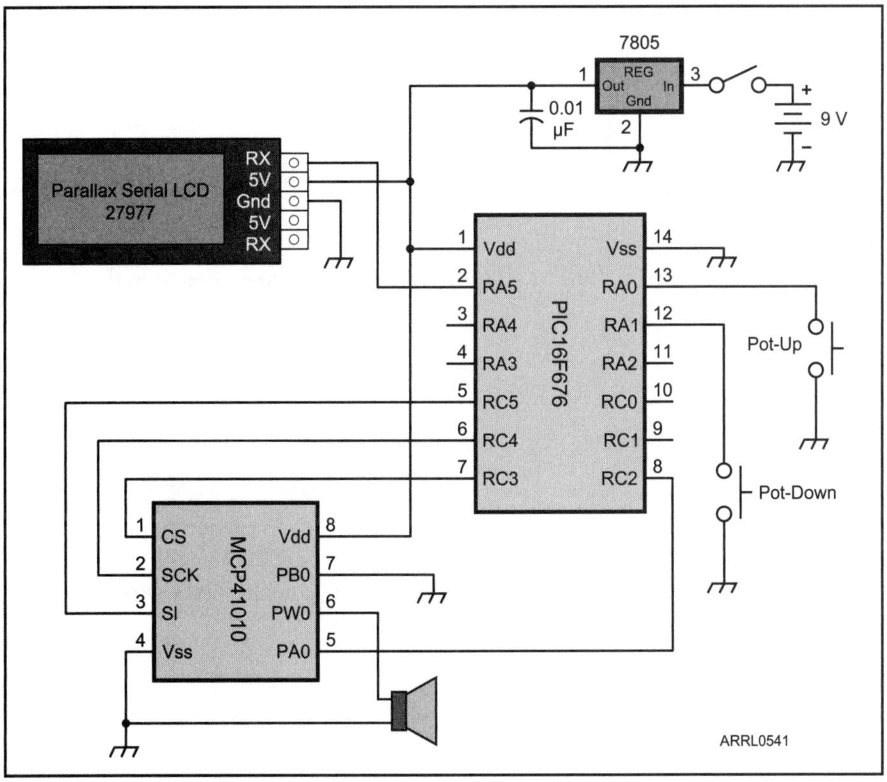

Load Project and Build Circuit

Load the project **Program Files/Ch 16 Program/SPI** into *MPLAB IDE*. Build the circuit for the following exercise as depicted in **Figure 16-1** and illustrated in **Figure 16-2**. The circuit includes two push button switches tied to PORTA I/O pins that are configured

Figure 16-1 — Serial Peripheral Interface (SPI) Synchronous Serial Data Link circuit diagram.

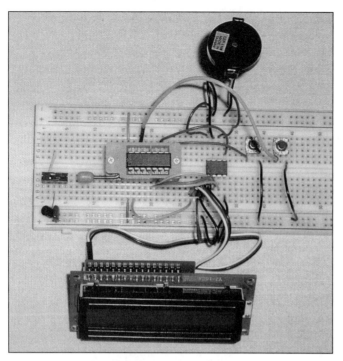

Figure 16-2 — The SPI Project.

as digital inputs with weak pull-up resisters enabled. The LCD is connected to PORTA, 5. The MCP41010 CS, SCK and SI pins are connected to the PORTC I/O pins 3, 4 and 5 respectively. These pins are configured as digital output pins. The TMR0 resource is set up to generate a 1000 Hz tone in the speaker. The speaker is connected to the digital potentiometer wiper pin which acts like a volume control for the tone.

Observe the Program Code

Turn your attention to the program code as it is being reviewed. The main program checks if one of the push buttons is pressed (for increasing or decreasing the volume). When one of the push buttons is pressed, the TMR0 interrupt is enabled and the tone is generated. In addition, the data value that is sent to the MCP41010 that sets the volume is either incremented or decremented as long as the button is pressed. The combined write command and data bytes are sent via the SPI subroutine to change the potentiometer and tone volume.

The Initialization section of the code should be familiar to you already. Scroll down to the main part of the program. The first lines of code set up the TMR0 register, SETS the CS line to disable the MCP41010 chip, CLEARS the SCK line, the resting state of the clock and sends some labeling text to the LCD. The main_loop section of the program reads the state on pins connected to the push button switches and jumps to the appropriate label to service the pin that is pressed:

```
main_loop
     btfss     PORTA,up
     goto      up_volume
     btfss     PORTA,down
     goto      down_volume
     goto      main_loop
```

We'll take a look at only the up_volume routines because both are similar. The portion of the code below sets up the TMR0 resource for interrupts to generate the 1000 Hz tone.

```
up_volume
     movlw     TMR0_scale
     movwf     TMR0
     bcf       INTCON,T0IF
     bsf       INTCON,T0IE
     bsf       INTCON,GIE
```

The repeat_up loop increments the data value that sets the potentiometer wiper position.

```
repeat_up
     incf      volume,f
     btfsc     STATUS,Z
     decf      volume,f
```

The btfsc opcode checks to see if the volume variable overflowed to zero when it was incremented. If an overflow occurred, the variable is decremented to keep it at a maximum of 255. Without this step, the volume of the tone would loop through the full volume range going up. There are a few lines of code that send the value of the volume data byte to the LCD for display.

The Command Byte

The data sent to the MCP41010 is 16 bits, or 2 bytes in length. The first 8 bits make up the command byte. In this simple device, there is only one command byte — to write a data byte that sets the wiper position on the potentiometer. The bit makeup of command byte can be found in the device documentation. The command byte to write to data to the MCP41010 is b'00010001'. Any other command byte will be ignored by the device. The data byte that determines the potentiometer wiper position then follows the command byte with the MSB sent first. For instance, to set the potentiometer wiper to the center position with a resistance of 5 kΩ, the data byte would be 128 (b'10000000'), which is ½ of 255 — the top position on the resistance ladder. The data stream that includes the command and data bytes would be b'00010001 10000000'. The device must receive all 16 bits or the command is discarded. Continue to scroll down through the code to see how this is done. While you are reviewing the code, take a look at the code flow diagram in **Figure 16-3**.

The bcf command sets the CS line low to signal the MCP41010 that is being addressed. The movlw instruction loads the bit pattern b'00010001' into the W-register. This bit pattern was defined and assigned to the label pot0 in the definition section of the code. The command byte is passed to the spi subroutine through the W-register.

```
bcf      PORTC, CS
movlw    pot0
call     spi
```

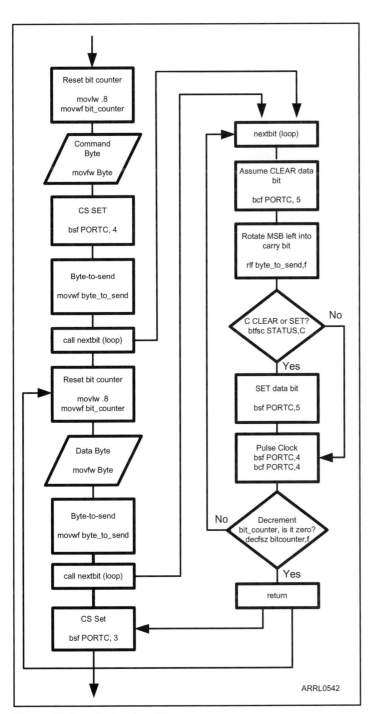

Figure 16-3 — Code Flow Diagram.

Scroll down to the spi subroutine, this is where the SPI communication work is done:

```
spi
        movwf       data_to_send
        movlw       .8
        movwf       bitcounter
trans_loop
        bcf         PORTC,SI
        rlf         data_to_send,f
        btfsc       STATUS, C
        bsf         PORTC,SI
        bsf         PORTC,SCK
        bcf         PORTC,SCK
        decfsz      bitcounter,f
        goto        trans_loop
        return
```

The byte to be sent is transferred from the w-register into an intra-loop working register data_to_send. The bitcounter variable is loaded with the number of bits to be sent. The bit to be sent is assumed to be CLEAR by using the bcf opcode. The first bit (MSB) to be sent is rotated left out of the data_to_send variable into the STATUS, C bit with the rlf instruction. Note that in the previous chapter on asynchronous serial communications, the data was sent LSB first which required that data rotate right into the carry bit. The carry bit is checked, and if CLEAR, the next instruction is skipped. The SI line is now in the corresponding state to the bit being sent. The SCK line is toggled high then low to latch the bit into the MCP41010 data register on the rising edge of the clock. The bitcounter is then decremented and checked if it is zero, if not, the loop continues to send the next bit, when done, the control of the program returns to the calling code.

The volume data byte is then loaded into the w-register and it is passed to the spi subroutine for transmission.

```
        movfw       volume
        call        spi
        bsf         PORTC,CS
        btfss       PORTA,up
        goto        repeat_up

        bcf         INTCON,GIE       ;if all done, disable tone
        bcf         INTCON,T0IE
        bcf         INTCON,T0IF
        goto        main_loop
```

The bsf command SETS CS to signal the MCP41010 to set the potentiometer wiper and await further commands. The state of the push button is checked with the btfss command. If it is still pressed (CLEAR) then the volume up process is repeated. If the button is released (SET) then the tone is turned off by disabling the TMR0 interrupt and the main program loop continues.

On a side note, scroll down into the LCDOutput subroutine. This is the routine that sends the characters to be displayed on the LCD via serial communication. You have studied this subroutine in the last chapter, but notice that in this version of the subroutine, instead of calling another subroutine to generate the bit time interval delay for 9600 baud transmission, the delay code is included in two locations within the subroutine, which seems a little inefficient. It is, but it also is required to work around the limitation imposed by the 8-level Stack in the PIC16F676. When the bit delay code is called as a subroutine, the Stack overflows and corrupts the program counter upon return from the subroutine and the program crashes. Imbedding the delay code within the LCDOutput subroutine prevents the Stack from overflowing. This is one thing to keep in mind if your programs crash even though they seem to work just fine when testing them in *MPLAB* Simulator. It is easy to over use nested subroutine calls and quickly overwhelm the Stack.

It is time to load the program into the PIC16F676, install it in the circuit, and power it up. The LCD should display the starting POT setting of 128. When you press the **UP** button, the tone will start and the volume will increase from the mid-volume to the maximum, coincident with the increasing POT setting number. Release the button and the tone will stop. Press the **DOWN** button. The tone will come on again and the volume will decrease from the previous setting to the minimum volume. This is similar to the operation of the volume controls of most modern electronics.

Summary

SPI techniques allow the user to serially pass information between a master device and multiple slave devices in both directions without regard to stringent timing specifications. The tradeoff when compared to asynchronous serial communication techniques is that it can take up to four signal lines to control the flow of data. In this chapter, a simplified, simplex (one direction), form of SPI was used to study the technique that required only three signal lines between the MCU and an MCP41010 Digital Potentiometer. Those three lines included a chip select line (CS), a clock line (SCK) and a data line (SI). In SPI, the CS line is CLEARED to gain the attention of the slave device, the command and data bytes are applied to the SI line one bit at a time (in proper sequence: MSB or LSB first), the clock is toggled to latch the data bits into the slave device's data register and finally the CS line is SET to cause the command to be executed by the slave device.

Review Questions

16.1 List the advantages and disadvantages of each serial communication technique (Asymmetrical and SPI).

16.2 If one SPI device needs a CLEAR CS line and another SPI device needs a SET CS line to operate, can these two devices share all three signal lines (CS, SCK and SI)?

16.3 If the wiper resistance in the MCP41010 is specified to be 52 Ω, what resistance would you expect when you command the wiper position to b'00000000'?

16.4 What line(s) of code would need to be changed if the attached SPI device required commands sent in LSB first format?

16.5 For the sake of code clarity, you decide that you would like to treat the command byte and the data byte as a single 16-bit variable with the labels dataH and dataL. To do so, write an amended SPI subroutine that would send all the data bits in one subroutine instead of two passes through one subroutine as was done in this exercise (once to send the command byte and then again to send the data byte). Hint: look to see how this was done in the b2_BCD subroutine (binary to BCD conversion subroutine), loop16 loop.

Working
With Data

Objective: To learn how to configure and use resources of the PIC16F676 to drive a 7-segment, single digit LED display and to use a data table within software to drive the display to generate numerical digits.

Reading: *PIC16F630/676 Data Sheet*, page 85 and *Single Digit Display Data Sheet* 335090.
Program: **Program Files/Ch 17 Program/7_Segment LED**.

The interface between the MCU device and the user is very software intensive and requires a lot of hardware resources. In previous programming examples, you have used serial communications techniques and data tables to display prompt messages on an LCD display. In this chapter, a technique to use data tables to generate numerical digits displayed on 7-segment LED displays will be explored.

LED Display Unit

A 7-segment LED display unit contains 7 LEDs arranged so that when the individual LEDs are turned on in the proper arrangement, a numeric from 0 through 9 is formed on the display. The display units come in two basic forms, common anode and common cathode. Regardless of the type of display, these units require a minimum of 7 MCU I/O resources to form the numbers (additional I/O resources if decimal point LEDs are required). More than one display unit can be multiplexed to increase the digit count (for instance four 7-segment LED display units to form a clock), but this would require an additional I/O pin resource for each digit, which could quickly limit the number of digits that could be handled by a single MCU device.

Anode Display and Cathode Display

In a common anode display, a single current source is required — the MCU I/O resources are used to provide the ground path for the individual LED segments by CLEARING the I/O pin. In a common cathode display, a single ground is required — the MCU I/O resources are used to provide the current source for the individual LED segments by SETTING the I/O pin. There are advantages and disadvantages to each configuration. Regardless of the configuration chosen for the display unit, consideration must be given to the current handling capabilities of the MCU individual I/O pins as well as the total current handling of the device. For the case of the PIC16F676, the maximum source or sink current handling capabilities of the individual pins is 25 mA and a total current for all I/O pins combined is 200 mA.

The Use of 7-Segment LED Displays

We are going to demonstrate and explore in this chapter the use of 7-segment LED displays with only a single digit. Build the circuit as illustrated in **Figure 17-1** and **Figure 2**. The display unit used in this circuit is a common cathode type. The PORTA and PORTC I/O pins connected to the individual LEDs of the display provide the current source through current limiting resistors. The approximate current required for each LED can be estimated by the use of Ohms law. The voltage provided at the I/O pin is 5 V. The current through the current limiting 470 Ω resistor would be approximately 0.01 A (5 V / 470 Ω = 0.011 A). This value is well within the specified current limits for the individual I/O pins of the PIC16F676 (25 mA) and also well within the total current handling capacity of the device (200 mA). If higher current handling capacities were required, transistor switches could be employed.

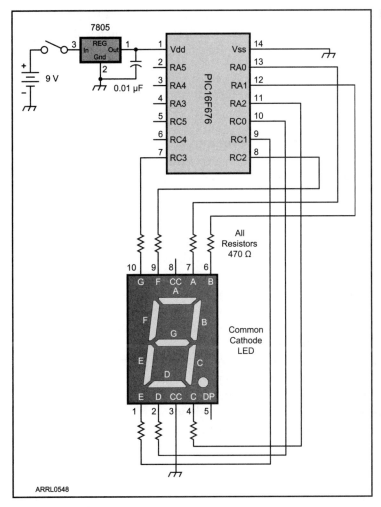

Figure 17-1

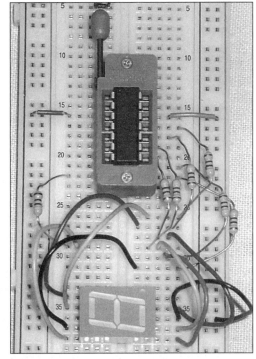

Figure 17-2

Survey of Contents of Table 17-1

Review the contents of **Table 17-1** which lists the sequence in which the individual LEDs of the display unit need to be illuminated to form the desired number digit. The individual LEDs are labeled A thorough G. Reviewing the data sheet for the display unit will tell you the specific pin connected to the individual LEDs. The bottom rows of the table identify the PIC16F676 I/O resource and physical pin connected to the individual LEDs. The left-hand column lists the number to be displayed. The columns below the letter designator for the individual LEDs list the state applied to the connected I/O resource to generate the number. A "1" applied to an LED would apply 5 V to that LED and it would illuminate. Conversely, a "0" would ground the LED and keep it off. The column on

Table 17-1

7-Segment LED Truth Table

Digit	G	F	E	D	C	B	A	Decimal
0	0	1	1	1	1	1	1	63
1	0	0	0	0	1	1	0	6
2	1	0	1	1	0	1	1	91
3	1	0	0	1	1	1	1	79
4	1	1	0	0	1	1	0	102
5	1	1	0	1	1	0	1	109
6	1	1	1	1	1	0	1	125
7	0	0	0	0	1	1	1	7
8	1	1	1	1	1	1	1	127
9	1	1	0	0	1	1	1	103
PORT# bit	RC3	RC2	RC1	RC0	RA2	RA1	RA0	
Pin#	7	8	9	10	11	12	13	

the far right lists the decimal value that equals the binary representation of the 7-bit bit pattern required to generate the number displayed. The right-hand column will be used in the data table in software that will be called to generate the numbers displayed on the 7-segment display unit.

Project

Load the project **Program Files/Ch 17 Program/7_Segment LED** into *MPLAB IDE* and display the .asm file contents while we explore the code. Scroll down to the bottom of the code in the subroutine table_get that includes the data table labeled simply "table."

```
table_get
    addwf PCL,f ;add the offset to the program counter to jump to character
table dt   .63, .6, .91, .79, .102, .109, .125, .7, .127, .103
```

The data table is formed by the use of the dt directive. Recall from Chapter 7 that the dt directive generates a series of retlw instructions in a data table that will load the w-register with the 8-bit value of the offset argument and return that value in the w-register to the calling program code when the retlw opcode is executed. The offset for the desired value in the data table is added to the low byte of the program counter which causes a jump to the desired value and the retlw opcode is executed. For example, if the "9" digit is to be displayed, the value of 9 is added to the program counter with the addwf PCL, f instruction and a jump is made to the 10th position in the data table (remember to start counting from 0). This generates a retlw with the w-register loaded with the literal decimal value 103.

Scroll up to the main part of the program.

```
main
    movlw    .10
    movwf    counter

next_count
    decf     counter
    movfw    counter
    call     table_get
```

Here the starting value is loaded into the variable counter which will be used to count through the digits 0 through 9 for display. The starting value of 10 is loaded the first time through because the counter is decremented within the loop so the first digit displayed will be 9, not 10. Within the next_count loop, the value of counter is decremented and loaded into the w-register before the call table_get instruction is executed to retrieve the desired bit pattern to generate the number digit.

```
    movwf    temp
    andlw    b'00000111'    ;mask upper 4 bits
    movwf    PORTA
    rrf      temp,f         ;shift out lower 3 bits
    rrf      temp,f
    rrf      temp,f
    movfw    temp
    andlw    b'00001111'
    movwf    PORTC
```

```
call        wait1sec
```

Upon return of the program execution to the main program with the bit pattern in the w-register, the bit pattern is stored in a working variable location labeled temp. The hardware connections between the MCU and the LED display are set up so that PORTA pins RA0, RA1, and RA2 are connected to LED segments A, B, and C respectively. To extract the bits for LEDs A, B, and C, the andlw opcode is used to mask those bits and convert all the other bits to zero before the bit pattern is loaded into the PORTA register to illuminate the appropriate LEDs. The three rrf opcodes rotate right the bits for LEDs A, B, and C out of position and the bits for LEDs D, E, F, and G into the lowest nibble of the byte temp. The contents of temp is then loaded into the w-register and the andlw opcode is used to mask the lower 4-bits and convert all the other bits to zero. This bit pattern is then loaded into the PORTC register to illuminate the appropriate LEDs to complete the number to be displayed. A delay of 1 second is then executed to give time for the number to be displayed before the next digit is displayed.

```
movf        counter
btfss       STATUS,Z
goto        next_count
goto        main
```

By simply moving the contents of counter back into counter, you can check if the value of counter has been decremented to zero. The btfss opcode skips the next opcode in code if the value of counter is zero and the main program repeats. If counter is not zero, the next digit to be displayed is generated by the next iteration of the next_count loop.

You can confirm the operation of the code by using the *MPLAB Simulator* and the **WATCH** window.

Build and Load the Program

Build and load the program into the PIC16F676. Install the device in the circuit and apply power. The 7-segment display will count down the digits from 9 through 0 and repeat the process until power is removed.

Summary

User interfaces with MCUs are software and hardware intensive. The use of data tables can reduce the amount of software overhead required to display messages or in this case to display a digit on a 7-segment LED. There are two kinds of 7-segment displays, common anode and common cathode. The user needs to consider the total current handling capacity of the MCU. The dt directive is used to create what is essentially a table of retlw opcodes that will load the w-register with the table entry and return to the calling program with the w-register intact. By adding an offset value to the program counter inside the data table subroutine, jumps to the desired data entry in the table are executed.

Review Question

17.1 Explain how you could multiplex four 7-segment display units to display all digits at one time. Draw a circuit diagram for the required circuit. Can this be accomplished with the PIC16F676 device?

Putting it All Together

Objective: To present a practical application that utilizes many of the software techniques used throughout this text. The culminating project is a Morse code electronic keyer.

Program: **Program Files/Ch 18 Program/Keyer**

Putting New Knowledge Together in a Final Project

You have come a long way during this journey to learn the basics of MCU programming. It is now time to tie many of the bits and pieces together in one culminating project to illustrate how you can develop your own PIC-MCU based project. The final project is a Morse code electronic keyer. You may or may not be a ham radio operator or interested in communicating with Morse code, regardless, the programming fundamentals and the use of the PIC16F676 resources is the real purpose of the project.

Morse Code and Keyers

Morse code is one of the first means of communication by electronic digital technology. The characters of the alphabet, numbers, punctuation and a few procedural signs are formed by a series of dit (dots) and dashes (dahs) that are transmitted by some medium between the sender and receiver. The basis of Morse code is the time length unit of the dit. The dash has a length of three dit time units. The time space between the dits and dahs that make up the character "byte" is one dit time unit. The time space between characters within a word is three dit time units (or one dah length). The time spacing between words in a sentence is seven dit time units. Morse characters can be formed by a hand key or switch that is turned on by the operator with the appropriate on and off-time. There are a number of mechanical and electronic devices that can be employed to assist the operator in making the Morse characters. These devices are mainly employed to improve the quality of the characters being sent, increase transmission speed or reduce operator fatigue. One such device is an electronic keyer. The electronic keyer has two input switch connections, one when closed will send a series of dits and the other that will send a series of dahs. The operator manipulates these switches alternately to form the Morse characters of dits and dahs. The electronic keyer is an excellent candidate for an MCU based project.

MCU Resources Needed for This Project

The first step in developing this project is to determine the MCU resources needed for the keyer while documenting the interconnections between components on a circuit diagram. For the keyer project:

a. Two input assigned I/O pin resources with weak pull-up resistors are required for the dit and dah switches.

b. One output assigned I/O pin resource is required to drive a transistor switch and indicator LED to actually key the transmitter equipment.

c. Another output assigned I/O pin resource is required to drive another transistor switch and indicator LED to enable or turn on the transmitter equipment to put it in the transmit mode — this is generally called the push-to-talk (PTT) line.

d. One output assigned I/O pin resource connected to a speaker is required to develop an audible tone that will provide Morse code feedback to the operator.

e. One ADC resource that is connected to a variable resistor that will allow the operator to control the dit time base unit length by varying the voltage on the ADC pin.

f. Finally, the TMR0 resource will be used to generate a 1000 Hz side tone to make the Morse bits audible, and the TMR1 resource will be used to hold the transmitter PTT line on for a specified period between Morse characters.

The Electronic Keyer Circuit

The circuit diagram of the electronic keyer with this resource configuration is depicted in **Figure 18-1**.

Build up this circuit on the prototyping board or if you have purchased the associated kit of parts for this text, the circuit can be built on the circuit board provided. Refer to the construction manual for this circuit board in Appendix C. The components for this project have been used in the circuits presented in the exercises throughout this text. Next load the project **Program Files/Ch 18 Program/keyer** into *MPLAB IDE*. View the contents of the code in the keyer.asm file for the following discussion of the application code.

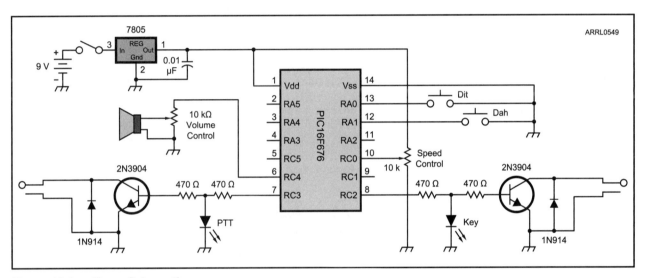

Figure 18-1 — Keyer Schematic

Discussion of the Application Code

Scroll down to the device initialization section of the code. You now should be able to compare the initialization code instructions to the listing of resources required above.

```
Init
        BANKSEL      Bank1
        call         0x3FF          ;retrieve factory calibration value
        movwf        OSCCAL

        BANKSEL      Bank0          ;select bank0
        clrf         PORTA          ;clear port bus
        clrf         PORTC
        movlw        b'00000111'    ;comparator disconnected, low
                                    ;power state
        movwf        CMCON
        movlw        b'11000000'    ;globals enabled, peripherals
                                    ;enabled,TMR0 disabled
        movwf        INTCON
        movlw        b'00010001'    ;left justified, Vdd ref, RC0 has ADC, ADC
                                    ;Stop, ADC turned on
        movwf        ADCON0
        movlw        b'00110001'    ;TMR1 prescale 1:8, internal clock, TMR1 ON
        movwf        T1CON
        BANKSEL      Bank1          ;select bank1
        movlw        b'00000001'    ;TMR0 set-up: pull-ups enabled,X,internal
                                    ;clk, X, pre-scale tmr0, pre-scale 1:2
        movwf        OPTION_REG
        movlw        b'00010000'    ;Fosc/8 for ADC
        movwf        ADCON1
        movlw        b'00000011'    ;RA0 and RA1 as input for paddle RA2
        movwf        TRISA          ;program PORTA
        movlw        b'00000011'    ;weak pull-ups on RA0, RA1
        movwf        WPUA
        movlw        b'00000001'    ;RC0 input for ADC
        movwf        TRISC          ;program PORTC
        movlw        b'00010000'    ;RC0 analog, all other digital
        movwf        ANSEL
        movlw        b'00000001'    ;TMR1 interrupt enabled
        movwf        PIE1
        BANKSEL      Bank0          ;back to bank0
        clrf         PORTC
```

Code for Closing the Key Switches

Scroll down to the main section of the code. Here you will find the code that we will monitor for the closure of the key switches and take appropriate action through subroutines.

```
get_key_loop
        movf         PORTA,f
        btfsc        STATUS,Z
        goto         iombic         ;use goto's here to avoid overwhelming
                                    ;limited stack space
        btfss        PORTA,0
        goto         send_dits
        btfss        PORTA,1
        goto         send_dahs
        goto         get_key_loop
```

The first opcode `movf` simply takes the contents of the PORTA register and loads in back into itself, but during the process, if the PORTA register is zero (both the dit and dah switches are closed) the STATUS, Z flag is SET and a jump to the iambic subroutine is made. If the PORTA register is not zero, then the individual switches are checked for closure and appropriate `gotos` are executed. As indicated in the comments, gotos are used instead of calls to avoid Stack overflow.

Set Up of Timer Resources for Sending Dit

The two timer resources are set up to generate the 1000 Hz tone (TMR0) and to generate the time interval that will hold the transmitter on (the PTT line) between characters. The voltage applied to the ADC resource will be used to determine the length of the dit delay. These timer resources are configured to generate interrupts and the individual interrupts are enabled as required within the subroutines. Scroll down to the send_dit subroutine.

```
send_dit
        bsf         PORTC, PTT          ;turn on PTT
        bsf         PORTC, key          ;close key
        clrf        TMR1H
        clrf        TMR1L
        bcf         PIR1,TMR1IF
        bsf         T1CON,TMR1ON
        bcf         INTCON,T0IF
        bsf         INTCON,T0IE
        goto        $+2                 ;skip over the bcf PORTC,key line
send_space
        bcf         PORTC, key          ;open key
        call        get_adc
        clrf        h_byte
        movwf       dit_count_low
dit_loop
;delay1mS                              ;delay routine contained here instead of
                                       ;using a called subroutine to avoid stack
                                       ;overflow issues

        movlw       .198
        movwf       count1
        nop
        goto        $+1
        goto        $+1
dly1mS1
        goto        $+1
        decfsz      count1, f
        goto        dly1mS1

        decfsz      dit_count_low, f
        goto        dit_loop
        bcf         INTCON,T0IF
        bcf         INTCON,T0IE
        return
```

When a dit is sent, the transmitter is put in the transmit mode by causing the switching transistor to conduct and close the PTT control of the transmitter by SETTING the RC3 pin and then the key line is also switched on by SETTING the RC2 pin. The TMR1 associated registers and flags are set up for a time interval interrupt to keep the transmitter PTT line on between Morse characters and TMR1 is enabled. Similarly, the TMR0 resource is also set up and enabled and the audio tone begins. Because the dit and space between bits of the Morse character are the same time interval, the same time delay code is used for both. However, during the dit time interval the transmitter needs to be keyed, during the space time interval the transmitter needs to be un-keyed. The instruction goto $+2 skips over the instruction that un-keys the transmitter during the dit time interval. The call get_adc subroutine retrieves the left justified ADC value that is determined by the setting of the variable resistor connected to the ADC resource. This value then is used to determine the number of iterations that the 1 ms delay loop is executed (nested loops) by the use of the dit_count_low counter variable. The area of the code labeled delay1mS should look familiar to you. This is the same code that generally is contained in the delay library of code. To avoid issues with Stack overflow, this delay code is included in the main body of the program code to avoid having to use subroutine calls to access the code. In this project the overall length of the program code is not restrictive. Once the dit delay is completed, the tone is stopped by disabling the TMR0 resource. If the dit time interval was intended to be the space between bits of the Morse character, the transmitter key line would need to be switched off. This is accomplished with the instruction bcf PORTC, key (that you will recall is skipped with the use of goto $+2 in the dit time interval use of this code).

Sending the Dah

The same basic code sequence is used when the dah is being sent, however, the dah is three times the length of the dit time interval so code needs to be added to the dah sequence to increase the time interval by a factor of three. Scroll to the send_dash subroutine and take note of the section of that code labeled x3 (for times 3).

```
x3
        movfw   l_byte      ;store a copy of the low byte in temporary
                            ;variable dash
        movwf   dash
        bcf     STATUS, C   ;make sure the carry bit is clear
        rlf     dash,w      ;multiplying by 2 with overrun in carry bit
        rlf     h_byte      ;multiply by 2 with carry bit placed in LSB
        bcf     STATUS, C   ;make sure the carry bit is clear
        addwf   l_byte,f    ;add in the original low byte to make times 3
        btfsc   STATUS, C   ;check if there was a carry, if not skip the
                            ;increment of the high byte
        incf    h_byte
```

This section of the code takes the dit time interval as determined by the setting of the variable resistor and retrieved by the get_adc subroutine and multiplies it by three. This is accomplished by multiplying the value by two and adding the value to the product. The rlf opcode multiplies the value by two (with any carry loaded into the h_byte through the STATUS, C bit). The original ADC value is then added with addwf and again, any carry that results from this operation is added to the h_byte variable. This value, now three times the value required to generate a dit time interval, is used in the nested delay loop to generate the dah time interval.

Scroll to the interrupt_service subroutine section of the code.

```
interrupt_service
        movwf     w_temp              ;copy w reg into a temporary variable
        swapf     STATUS, w           ;using swap here because it does not affect
                                      ;STATUS
        movwf     status_temp         ;copy swapped STATUS into temporary
                                      ;variable
        btfsc     PIR1,TMR1IF         ;check if TMR1 caused interrupt
        goto      PTT_service         ;if so, turn off PTT
        bcf       INTCON,T0IF         ;clear TMR0 interrupt
        movlw     TMR0_scale          ;reset TMR0 scaling
        movwf     TMR0
        movlw     b'00010000'         ;set up to toggle RC4
        xorwf     PORTC, f
        bcf       INTCON, T0IF        ;clear TMR0 interrupt
        goto      return_interrupt    ;to not affect TMR1 and the PTT line
```

The first part of the code that stores the contents of the w-register and the STATUS register should look familiar to you. There are two interrupts enabled in this application. The btfsc PIR1, TMR1IF instruction is used to check the TMR1 interrupt flag to determine if the interrupt was generated from TMR1. If not, the interrupt, by default, must have been generated by TMR0. If the interrupt was from TMR0, the code toggles the I/O resource that drives the speaker to generate the tone and the TMR0 resource is reset for the next interrupt. If the interrupt was generated by TMR1, then the PTT line needs to be serviced.

```
PTT_service                           ;called when PPT time is expired
        btfsc     PORTC, key          ;if key is still down reset PTT
        goto      reset_PTT
        bcf       PORTC, PTT          ;turn off PTT
        bcf       T1CON,TMR1ON        ;turn off TMR1
        bcf       PORTC,4             ;make sure speaker I/O line is low to reduce
                                      ;current consumption

        movlw     b'01000000'         ;allow peripheral interrupts from TMR1
        movwf     INTCON
;
reset_PTT
        movlw     b'00000011'
        xorwf     PORTA, w
        btfss     STATUS, Z
        bsf       PORTC, PTT
        bcf       PIR1,TMR1IF         ;clear TMR1 interrupt flag
```

In the TMR1 interrupt service section of the code, the state of the transmitter key line is checked. If the key line is closed the PTT line needs to be maintained in the closed state also and the TMR1 interrupt is reset. If the key line is open (turned off), then the PTT line is opened because the specified time interval has expired (by virtue of the interrupt). The TMR1 interrupt is disabled until the next time either the dit or dah switch is closed. The interrupt_service routine is closed by returning the w-register and STATUS register to their pre-interrupt values and the enabled interrupts are globally enabled with the retfie opcode.

The last section of the code to be discussed is inside the get_adc subroutine.

```
get_adc
    bsf             ADCON0,GO           ;set GO bit to begin ADC conversion
wait_ADC
    btfsc           ADCON0,NOT_DONE     ;check if ADC complete (cleared
                                        ;bit)
    goto            wait_ADC            ;if not, loop and wait until clear

    movlw           .252                ;low side limit for resistor value
    subwf           ADRESH, w
    btfss           STATUS, C
    goto            check_low_limit
    movlw           .252
    movwf           l_byte
    return
check_low_limit
    movlw           .24                 ;high side limit for resistor value
    subwf           ADRESH, w
    btfss           STATUS, C
    goto            exit_ADC
    movfw           ADRESH
    movwf           l_byte
    return

exit_ADC
    movlw           .24
    movwf           l_byte
    return
```

Only the top 8-bits of the 10-bit ADC value are used to determine the dit time interval. The lower 2-bits are truncated by using the left hand justification of the ADC registers and loading the top 8-bits into l_byte and clearing the value in h_byte. The first part of the code loops until the ADC conversion is completed. It was found through experimentation and development of this project that the highest and lowest values of the ADC were not usable for generating Morse code, consequently, a software trap was developed to eliminate those ADC values above 252 and those below 24. For those values above 252, the literal 252 is subtracted, using subwf, from the ADC value in ADRESH. If the result does not generate a carry (the value of ADRESH is less than 252) then the low limit is checked. If the result generates a carry (the value of ADRESH is greater than 252) then l_byte is loaded with 252. Similarly, the low limit is checked by subtracting the literal 24 from the value of ADRESH and the appropriate value is loaded into l_byte. If you are going to use a similar technique in your own code, you can use *MPLAB Simulator* and the **WATCH** window to view the operation of your code to ensure you get the outcome that you expect.

In operation, when you close the dit switch, a string of dits will be generated. You will hear the audio tone of the dits. The PTT LED will illuminate indicating the transmitter is enabled, and the KEY LED will flash in step with the dits being sent. Likewise, closure of the dah switch will generate a series of dahs. When the switches are opened, the PTT LED will extinguish a moment later putting the transmitter in the stand-by mode. Closing both the dit and dah switches at the same time will generate a series of alternating dits and dahs. The Morse operator uses a mechanical switching device called a paddle that is connected to the dit and dah lines of the electronic keyer. The paddle is set up for side to side movements with the fingers to close the switches. To generate the letter "A" for instance (dit-dah), the operator would momentarily close the dit switch with a thumb movement, and then momentarily close the dah switch with the pointing and middle finger movement. The electronic keyer will keep track of proper dit interval timing and make sure that the transmitter controls are on and off at the proper time intervals. To generate the letter "B" (dah-dit-dit-dit), the operator would momentarily close the dah switch and then hold the dit switch closed for a long enough time to generate a series of three dits.

Conclusion

You have come a long way in this journey to learn more about MCU programming, and that journey has only begun. Now that you have the basic tools you need to tap into the power that these common yet very powerful devices have to offer, it is time for you to experiment and develop your own application. The real learning comes from adapting the MCU to accomplish a task that you dictate.

The next leg of your journey begins by dividing your intended project into simple, individual tasks that need to be accomplished to reach the end goal. Then match the available resources of the MCU device to those individual tasks and illustrate the connecting bits and parts needed to interface the MCU to the outside world in a circuit diagram. Then armed with the resource listing and your circuit diagram, it is time to develop the program code to accomplish each task (or step). Begin your code by defining constants and variables. Next, write the code to configure the resources of the MCU to meet your needs. When you write the 'meat' of your code, try to use subroutines to accomplish the individual tasks if possible. This will make your code easier to debug and also make it more readable. Get the individual subroutines to work to your satisfaction and then move on. The main part of your program is then simply a matter of calling upon the subroutines to take you from point A to point Z of your application journey.

Review Questions

18.1 How can you customize the keyer project to include a start-up sequence of Morse code characters, for instance to send "HI" or send your ham radio call sign? Consider if you want this start-up sequence to be transmitted over the air waves or not.

18.2 Develop circuit and software changes to automatically send common Morse code sequences like sending CQ calls.

18.3 Develop circuit and software changes to add a power-on LED to the project.

18.4 Develop software changes that will increase or decrease the amount of time the PTT line is held closed after the last Morse character is sent.

Appendix A

Glossary

ASCII — American Standard Code for Information Interchange is a numerical based code used to represent text in computer equipment, and other devices that work with text and/or display text. ASCII includes definitions for 128 characters: 33 are non-printing, that affect how text is processed; 94 are printable characters; and the space character.

Assembly — Language. Assembly is a low-level programming language that is based on mnemonics that represent instructions or opcodes. The use of mnemonics helps to make the code more readable. The instructions authored in assembly are then assembled, compiled, or translated into machine language, which is the program in a sequence of binary code that is actually run in the microcontroller. High-level languages such as C++ or PASCAL are used for writing more complex programs to perform larger tasks. The use of high-level languages is much easier. Programs written in high-level code also need to be compiled.

Asynchronous Serial Communication — Asynchronous describes a serial transmission protocol that requires that a *start signal* is sent prior to each byte, character or code word and a *stop signal* is sent after each code word. The use of asynchronous serial communication does not require that clocking of the sending and receiving devices be synchronized, which means that data transmission can occur at any time. This scheme then requires that some part of the protocol is used to signal that data is being transmitted. The start signal serves to prepare the receiving mechanism for the reception of the data bits that follow. The stop signal signals the receiving device to reset in preparation for the next byte.

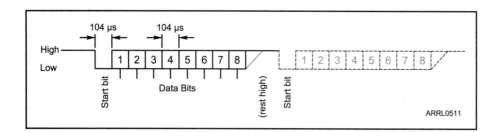

In the above diagram, a start bit is sent, followed by eight data bits, no parity bit and one stop bit, for a 10-bit character frame. The number of data and formatting bits, and the transmission speed are specific to the device. After the stop bit, the line may remain idle indefinitely, or another character may immediately be started.

Opcode — An opcode (operational code) is the portion of a programming instruction that specifies the operation to be performed. The opcode, in combination with the operand, make up the programming instruction.

Operand — An operand is the portion of a programming instruction that is changed, modified, or provides arguments for action upon by the opcode. Operands may include constants, register or memory locations, values stored in memory locations or registers, or I/O port pin assignments.

Microcontroller or MCU — A microcontroller or MCU is a functional computer system-on-a-chip. An MCU has a central processing unit (CPU), a small amount of RAM memory, programmable peripherals, and input/output pins (I/O). MCUs are used in automatically controlled products and devices, such as automobile engine control systems, remote controls, office machines, appliances, power tools, and toys.

PIC® — PICs are a family of Microchip Technology microcontroller products. The term PIC is a registered trademark of Microchip; however, the term is frequently used to refer to generic microcontroller devices. PIC has also referred to Programmable Interface Controller, Peripheral

Interface Controller, and Programmable Intelligent Computer. In this text, the use of PIC will be in reference to the Microchip family of microcontrollers.

SPI™ — Serial Peripheral Interface is a communication protocol that allows devices to communicate using a master/slave relationship, in which the master initiates the data frame. When the master generates a clock and selects a slave device, data may be transferred in either or both directions simultaneously. SPI specifies four signals: *clock* (SCLK); *master data output, slave data input* (MOSI); *master data input, slave data output* (MISO); and *slave select* (CSS).

Appendix B

Answers

Chapter 2 — Inside the PIC16F676

2.1 What is the physical pin assigned to PORTA RA3?
Answer: Pin 4

2.2 What is the purpose of the comparator module?
Answer: To compare the relative voltage magnitudes on two pins RA0 and RA1 or physical pins 13 and 12. The output of the comparator can be programmed to be put on pin RA2 or physical pin 11.

2.3 What is the physical pin assigned to the ADC channel AN5?
Answer: Pin 9

2.4 What is the bit resolution of the ADCs within the PIC16F676?
Answer: 10-bits

2.5 How many internal general purpose timers are available in the PIC16F676?
Answer: Two, timer 0, an 8-bit timer/counter, and timer 1, a 16-bit timer/counter

2.6 How much RAM is available for your programs?
Answer: 1024 words of FLASH RAM

2.7 Once a PIC16F676 is programmed, how long can you expect that program to be retained in the PIC (if it is not over-written by another program)?
Answer: Greater than 40 years

Chapter 3 — Software and Hardware Setup

3.1 What icon and *MPLAB IDE* operation must you use with caution, or not at all as recommended by the author?
Answer: The **ERASE THE TARGET DEVICE MEMORIES** button.

3.2 If an MCU device suddenly stops working when developing your code and reloading the adjusted code in the device, what can you check in the device memory to try and troubleshoot the problem?
Answer: The device memory may have been inadvertently erased. Click on the **READ TARGET DEVICE MEMORIES** icon, then display the **Program Memory** page with **View/Program Memory**, and scroll down to address 0x3ff. If you see 0x00 at that memory location, the device has probably been erased. The work-around for this problem is to not use the internal RC oscillator of the device or use the internal oscillator uncalibrated (OSCCAL).

3.3 What is the web URL that you can visit to find the latest version and/or check for recent updates of *MPLAB IDE*?
Answer: **www.microchip.com/** and then do a site search for *MPLAB IDE*

Chapter 4 — Program Architecture

4.1 In which section of the program will you identify the type of device for which the program is intended?

Answer: In the Directives section of the program code, at the beginning of the program listing after the comments that summarize the purpose of the program.

4.2 In which section of the code will you identify additional files that contain information that is needed to complete the program?

Answer: In the Directives section of the program code, right after you identify the type of MCU to be used.

4.3 Why do you not write the main body of the program in the reset section of the program since that is where the program counter will be starting from upon initial power-up or reset of the device?

Answer: There are only 4 memory locations between the reset vector and the interrupt vector. This is just enough room to write a goto to the routine that makes up the main program.

4.4 What is the main difference between the code segment in the Initialize section and the main section of the code?

Answer: The Initialization section of the code is where you configure the device resources by manipulating the SFRs. The Initialization section of the code is generally only run one time, when the power is first applied to the device or after a hard reset. The device resources and controlling SFRs can, and frequently are, manipulated in the main section of the code after first being configured in the Initialization section of the code.

4.5 List two purposes for writing code in subroutines as opposed to writing the same code in the main program?

Answer: The use of subroutines allows you to use sections of code that may be repeated often throughout the program to perform redundant tasks. The use of subroutines makes your code easier for other users to follow and read. Carefully authored subroutines can be used in other applications by collecting the subroutines in a library that can be cut and pasted into other code. Subroutines can save memory space. Care should be taken to ensure that the use of subroutines does not overwhelm the limited Stack space of the device, particularly when using nested subroutines and interrupts.

Chapter 5 — Program Development

5.1 List the steps required to list the files that make up a project.

Answer: Use the *WINDOWS Explorer* utility and navigate to the file where the program has been compiled. The main files include the file extensions .asm, .cod, .hex, .lst, .project, and .workspace.

5.2 Can you develop, test, and debug programs without attaching the programmer?

Answer: Yes, however those icons and functions specifically related to working with the programmer will not be available until the programmer is connected.

5.3 Will the *MPLAB IDE* allow you to load a program into the target MCU device if the program did not assemble properly?

Answer: No, if the build fails, the current program will not be compiled and will not be loaded into the device. The previous program will remain in the device which may cause some confusion if you do not pay attention to the build error message. It would appear that the programming was successful because the device functions in circuit, however your programming adjustments will not have been made in the program in the device.

5.4 Which of the icons that allow you to access the target device memory should you use with great caution, or not at all?

Answer: The **ERASE THE TARGET DEVICE MEMORIES**. I know you are probably tired of seeing reference to the use of this icon but be assured, the redundant reference is on purpose. I have trashed too many devices by making this error and want to ensure it doesn't happen to you more than one time.

5.5 Why is it important to use the standard default file structure when installing *MPLAB IDE* on your computer?

Answer: So that you can find the required .inc file for the device. *MPLAB IDE* utilities are set up for the default file structure. You can override the use of the default file structure, but other users of your programs may not be aware of your unique file locations when they try to compile your programs from the source code.

5.6 Which type of file is unique to each particular MCU device?

Answer: The include file with extension .inc. The include files are placed in the **C:\Program Files\Microchip\MPASM Suite directory** when using the defaults during *MPLAB IDE* installation.

Chapter 6 — Working With Registers

6.1 Define SET and CLEAR.

Answer: SET means that the addressed pin, or register bit is in the high state, 1, or +5 V is applied as appropriate. CLEAR means that the addressed pin, or register bit is in the low state, 0, 0 V, or ground.

State the appropriate register and bit to accomplish the following actions. In your answer list the register label name, the actual memory location in hexadecimal, the bit label, and the bit number. Use the Question 6.2 as the example.

6.2 Which bit is manipulated to switching to Bank 1?

Answer: STATUS, 0x03 or 0x83, RP0, bit 5. SET RP0 for Bank 1.

6.3 What register and bit would you read to determine if an arithmetic action resulted in a zero result?

Answer: STATUS, 0x03 or 0x83, Z, bit 3. Z is SET if the result is zero.

6.4 Enable the weak pull-up resistors on PORTA, 2?

Answer: WPUA, 0x95, WPUA2, bit 2. SET WPUA2 to enable the weak pull-up on PORTA, 2. OPTION_REG, 0x81, RAPU, bit 7. CLEAR RAPU to enable all individually enabled weak pull-ups.

6.5 Disable all weak pull-up resistors associated with PORTA?

Answer: OPTION_REG, 0x81, RAPU, bit 7. SET RAPU to disable all individually enabled weak pull-ups.

6.6 To what register would you load the factory determined internal oscillator calibration value?

Answer: OSCCAL, 0x90. The value loaded into OSCCAL is retrieved from memory location 0x3ff.

6.7 How would you configure the appropriate registers to make PORTA, 0; PORTA, 2; and PORTA, 4 as digital outputs, and PORTA, 1 as an analog input?

Answer: TRISA, 0x85, TRISA0, bit 0, TRISA2, bit 2, TRISA4, bit 4, TRISA1, bit 1. CLEAR TRISA0, TRISA2, and TRISA4 to make those pins output; SET TRISA1 to make that pin input. ANSEL, 0x91, ANS0, bit 0, ANS1, bit 1, ANS2, bit 2, ANS3, bit 3. CLEAR ANS0, ANS2, and ANS3 to make these pins digital, SET ANS1 to make this pin an analog input pin.

Chapter 7 — Instruction Set Overview

7.1 Does the `movf` instruction affect the Z flag of the STATUS register?

Answer: Yes

7.2 What value would the instruction `movf var1, f` serve?

Answer: This is a programming technique that can be used to check if the value in var1 is zero or not.

7.3 What precautions should you consider when executing nested call instructions?

Answer: You can overwhelm the available Stack space (8-bytes deep) if you have more than 8 calls to subroutines before returning from a subroutine.

7.4 Which of the opcode instructions is useful if you want to toggle an I/O pin to turn on and off an attached LED?

Answer: `xorwf`.

7.5 What kind of information is included in the device .inc file? What directive would you use to include the contents of the device .inc file in your program code?

Answer: The .inc file contains the mnemonic labels assigned to various device specific SFRs, register bits, and configuration words that match the documentation for the device. This allows you to author code that can be more easily followed by another user. The assembler directive to add the .inc file is

```
#include <p16f676.inc>.
```

7.6 Which INTCON bit is automatically SET when the `retfie` opcode is executed?

Answer: The GIE bit which enables global interrupts. The GIE bit is CLEARED automatically when an interrupt occurs.

7.7 When using the `rrf` and/or the `rlf` opcodes to rotate bits through the C bit of the STATUS register, what are some precautions that you need to consider?

Answer: The previous contents of the C bit is rotated into the target location before it accepts the bit rotated out of the location. You need to make sure that the previous contents of the C register will not contaminate the target register contents.

7.8 Is it possible to move values from one memory location or register directly into another? Write a sample of code that would accomplish this task.

Answer: No, when moving contents from one register to another, the value must pass through the w-register.

```
movfw    variable1    ;load contents in variable1 into the w-register
movwf    variable2    ;load the contents in the w-register into variable2
```

The above code affects the STATUS, Z flag.

```
swapf    variable1, w ;swap the nibbles in variable1 and load into
                      ;the w-register
movwf    temp         ;put swapped contents into a temp variable
swapf    temp, w      ;un-swap nibbles that were in temp
movwf    variable1    ;return original contents into varible1
```

The above code does not affect the STATUS, Z flag.

Chapter 8 — Device Setup

8.1 Write the code segments required to configure PORTA pins 0, 2, 4 and 5 as digital outputs, all other port pins as digital inputs with weak pull-up resistors enabled.

Answer:

```
BANKSEL    Bank1                     ;select bank 1
movlw      b'00000000'               ;weak pull-ups enabled
movwf      OPTION_REG
movlw      b'00001010'               ;0, 2, 4, 5 output, 1, 3 input
movwf      TRISA                     ;program PORTA
movlw      b'00000010'               ;weak pull-up on 1, no pull-up on 3
movwf      WPUA
movlw      b'00000000'               ;all digital
movwf      ANSEL
BANKSEL    Bank0                     ;back to Bank 0
```

8.2 Write the code segments required to configure PORTA pin 0 as an ADC with a clock frequency of Freq/8 and left-hand justified.

Answer:

```
BANKSEL    Bank1                     ;select bank 1
movlw      b'00000001'               ;0 input, all others (except 3) output
movwf      TRISA                     ;program PORTA
movlw      b'00010000'               ;'Freq/8
movwf      ADCON1
movlw      b'00000001'               ;0 analog, all others digital
movwf      ANSEL
BANKSEL    Bank0                     ;BACK TO BANK 0
movlw      b'00000010'               ;left justified, Vdd as ref, ch 0 AN0
movwf      ADCON0
```

8.3 Write the code segments required to disable all weak pull-up resistors.

Answer:

```
BANKSEL    Bank1                     ;select bank 1
bsf        OPTION_REG, 7             ;SET RAPU bit
BANKSEL    Bank0                     ;back to bank 0
```

8.4 Can the direction of a PORT pin be changed after it is initialized in the Initialization section of the code? If the direction can be changed, write the code required to change the direction of pin 5 of PORTC.

Answer: Yes, (assuming that PORTC, 5 is an output to start, change to input in code)

```
BANKSEL    Bank1                     ;select bank 1
bsf        TRISC, 5                  ;SET to change PORTC, 5 to input
BANKSEL    Bank0                     ;back to bank 0
```

or to toggle PORTC, 5:

```
BANKSEL    Bank1                     ;select bank 1
movlw      b'00100000'
xorwf      TRISC, f                  ;toggle PORTC, 5
BANKSEL    Bank0                     ;back to bank 0
```

Chapter 9 — Delay Subroutines

9.1 Serial communications is based on precise timing of pulse widths. The pulse widths can be calculated by the formula *time* = 1 / *baud*. For 4800 baud, the time interval is .000208 seconds. Write a delay subroutine to generate bit pulses of this duration and test your code using the *MPLAB Simulator* tool.

Answer: (the code below will create a delay of .000208 seconds)

```
bitdelay
movlw      66         ;this number works if the user uses the calibrated
                      ;value for the internal clock. This routine, including
                      ;the goto and nop statements below allow the user to develop
                      ;an anticipated delay of 208 µs for the bits at 4800 Baud.
                      ;This delay can be verified by using the stop
                      ;watch function of MPLAB Simulator
movwf      count
goto       $+1        ;these goto statements allow you to tweak the
                      ;time of the
goto       $+1        ;delay. goto statements like this take 2 clock
                      ;cycles
nop                   ;while the nop statement takes 1 clock cycle
                      ;to complete
bit
decfsz     count, f
goto       bit
return
```

Chapter 10 — Basic Input/Output

10.1 List the code that would be required to configure the I/O resources of the MCU so that RA0, RA3, RA4, RC1, and RC2 are digital inputs, the rest of the pins are digital outputs and Weak pull-up resistors are enabled on the PORTA input pins.

Answer:
```
BANKSEL    Bank1                ;select bank 1
movlw      b'00011001'          ;0, 3, 4 input
movwf      TRISA
movwf      WPUA                 ;same pins have weak pull-ups
movlw      b'00000110'          ;1, 2 input
movwf      TRISC
movlw      b'00000000'          ;CLEAR RAPU to enable weak pull-ups
movwf      OPTION_REG
BANKSEL    Bank0                ;back to bank 0
```

10.2 List the I/O restrictions on RA3.

Answer: PORTA, 3 or RA3 is restricted to general input only because it also can be configured to serve as a master clear reset from an external source.

10.3 You have a pin in PORTA configured as an input with the weak pull-up resistor enabled for that pin. Inside the main program, you would like to momentarily change the direction of that pin to an output. What command(s) would you need to include to do the switching from input to output and back again?

Answer:
```
BANKSEL    Bank1                ;select bank 1
bcf        TRISA, #             ;CLEAR the appropriate bit to make output
BANKSEL    Bank0                ;back to bank 0
```
There is no need to change the WPUA register because the enabled weak pull-up resistors are automatically disabled when a pin is changed to an output.

10.4 Write a command line that is an alternative to:
```
movlw      b'00000000'
movwf      PORTA
```
Answer:
```
Clrf       PORTA
```

10.5 The following command segment will toggle the status on pin PORTA, 4, which means if the pin is SET, the program will CLEAR the pin, and vice versa:
```
btfsc      PORTA,4
bcf        PORTA,4
btfss      PORTA,4
bsf        PORTA,4
continue_with_program
```
Write a tighter (more efficient code) that will accomplish the same task. (Hint: look at the xorwf command.)

Answer:
```
movlw      b'00010000'          ;addressing bit 4
xorwf      PORTA, f             ;if 1 then 0, if 0 then 1
```

10.6 Switches are notorious for contact bouncing, which means that when the contacts within a switch are opened or closed, there is not an instantaneous make or break of the switch contacts. When the switch closure or opening is sampled fast enough with a computer, multiple closures or openings could be detected with potentially disastrous results. Write a code segment that would help to alleviate the switch contact bounce issue.

Answer:

```
switch_on
btfsc       PORTA, 0              ;switch connected to PORTA, 0
goto        switch_on
wait
btfss       PORTA, 0              ;skip if switch open
goto        wait                 ;hold while closed
```

10.7 Write out the default configuration for the ANSEL, TRISA, TRISC, OPTION_REG, and WPUA registers. Under what resource configuration conditions would the default configurations of these registers be okay, meaning you would not have to address these registers in the Initialization segment of your program? Would it be advisable to use the default configuration instead of deliberately configuring these registers, why or why not?

Answer:

```
ANSEL = b'11111111'
TRISA = b'xx111111'
TRISC = b'xx111111'
OPTION_REG = b'11111111'
WPUA = b'xx11x111'
```

Not very often, maybe when all PORT I/O resources are going to be used as analog inputs. Deliberately configuring the registers in the Initialization of the code would facilitate the author and users of the software to focus on resource setup to match the resource configuration to the objectives of the code.

10.8 Adjust the code that you used during this chapter to flash an LED when the switch was pressed so that two LEDs flash but alternately (when one LED is on, the other is off and vice versa).

Answer:

```
bsf         PORTC, 4             ;one LED on pin 4
bcf         PORTC, 3             ;one LED on pin 3
main
btfsc       PORTA,4              ;check if button pressed (0)
goto        main                 ;if 0 then skip this goto
movlw       b'00011000'          ;mask 3, 4
xorwf       PORTC                ;flash LED
call        wait1sec             ;wait for 1 second
goto        main                 ;do it again
```

10.9 Adjust the same code so that the LED is flashing when the switch is open and stops flashing when the switch is closed.

Answer:

```
bsf      PORTC, 4          ;one LED on pin 4
bcf      PORTC, 3          ;one LED on pin 3
main
btfss    PORTA,4           ;check if button open (1)
goto     main              ;if 0 then skip this goto
movlw    b'00011000'       ;mask 3, 4
xorwf    PORTC             ;flash LED
call     wait1sec          ;wait for 1 second
goto     main              ;do it again
```

10.10 Adjust the same code to make a stop light simulation. In this simulation, the red LED is on until the switch is pressed. Then like the operation of a stop light, there is a pause, then the red light goes out and the green LED comes on for a short period. After the green period, the yellow LED comes on, the green goes out for a short period. Finally, the red LED is turned on and the yellow is turned off and the program awaits for the next switch press (the car).

Answer:

```
bsf      PORTC, 4          ;red LED on pin 4
bcf      PORTC, 3          ;yellow LED on pin 3
bcf      PORTC, 5          ;green LED on pin 5
main
btfsc    PORTA,4           ;check if button pressed (0)
goto     main              ;if 0 then skip this goto
movlw    b'00100000'       ;green on others off
movwf    PORTC
call     wait5sec          ;green for 5 seconds
movlw    b'00001000'       ;yellow on others off
movwf    PORTC
call     wait1sec          ;yellow for 1 second
movlw    b'00010000'       ;red on others off
movwf    PORTC
goto     main              ;do it again
```

Chapter 11 — Analog to Digital

11.1 The ADC resources of the PIC16F676 share common input circuitry. What considerations must be taken because of this common circuitry?

Answer: The ADC resources share common input circuitry which includes the capacitor that is charged to sample and hold the input voltage to the ADC. If you are going to use multiple ADCs, you need to consider this. There must be enough time between ADC samples to switch the ADC channels, and then allow enough time for the new voltage to stabilize on the capacitor before the ADC reading is attempted.

11.2 Which register and bit are used by the PIC16F676 hardware to signal that the conversion is still in progress?

Answer: ADCON0, GO/DONE

11.3 Which register and bit can be used to disable the ADC circuits (this also would reduce chip power consumption)?

Answer: ADCON0, ADON

11.4 Can you read both the ADRESH and ADRESL registers while operating in memory Bank 0?

Answer: No, ADRESH is in Bank 0, ADRESL is in Bank 1.

11.5 Is bank switching required in this code snippet? Explain your answer.

```
BANKSEL    Bank1
movfw      ADRESL
BANKSEL    Bank0
movwf      l_byte
```

Answer: No, but it is a good idea to do so. The l_byte variable location would be in the general purpose registers between 0x20 and 0x5f in Bank 0. However, the general purpose registers are cross accessed to Bank 1 between 0xao and 0xdf, so you should be able to access l_byte from either bank.

11.6 What could you do if you wanted to reduce the noise present on the LSB of the ADC output by changing the ADC output from 10-bits to 8-bits? Write a short code segment to efficiently accomplish this change. (Hint: look at left justifying the ADC data.)

Answer:

```
bcf     ADCON0, ADFM    ;left justify the ADC result
movfw   ADRESH          ;put upper 8-bits into w-register
movwf   l_byte          ;put the upper 8-bits into the low working
                        ;register
```

Simply using the left justify of the ADC output truncates the lower 2 bits of the 10-bit ADC output and this reduces any noise that will show up in the lowest bits of the ADC output.

11.7 What would happen to the contents of the ADRESH and ADRESL registers if you clear the ADCON0, GO bit before the ADC conversion is completed?

Answer: The ADRESH and ADRESL registers will not be updated and will contain the previous ADC result if the ADC conversion is aborted before it is completed.

Chapter 12 — Comparator

12.1 What comparator mode configures the comparator to consume the lowest power?

Answer: Comparator Off mode, CMCON, CM2:CM0 b'111'.

12.2 Which comparator mode connects the C_{IN-} and C_{IN+} comparator inputs to RA0 and RA1 and does not connect the C_{OUT} bit to RA2? Does the use of this mode create a conflict if your application does not even use the comparator circuit?

Answer: Comparator without output, CMCON, CM2:CM0 b'010'. Not really. This mode may only conflict if RA0 and RA1 are digital outputs, but the I/O pins in this mode would automatically disconnect analog inputs anyway. It would be good practice to configure resources you are going to use.

12.3 What is the value of the internal reference voltage applied to comparator input C_{IN+} in the mode dictated by CM2:CM0 loaded with b'011" and VREN loaded with b'10001011'?

Answer: If V_{dd} = 5 V. Vref is internal and in the high range. VR3:VR0 = b'1011'=11
Use:

$$V = \frac{V_{dd}}{4} + \left(\frac{VR3:VRO}{32} \right) \times V_{dd} = 2.989 \; volts$$

Chapter 13 — Interrupts

13.1 What would happen if an interrupt "flag" is not reset before the interrupt service subroutine returns control back to the main program?

Answer: The interrupt would be generated immediately after the interrupts are enabled.

13.2 Describe the difference between globally enabling interrupts (SETTING the INTCON, GIE bit) and enabling a specific interrupt, for instance TMR0 (SETTING the INTCON, T0IE bit).

Answer: Enabling specific interrupts simply puts those interrupts in stand-by mode ready to go. Globally enabling interrupts gives all those specifically enabled interrupts the go signal. You can turn on and off all enabled interrupts with GIE. You can turn on and off specific interrupts by manipulating the specific interrupt enable bit.

13.3 Does an interrupt have to be enabled for the associated interrupt flag to be SET by the interrupt condition?

Answer: No, the interrupt flags operate independently of the enable status of the interrupt.

13.4 What is the depth (number of bytes) of the Stack? What precautions must be considered when working with the Stack?

Answer: The Stack is only 8 layers deep. If nested calls to subroutines or nested interrupts occur that cause more than 8 PC pushes onto the Stack, each subsequent push will cause a PC to fall out the bottom of the Stack. When returns try to retrieve those lost PC values, the program will crash.

13.5 What precautions must be considered when using interrupts and other subroutine calls that deal with the W-register and the STATUS register?

Answer: The W-register is used frequently in the program. The STATUS register is frequently modified by opcode execution. If the calling program is interrupted while manipulating the W-register or STATUS register, if your interrupt service routine also affects these two registers, the original register contents will be lost with probably catastrophic effect upon the return to the calling program. Temporarily storing the W-register and STATUS register values at the beginning of the interrupt service routine and restoring those values before returning from the subroutine will prevent problems.

13.6 How can "break points" be used in program debugging?

Answer: Break points at strategic locations in the program will stop a program simulation so that you can view the contents of various registers and note the elapsed time of execution using the **Stopwatch** window.

Chapter 14 — Timer 0 and Timer 1 Resources

14.1 At what rate (in instruction cycles) does the TMR0 register increment when there is no pre-scaler assigned to the resource. Alternatively, at what rate does the TMR1 register increment when a pre-scaler ratio of 0:0 is assigned?

Answer: Both TMR0 and TMR1 increment every instruction cycle.

14.2 What command begins the incrementing of the TMR0 register? When does the TMR1 register begin to increment?

Answer: TMR0 begins to increment its register when the OPTION_REG register is loaded. TMR1 begins to increment its registers when the T1CON, TMR1ON bit is SET.

14.3 Do the timer resources operate even if their interrupt function is not enabled?

Answer: Yes

14.4 Can you monitor the progress of the timer resources between interrupts? If so, how?

Answer: Yes, you can check the status of the interrupt flags and you also can access the resource registers TMR0, TMR1L, and TMR1H values anytime in code.

14.5 Why is it important to CLEAR the associated interrupt flag in the interrupt service subroutine before returning control back to the main program?

Answer: If the interrupt flag is not CLEARED, then an immediate interrupt will be generated as soon as the interrupts are enabled.

14.6 In the programming exercises in this chapter, the interrupt service subroutines did not contain code designed to temporarily store the w-register and STATUS register contents while servicing the interrupt and then reload the pre-interrupt values into these registers when returning to the main program as was recommended in the chapter on interrupts. Why was this not a problem during the execution of the exercise programs? Amend the exercise code to take these precautions.

Answer: There were no subroutine calls from the main program so there was no danger of nested subroutine calls. Only one interrupt was allowed at a time in the exercise code so there was no danger of nested interrupts. The following snippet of code would temporarily store the w-register and STATUS register contents and then retrieve the data prior to the return opcode.

```
movwf      w_temp                ;copy contents of w_reg into a temp register
swapf      STATUS,w              ;swap the nibbles of STATUS and place into
                                 ;the w_register, these nibbles will be swapped
                                 ;back when the STATUS register is recovered
                                 ;at the end of the interrupt service routine
BANKSEL    Bank0                 ;forces a return to Bank 0 regardless of bank
                                 ;when interrupt occurred
movwf      status_temp           ;put the swapped old STATUS reg value in a temp

swapf      status_temp,w         ;swap the nibbles in status_temp and put result
in                               ;w_register
movwf      STATUS                ;STATUS now returned to pre-interrupt value
swapf      w_temp,f              ;take the old value of w_reg and swap nibbles
swapf      w_temp,w              ;swap nibbles again and place into w_reg, w_reg
                                 ;now returned to pre-interrupt value
retfie                           ;this command also sets GIE to enable global
                                 ;interrupts
```

14.7 You can very accurately determine the interrupt time interval due to program code execution. What factor other than code determines the actual interrupt time interval? How might you measure the actual interrupt time interval?

Answer: The accuracy of the MCU clock source contributes to the accuracy of interrupt and other delay time intervals. The clock accuracy depends on the device, voltage, temperature, and other environmental factors. You can use an oscilloscope tied to an I/O pin that is toggled at the edges of the interrupt to measure the time interval of the interrupt.

14.8 Thinking in general terms of the resources available in the PIC16F676, how would you configure the resources to build a basic frequency counter?

Answer: The TMR1 resource would be configured as a counter, the TMR0 resource would be configured to interrupt at a specific time interval, for instance 500 mseconds. The program would start TMR0 and TMR1 simultaneously. At the expiration of the TMR0 interval, the number of counts in the TMR1H and TMR1L registers would be sampled, then the number doubled, to calculate the frequency in Hertz.

Chapter 15 — Asynchronous Serial Communication

15.1 In looking at the bitdelay subroutine in the example code, what value would be loaded into the count variable to produce a delay appropriate for 2400 baud serial communications?

Answer: Approximately 130, though the actual value would have to be determined by use of the simulator to compensate for code overhead.

15.2 What code adjustments are required if the data stream was increased from 8-bits to 16-bits? What else must be considered if there is a significant increase in the number of data bits that are transmitted at one time (hint: think about the bit time interval produced by the delay routines and the code overhead contribution to the delay)?

Answer: The bitcounter variable would have to start at 16. You would need to check to see if the lengthened character would cause enough delay in the bit delay time interval to prevent sampling the bit state in approximately the middle of the bit.

15.3 The *MPLAB Simulator* can be used to predict the length of a delay produced by code. What other factor also contributes to these timing delays? How can you determine the actual timing of a serial data stream?

Answer: The accuracy of the system clock also affects the length of program delays. Using an oscilloscope connected to the data line can allow you to measure the length of the bit delay.

15.4 What is(are) the ASCII code(s) required to send the number 127 to the LCD?

Answer: "1" in ASCII = 49, "2" in ASCII = 50, "7" in ASCII = 55. Three values that represent the ASCII characters would have to be sent, 49, 50, and 55.

15.5 What is the code that you would send to the LCD to clear the display and move the cursor to the upper left corner?

Answer: 0x0c to clear the display, 0x80 to move the cursor to the upper left corner, line-0.

15.6 What adjustment to the exercise code would be required if the LCD used data sent with the MSB sent first?

Answer: You would use the `rlf` opcode versus `rrf`.

15.7 In the previous chapter on Interrupts, the temporary storage of the contents of the w-register and the STATUS registers was emphasized. Why would that strategy be important if the timer interrupt resources are used to generate the bit interval delays?

Answer: Because the w-register and STATUS register are used extensively while sending data to the external device. If the interrupt occurred in midstream, the critical values in those registers in all likelihood would be lost or corrupted.

15.8 In the program exercise, the individual bit being sent was rotated through the carry bit that is included in the STATUS register. What code alternative might be used to determine the state of the bit to be transmitted?

Answer: Though not particularly efficient, the operand argument for the bit to be checked could be a variable. Then you could use a loop to increment the bit variable to be checked.

```
        movwf    byte_to_send
        movlw    .8
        movwf    bitcounter              ;set up to send 8 bits
        bcf      PORTA,5                 ;send start bit
        call     bitdelay
nextbit
        bcf      PORTA,5
        btfsc    byte_to_send, bitcounter ;sends MSB first
        bsf      PORTA,5
        call     bitdelay
        decfsz   bitcounter,f
        goto     nextbit
        bsf      PORTA,5                 ;set to high for resting state
        call     delay5mS
        return
```

Chapter 16 — Serial Peripheral Interface Communication

16.1 List the advantages and disadvantages of each serial communication technique (Asymmetrical and SPI).

Answer: Asymmetrical advantage: one data line required; disadvantages: timing is critical, relatively slow. SPI advantages: relatively fast, timing not critical; disadvantage: multiple lines needed.

16.2 If one SPI device needs a CLEAR CS line and another SPI device needs a SET CS line to operate, can these two devices share all three signal lines (CS, SCK, and SI)?

Answer: Yes.

16.3 If the wiper resistance in the MCP41010 is specified to be 52 Ω, what resistance would you expect when you command the wiper position to b'00000000'?

Answer: 52 Ω.

16.4 What line(s) of code would need to be changed if the attached SPI device required commands sent in LSB first format?

Answer:

```
rrf         data_to_send,f      ;rotate command right into carry
```

16.5 For the sake of code clarity, you decide that you would like to treat the command byte and the data byte as a single 16-bit variable with the labels dataH and dataL. To do so, write an amended SPI subroutine that would send all the data bits in one subroutine instead of two passes through one subroutine as was done in this exercise (once to send the command byte and then again to send the data byte). Hint: look to see how this was done in the b2_BCD subroutine (binary to BCD conversion subroutine), loop16 loop.

Answer:

```
movwf       dataH               ;new variables declared and loaded with data
movwf       dataL
spi
movlw       .16                 ;reset bit counter for 16 bits
movwf       bitcounter
trans_loop
bcf         PORTC,SI            ;assume 0 bit
rlf         dataL, f            ;rlf low byte through carry
rlf         dataH, f            ;rlf high byte accept bit from carry
btfsc       STATUS, C           ;if carry is high, set bit high/else skip
bsf         PORTC,SI
bsf         PORTC,SCK           ;clock in the bit
bcf         PORTC,SCK
decfsz      bitcounter,f        ;check if 16 bits sent, if not, go back
goto        trans_loop
return
```

Chapter 17 — Working With Data

17.1 Explain how you could multiplex four 7-segment display units to display all digits at one time. Draw a circuit diagram for the required circuit. Can this be accomplished with the PIC16F676 device?

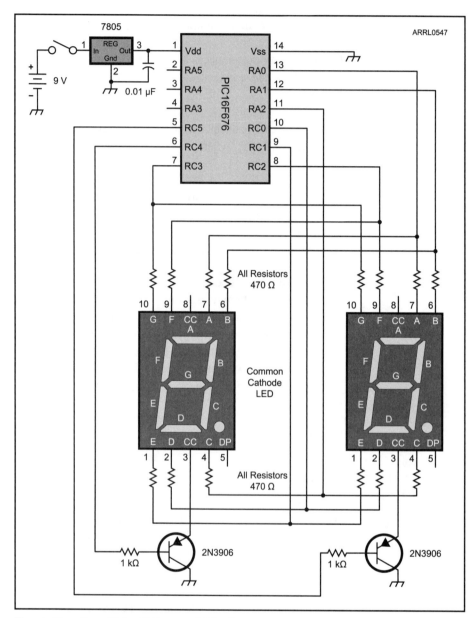

Figure Question 17-1 – 7-Segment Display

Answer: Use switching transistors on each common cathode line to turn on the digit and then move on to the next digit. If you do this fast enough, the viewer will not be able to detect that the digits are really only on one at a time. The PIC 16F676 has enough I/O lines to handle two more switching transistors.

Chapter 18 — Putting It All Together

18.1 How can you customize the keyer project to include a start-up sequence of Morse code characters, for instance to send "HI" or send your ham radio call sign? Consider if you want this start-up sequence to be transmitted over the air waves or not.

Answer: Use a data table with the text that you would like to send and call a routine to get each character to send in turn. This may require building a character table for each letter in the alphabet made up of the dits and dahs that make up the character. If you do not want this start-up message sent over the air, simply do not key the transmitter.

18.2 Develop circuit and software changes to automatically send common Morse code sequences like sending CQ calls.

Answer: Build on the program adjustments above. Add a push button switch that is polled in the program. When this button is pressed, a jump to a subroutine sends the desired message.

18.3 Develop circuit and software changes to add a power-on LED to the project.

Answer: Connect an LED to an unused I/O pin that is programmed as a digital output pin. The SET this bit early in the program, probably in the Initialization section of the code.

18.4 Develop software changes that will increase or decrease the amount of time the PTT line is held closed after the last Morse character is sent.

Answer: Look at the delay loop created using the TMR1 resource and adjust the starting register values to achieve the desired delay.

Appendix C

Keyer Project
Circuit Board
Construction Manual

Introduction

Use the following steps to install the components into the keyer project circuit board. The components are the same ones that you used while performing the exercises in the text. The components are mounted flush against the board surface unless indicated in the individual steps (for the voltage regulator and the two transistors). All the components are mounted from the silkscreen side of the board (the side with the components outlines and lettering) except the battery holder, which is installed last and is installed from the back side (foil side) of the board.

When soldering, remember that more solder is not necessarily better. Use just enough solder to make a good mechanical and electrical connection. Use care to double-check that the proper components are being installed and with the correct orientation. The board is a high quality, plated through hole construction, which makes for a professional and durable project, but the plated through holes are not very forgiving for de-soldering and reinstalling mis-placed components.

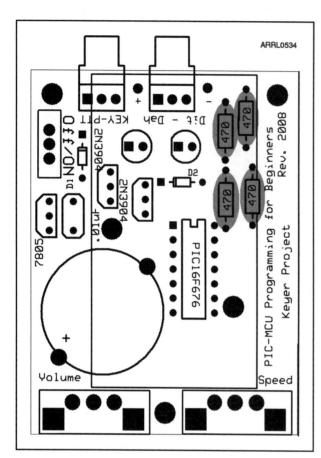

Figure C-1

Step 1

Orient your circuit board as indicated in **Figure C-1**. Find the four 470 Ω resistors (yellow, violet, brown) and install them at the indicated locations. Bend the leads at 90°, close to the resistor body, put the leads through the appropriate circuit board holes and press the resistor bodies flush with the circuit board surface. Resistors can be installed in either direction. On the foil side of the board, bend the leads outward slightly to hold the resistors in place while soldering. Solder each of the leads and then clip the excess leads as close to the circuit board surface as practicable.

Step 2

Locate the two 1N914 diodes (similar in appearance to the resistors but having a glass body). Note that one end of the diode has a band. The unbanded end is the anode (goes toward the positive current), the banded end is the cathode (goes toward the negative current). Locate the diode component outlines on the circuit board, D1 and D2. Note that the component outlines have banded ends also — this is to assist you in installing the diodes with the proper orientation. As with the resistors, bend the diode leads at 90°, close to the component body and install the diodes in the indicated locations, pay particular attention to the banded ends. See **Figure C-2.**

Step 3

a. The 7805 voltage regulator looks just like the 2N3904 transistors and it is easy to confuse the parts. Locate the 7805 voltage regulator and double-check that you in fact have the voltage regulator by making sure it is marked with the numbers 7805 (there may be some additional lettering on the specific component, but it definitely will have the numbers 7805. The transistors will not have those numbers). Note that the regulator has a flat surface

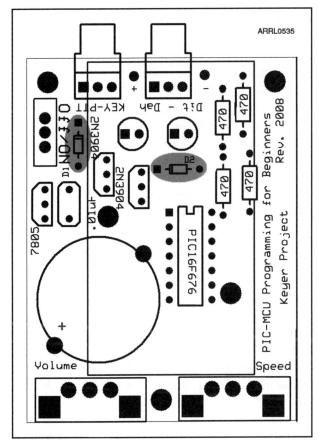

Figure C-2

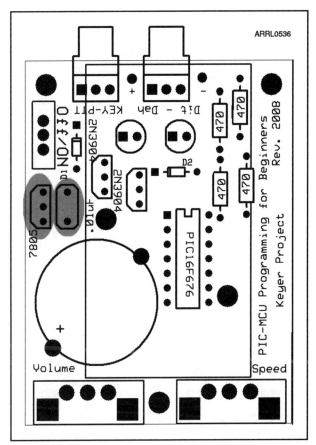

Figure C-3

opposite a round surface and three wire leads. Locate the 7805 regulator outline on the circuit board. Note that the component outline also has a flat and round outline to help you correctly orient the regulator. Bend the leads slightly so that they fit in the holes in the circuit board. Push the regulator down toward the board surface until there is approximately ¼ inch distance between the regulator body and the circuit board surface. Do not attempt to push the component body down so that it is flush with the board surface or you might damage the component. Slightly bend the outer leads of the regulator to hold the component in place and solder and clip the three leads.

b. Locate the capacitor. It is marked with 103 on the side of the component. This capacitor can be installed in either direction. Locate the component outline on the circuit board and install the capacitor with the bottom of the component flush with the circuit board surface. Solder and clip the excess leads. See **Figure C-3**.

Step 4

Locate the 14-pin IC socket. Note that one end of the socket has a half-moon notch in it. Locate the IC socket component outline on the circuit board and note that it also has a half-moon notch in the outline. Install the IC socket so that the notches are lined up. Hold the IC socket in place while you solder <u>only one</u> socket lead on the bottom of the board. Inspect the IC socket installation and ensure that the socket body is flush against the board surface. If necessary re-melt the soldered pin and re-seat the IC socket. Once you are satisfied that the socket is flush against the circuit board surface, solder the remaining 13 pins. Do not solder the PIC16F676 in this location; this would make it impossible for you to program or re-program the device later. See **Figure C-4**.

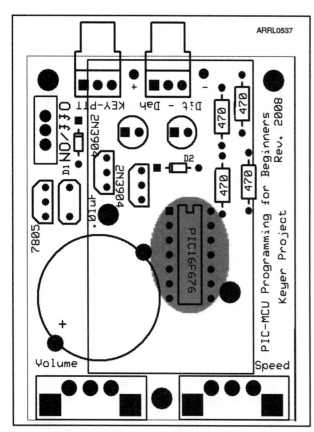

Figure C-4

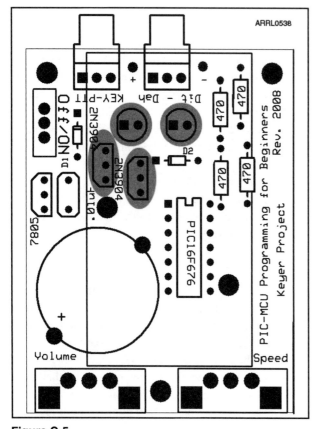

Figure C-5

Step 5

a. Locate the two 2N3904 transistors and note that they have flat surfaces just like the regulator did. Also confirm that you have the transistors by ensuring that the components have the 2N3904 identification labels. Locate the transistor outlines on the circuit board, and — while matching the flat side of the transistor with the flat side of the component outline — install the two transistors. Push the transistors down toward the circuit board surface until you have approximately ¼ inch clearance between the component body and the circuit board surface as you did with the voltage regulator. Solder and clip the excess leads.

b. Locate the two light emitting diodes (LEDs), one will be red, and one will be green. Note that one of the LED leads is longer than the other. The longer lead is the anode; the shorter is the cathode lead. Also note that there is a flat spot on the rim of the LED lens. The flat spot corresponds with the short, or cathode, lead of the LED. Find the LED component outlines on the circuit board and note that each LED component outline has a flat side also. When installing the LEDs, make sure the short lead, and the flat side of the LED body, are lined up with the component outline (the short lead goes in the hole with the square pad). You'll have to make a decision as to which LED color you want to indicate keying the transmitter and which LED color you want to indicate the Push to Talk (PTT.) I used red for keying and green for PTT. The keying LED is adjacent to the words "dit-dah" on the board; the PTT LED is adjacent to the words "KEY-PTT" on the board. Install the LEDs with the component bodies flush against the circuit board surface. Solder and clip the excess leads. See **Figure C-5.**

Step 6

a. Locate the speaker and the speaker location on the circuit board. If the speaker has the polarity marked on the component, take note of the positive (+) lead of the speaker. Insert the speaker into the appropriate holes and hold the speaker flush against the circuit board surface while soldering in place.

b. Locate the slide switch and the switch component outline on the circuit board. Hold the switch in place while you solder only one lead of the switch. Inspect the switch installation and make sure the switch body is flush with the circuit board surface. Melt and re-solder the pin until you are satisfied with the switch installation and then solder the remaining two pins.

c. Locate the two connectors and the connector component outline. Using the same technique as used

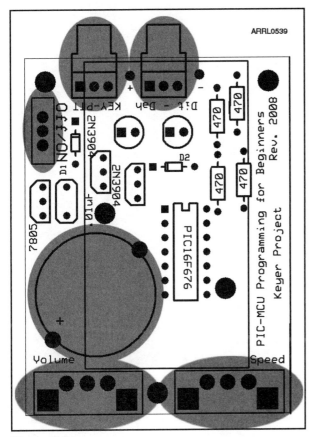

Figure C-6

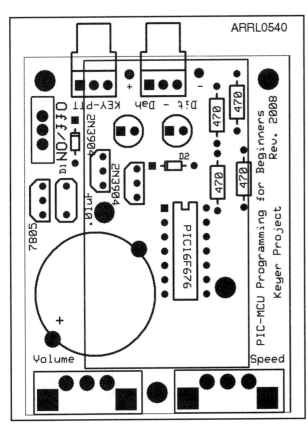

Figure C-7

to install the switch, install the two connectors.

d. Locate the two variable resistors and the variable resistor outlines on the circuit board. Install these resistors one at a time, they are identical resistors. Install the resistors with the adjustment shaft facing outward from the circuit board. Mechanically, slightly bend the tabs on the resistor body just enough to hold the resistor body flush against the circuit board surface. You may have to hold the resistor body flush with your finger while you solder one resistor lead only (not the body tabs just yet). Inspect the resistor installation and melt and re-solder the component as necessary to get the component body flush against the circuit board surface. Solder the two remaining resistor leads; then solder the tabs of the resistor body. You don't need to fill the holes around the tabs with solder, just apply enough solder to make a good mechanical connection between the tab and the circuit board ground plane (the solder pad). In a similar manner, install the second variable resistor. See **Figure C-6.**

Step 7

You are almost completed with the board. Find the 9 V battery clip, the nylon washers, and the two screws and nuts. The battery clip is installed on the bottom of the circuit board and the two battery clip leads are soldered from the top side of the board. The battery clip installation will take a little mechanical dexterity to get everything in place before you solder. Install the two screws into the mounting holes of the battery clip. Put a piece of tape over each screw head to hold the screws in place. Place two nylon washers over each screw on the bottom side of the battery clip. Now insert the screws through the two mounting holds of the circuit board from the back side of the board (solder side). Line up the battery clip leads with the two holes in the board and with all four holes, two screws, and two leads lined up, install the battery clip. Put the nuts on the screws from the component side of the board and tighten things down snugly (but not so snug as to crack the circuit board or battery clip). Once you are satisfied that the battery clip is installed with good mechanical integrity, solder the two leads from the component side and clip off the excess leads.

Once you have loaded the keyer program into the PIC16F676, you can install the device in the IC socket (making sure the notch on the IC matches the notch on the IC socket). Wire up the companion sockets to your paddle and transmitter connectors. Install the battery, turn on the board, and fire it up...you're ready to go. Congratulations.

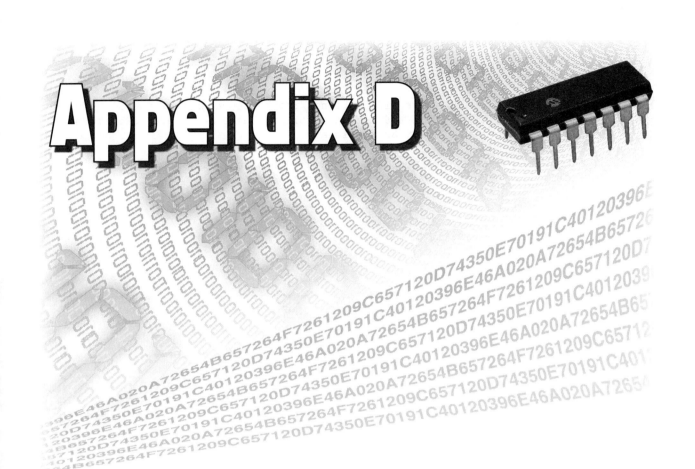

Appendix D

PIC 16F676 Include
File Contents

```
      LIST
; P16F676.INC  Standard Header File, Version 1.00     Microchip Technology, Inc.
      NOLIST

; This header file defines configurations, registers, and other useful bits of
; information for the PIC16F676 microcontroller. These names are taken to match
; the data sheets as closely as possible.

; Note that the processor must be selected before this file is
; included.  The processor may be selected the following ways:

;    1. Command line switch:
;           C:\ MPASM MYFILE.ASM /PIC16F676
;    2. LIST directive in the source file
;           LIST   P=PIC16F676
;    3. Processor Type entry in the MPASM full-screen interface


;==============================================================================
;
;    Revision History
;
;==============================================================================
;1.00   05/13/02 Original


;==============================================================================
;
;    Verify Processor
;
;==============================================================================

      IFNDEF __16F676
              MESSG "Processor-header file mismatch. Verify selected
processor."
      ENDIF


;==============================================================================
;
;                          Register Definitions
;
;==============================================================================

W                           EQU      H'0000'
F                           EQU      H'0001'

;----- Register Files-------------------------------------------------------

INDF                        EQU      H'0000'
TMR0                        EQU      H'0001'
PCL                         EQU      H'0002'
STATUS                      EQU      H'0003'
FSR                         EQU      H'0004'
PORTA                       EQU      H'0005'

PORTC                       EQU      H'0007'

PCLATH                      EQU      H'000A'
INTCON                      EQU      H'000B'
PIR1                        EQU      H'000C'

TMR1L                       EQU      H'000E'
```

```
TMR1H                          EQU        H'000F'
T1CON                          EQU        H'0010'

CMCON                          EQU        H'0019'

ADRESH                         EQU        H'001E'
ADCON0                         EQU        H'001F'


OPTION_REG                     EQU        H'0081'

TRISA                          EQU        H'0085'
TRISC                          EQU        H'0087'

PIE1                           EQU        H'008C'

PCON                           EQU        H'008E'

OSCCAL                         EQU        H'0090'
ANSEL                          EQU        H'0091'

WPU                            EQU        H'0095'
WPUA                           EQU        H'0095'
IOC                            EQU        H'0096'
IOCA                           EQU        H'0096'

VRCON                          EQU        H'0099'
EEDATA                         EQU        H'009A'
EEDAT                          EQU        H'009A'
EEADR                          EQU        H'009B'
EECON1                         EQU        H'009C'
EECON2                         EQU        H'009D'
ADRESL                         EQU        H'009E'
ADCON1                         EQU        H'009F'


;----- STATUS Bits ----------------------------------------------------

IRP                            EQU        H'0007'
RP1                            EQU        H'0006'
RP0                            EQU        H'0005'
NOT_TO                         EQU        H'0004'
NOT_PD                         EQU        H'0003'
Z                              EQU        H'0002'
DC                             EQU        H'0001'
C                              EQU        H'0000'

;----- INTCON Bits ----------------------------------------------------

GIE                            EQU        H'0007'
PEIE                           EQU        H'0006'
T0IE                           EQU        H'0005'
INTE                           EQU        H'0004'
RAIE                           EQU        H'0003'
T0IF                           EQU        H'0002'
INTF                           EQU        H'0001'
RAIF                           EQU        H'0000'
```

```
;----- PIR1 Bits ------------------------------------------------------

EEIF                          EQU        H'0007'
ADIF                          EQU        H'0006'
CMIF                          EQU        H'0003'
T1IF                          EQU        H'0000'
TMR1IF                        EQU        H'0000'

;----- T1CON Bits -----------------------------------------------------

TMR1GE                        EQU        H'0006'
T1CKPS1                       EQU        H'0005'
T1CKPS0                       EQU        H'0004'
T1OSCEN                       EQU        H'0003'
NOT_T1SYNC                    EQU        H'0002'
TMR1CS                        EQU        H'0001'
TMR1ON                        EQU        H'0000'

;----- COMCON Bits ----------------------------------------------------

COUT                          EQU        H'0006'
CINV                          EQU        H'0004'
CIS                           EQU        H'0003'
CM2                           EQU        H'0002'
CM1                           EQU        H'0001'
CM0                           EQU        H'0000'

;----- ADCON0 Bits ----------------------------------------------------

ADFM                          EQU        H'0007'
VCFG                          EQU        H'0006'
CHS2                          EQU        H'0004'
CHS1                          EQU        H'0003'
CHS0                          EQU        H'0002'
GO                            EQU        H'0001'
NOT_DONE                      EQU        H'0001'
GO_DONE                       EQU        H'0001'
ADON                          EQU        H'0000'

;----- OPTION Bits ----------------------------------------------------

NOT_GPPU                      EQU        H'0007'
NOT_RAPU                      EQU        H'0007'
INTEDG                        EQU        H'0006'
T0CS                          EQU        H'0005'
T0SE                          EQU        H'0004'
PSA                           EQU        H'0003'
PS2                           EQU        H'0002'
PS1                           EQU        H'0001'
PS0                           EQU        H'0000'

;----- PIE1 Bits ------------------------------------------------------

EEIE                          EQU        H'0007'
ADIE                          EQU        H'0006'
CMIE                          EQU        H'0003'
T1IE                          EQU        H'0000'
TMR1IE                        EQU        H'0000'

;----- PCON Bits ------------------------------------------------------
```

```
NOT_POR                         EQU     H'0001'
NOT_BOD                         EQU     H'0000'

;----- OSCCAL Bits -------------------------------------------------------------

CAL5                            EQU     H'0007'
CAL4                            EQU     H'0006'
CAL3                            EQU     H'0005'
CAL2                            EQU     H'0004'
CAL1                            EQU     H'0003'
CAL0                            EQU     H'0002'

;----- ANSEL Bits --------------------------------------------------------------

ANS7                            EQU     H'0007'
ANS6                            EQU     H'0006'
ANS5                            EQU     H'0005'
ANS4                            EQU     H'0004'
ANS3                            EQU     H'0003'
ANS2                            EQU     H'0002'
ANS1                            EQU     H'0001'
ANS0                            EQU     H'0000'

;----- VRCON Bits --------------------------------------------------------------

VREN                            EQU     H'0007'
VRR                             EQU     H'0005'
VR3                             EQU     H'0003'
VR2                             EQU     H'0002'
VR1                             EQU     H'0001'
VR0                             EQU     H'0000'

;----- EECON1 Bits -------------------------------------------------------------

WRERR                           EQU     H'0003'
WREN                            EQU     H'0002'
WR                              EQU     H'0001'
RD                              EQU     H'0000'

;----- ADCON1 Bits -------------------------------------------------------------

ADCS2                           EQU     H'0006'
ADCS1                           EQU     H'0005'
ADCS0                           EQU     H'0004'

;==============================================================================
;
;                               RAM Definition
;
;==============================================================================

__MAXRAM H'FF'
__BADRAM H'06', H'08'-H'09', H'0D', H'11'-H'18', H'1A'-H'1D', H'60'-H'7F'
__BADRAM H'86', H'88'-H'89', H'8D', H'8F', H'92'-H'94', H'97'-H'98', H'E0'-H'FF'

;==============================================================================
;
;                               Configuration Bits
;
```

```
;=============================================================================
_CPD                        EQU     H'3EFF'
_CPD_OFF                    EQU     H'3FFF'
_CP                         EQU     H'3F7F'
_CP_OFF                     EQU     H'3FFF'
_BODEN                      EQU     H'3FFF'
_BODEN_OFF                  EQU     H'3FBF'
_MCLRE_ON                   EQU     H'3FFF'
_MCLRE_OFF                  EQU     H'3FDF'
_PWRTE_OFF                  EQU     H'3FFF'
_PWRTE_ON                   EQU     H'3FEF'
_WDT_ON                     EQU     H'3FFF'
_WDT_OFF                    EQU     H'3FF7'
_LP_OSC                     EQU     H'3FF8'
_XT_OSC                     EQU     H'3FF9'
_HS_OSC                     EQU     H'3FFA'
_EC_OSC                     EQU     H'3FFB'
_INTRC_OSC_NOCLKOUT         EQU     H'3FFC'
_INTRC_OSC_CLKOUT           EQU     H'3FFD'
_EXTRC_OSC_NOCLKOUT         EQU     H'3FFE'
_EXTRC_OSC_CLKOUT           EQU     H'3FFF'

        LIST
```

Appendix E

Parts Sources

The PIC programming kit available from the ARRL (produced by Cana Kit Corporation of British Columbia, Canada) includes all the parts listed below. Alternatively, you may wish to obtain the parts and PIC programmer yourself.

Cana Kit: tel 888-540-KITS; **www.canakit.com**
DigiKey: tel 800-344-4539; **www.digikey.com**
Paralax: tel 888-512-1024; **www.paralax.com**
Jameco: tel 800-831-4242; **www.jameco.com**
Microchip: **www.microchipdirect.com**

Quanity	Part	DigiKey	Paralax	Jameco	Cana Kit	Microchip
1	PIC Programmer				UK1301	DV164120
1	Prototype Board and Wire Kit	438-1046-nd			BB-102W	
1	LCD Display		27977		PX-27977	
1	LCD Extension Cable		805-00011		PX-805-00011	
2	PIC16F676	PIC16F676-I/P-ND			IC-PIC16F676	
1	MCP41010 Digital Pot 10K	MCP41010-I/P-ND			IC-MCP41010	
4	470 Ω 1/4 Watt Resistor	470QBK-ND			R5-25-470R	
1	.01uF Capacitor	P4582-ND			CP-103-50V	
2	1N914 Diode	1N914-TPCT-ND			DS-1N914	
1	5V Regulator 7805	LM78L05ACZFS-ND			IC-LM78L05	
1	9V Battery Clip	BH9V-PC-ND			DX-BH9V-PC	
4	Button Switch	SW403-ND			SW-1102B	
2	Red LED	67-1105-ND			LED-5MRED	
2	Yellow LED	67-1116-ND			LED-5MYEL	
2	Green LED	67-1098-ND			LED-5MGRN	
2	2N3904 Transistor	2N3904FS-ND			TR-2N3904	
1	Slide Switch	EG1903-ND			SW-SPDT	
2	10K Potentiometer	CT2254-ND			P16-10KB-SP1	
1	Speaker	102-1142-ND			DX-102-1142	
1	7-Segment LED			334896	7SEG-CCR-56	
1	14-Pin DIP Socket	AE9989-ND			SKT-14	
1	8-Pin DIP Socket	AE9986-ND			SKT-8	
2	3-Pin Male Connector	WM2001-ND			DX-WM2001	
2	3-Pin Female Connector	WM4301-ND			DX-WM4301	
10	Connector Pins	WM1114-ND			DX-WM1114	
1	Keyer Circuit Board				C120-ARRL	

Index